Instructor's Resource Guide

A Problem Solving Approach to Mathematics

for Elementary School Teachers

Sixth Edition

Instructor's Resource Guide

A Problem Solving Approach to Mathematics

for Elementary School Teachers

Sixth Edition

Rick Billstein

University of Montana
Missoula, Montana

Shlomo Libeskind

University of Oregon
Eugene, Oregon

Johnny W. Lott

University of Montana
Missoula, Montana

 **ADDISON-WESLEY**

An imprint of Addison Wesley Longman, Inc.

Reading, Massachusetts • Menlo Park, California • New York • Harlow, England
Don Mills, Ontario • Sydney • Mexico City • Madrid • Amsterdam

ISBN   0-201-44084-9

2 3 4 5 6 7 8 9 10 CRS 9998

TABLE OF CONTENTS

Sample Assessment

1.   List the terms that complete a possible pattern in each of the following:

   (a)   38, 33, 28, 23, 18,___,___,___
   (b)   640, 320, 160, 80,___,___,___
   (c)   7, 8,15, 23, 38,___,___,___
   (d)   4, 8, 16, 32, 64 ,___,___,___
   (e)   1,___,___,___,25, 36, 49

2.   Classify each of the sequences in Problem 1 as arithmetic, geometric, or neither.

3.   Find the nth term in each of the following:

   (a)   6, 8, 10, 12, 14, ...
   (b)   2, 5, 10, 17, 26, ...
   (c)   5, 25, 125, 625, ...

4.   Find the first five terms of the sequences with the nth term given as follows:

   (a) $3n + 2$
   (b) $n^2 + n$
   (c) $n(n + 7)$

5.   Find the following sum.

   $6 + 8 + 10 + 12 +... + 100$

6.   (a)   Determine a possible pattern in the following sequence if the tenth term is supposed to have four digits.

      101, 212, 323, 434, 545, 656, 767, ...

   (b)   What is the 100th term of the sequence in (a)?

7.   A person writing a book numbered the pages consecutively starting with 1 and had written 4553 digits. How many pages had she numbered? Explain your reasoning.

8.   Place the numbers 3, 4, 7, 9 in the squares below to obtain the greatest product.

   □□
X □□
   ‾‾‾

9. John is responsible for seating arrangements at a dinner party. He has seven tables which individually seat six people as shown. He wants to make one large table by pushing them together. He expects a total of 15 couples.

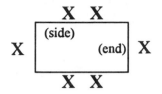

(a) Can he accommodate all the expected guests if he lines the tables up side-to-side? Explain.
(b) Can he accommodate all the expected guests if he lines the tables up end-to-end? Explain.

10. A novice rabbit breeder started with two pregnant females. One delivered six female young, the other delivered three males and five females. He recently bred all the females he owned and each delivered five young. If he has kept all of the rabbits, how many does he have?

11. A rectangle is 6 cm wide. The length is 1 cm less than 3 times the width.

(a) What is the length of the rectangle?
(b) What is the perimeter of the rectangle?

12. How many different ways can you make change for a $100 bill using $5, $10, $20, and $50 bills?

13. How many different rectangles are in the following figure?

Sample Assessment

1. List the terms that complete a possible pattern in each of the following:

   (a) 47, 87, 67, 107, 87,___,___,___
   (b) 2, 10, 50, 250, 1250,___,___,___
   (c) 8, 15, 22, 29, 36,___,___,___
   (d) 4, 0, 8, 0, 16, 0,___,___,___
   (e) 5, 9, 13, 17, 21,___,___,___

2. Classify each of the sequences in Problem 1 as arithmetic, geometric, or neither.

3. Fine the nth term in each of the following:

   (a) 4, 9, 14, 19, 24,___,___,___
   (b) 6, 12, 24, 48, 96,___,___,___
   (c) 1, 4, 9, 16, 25,___,___,___

4. Find the first five terms of the sequences with the nth term given as follows:

   (a) $4n + 7$
   (b) $n^2 + 2n$
   (c) $n(n - 1)$

5. Find the following sum:

   $3 + 6 + 9 + 12 +... + 84$

6. In order to divide a P.E. class into two teams, the gym teacher has the students stand in a circle and count off 1, 2, 3, ... all the way around the circle. If the teacher divides the circle in half between the numbers 3 and 4 and between the number 12 and 13, how many students are on each team?

7. A 200 mL test tube collects 25 mL of condensation every night and loses 9 mL to evaporation every day. When will the test tube overflow? Explain your reasoning.

8. Charlie is designing an 80 ft x 120 ft rectangular fence. He wants to put posts 10 ft apart along one of the 120 ft sides. The posts will be 8 ft apart along the other three sides of the fence. How many posts does Charlie need? Explain your reasoning.

9. Catarina had a total of $2.00. This money consisted of the same number of nickels, dimes, and quarters. How many of each did she have?

10. What is the 200th letter in the sequence A, B, C, D, E, F, A, B C, D, E, F, ...?

11. Gerald and Betty Joggette ran 5 blocks on their first day out. They increased their run by 3 blocks each day until they were running 35 blocks. How many days did it take to do this?

12. Place the digits 2, 3, 4, 5, and 6 in the squares below to obtain the product shown.

$$\begin{array}{r} \square\square\square \\ \times\ \ \square\square \\ \hline \mathbf{10695} \end{array}$$

13. How many numbers are there between 100 and 1000 that contain the digits 7, 8, or 9?

Sample Assessment

1. Write the set of vowels in the name of the creator of "set theory" using set-builder notation.

2. List all the subsets of {2,o,t}.

3. Let   U = {x | x is a female}
          A = {x | x is a mathematician}
          B = {x | x owns a pickup}
          C = {x | x owns a dog}

    Describe in words a member of each of the following:

    (a) $\overline{B}$ (b) B ∪ C   (c) A – C
    (d) $\overline{A \cup C}$ (e) B – A   (f) A

4. Let   U = {u,n,i,t,e}
          A = {n,i,t}
          B = {n,e}
          C = {u,n,i,t,e}
          D = {u,e}

    Find each of the following:

    (a) A ∩ B   (b) C ∪ D   (c) $\overline{D}$
    (d) $\overline{A \cup D}$ (e) B ∩ $\overline{C}$ (f) (B ∩ C) ∩ D
    (g) (A ∩ B) ∩ (C ∪ D)   (h) (C – D) ∩ $\overline{A}$ (i) n(C)
    (j) n(C ∪ D)

5. Indicate the following sets by shading.

    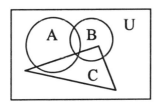   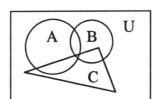

    (a) (A ∪ B) ∪ C   (b) A ∩ (B ∪ C)

6. Let C = {p,l,u,s}. How many proper subsets does C have?

7. How many possible one-to-one correspondences are there between sets D and E if D = {w,h,y} and E = {n,o,t}?

8. How many elements are there in the Cartesian product of sets D and E in Problem 7?

9. Use a Venn diagram to determine whether $A \cup (B - C) = (B \cup A) - C$ for all sets A, B, and C.

10. Describe using symbols, the shaded portion in each of the following:

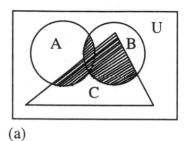

(a)

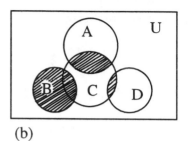

(b)

11. Use $A = \{o,n,e\}$, $B = \{t,w,o\}$, $C = \{z,e,r,o\}$, to illustrate the equality
    $A \times (B \cup C) = (A \times B) \cup (A \times C)$.

12. Classify each of the following as true or false. If false, tell why or give an example showing that it is not true.

    (a) For all sets A and B, $A - B = B - A$
    (b) For all sets A, $\emptyset \subseteq A$
    (c) For all sets A, $A \subseteq A \cup \emptyset$
    (d) The set $\{r,s,t,\ldots,z\}$ is a finite set.
    (e) No set can be equivalent to all of its subsets.

13. In an interview of 50 math majors,
    12 liked calculus and geometry
    18 liked calculus but not algebra
    4 liked calculus, algebra, and geometry
    25 liked calculus
    15 liked geometry
    10 liked algebra but neither calculus nor geometry
    2 liked geometry and algebra but not calculus.
    Of those surveyed, how many liked calculus and algebra?

14. Which of the following sets are functions from the set of first components to the set of second components?

    (a) $\{(b,a),(d,c),(a,e),(g,f)\}$
    (b) $\{(a,b),(b,a),(c,c),(a,c)\}$
    (c) $\{(b,a),(c,a),(b,b),(c,b)\}$

15. Give the following function rules and domains, find the associated ranges.

   (a) $f(x) = 5x + 3$, Domain = $\{0,1,2,3,4\}$
   (b) $f(x) = x^2 - 1$, Domain = $\{1,9,4\}$
   (c) $f(x) = 2x + x^2$, Domain = $\{1,0,2\}$

16. If $f(x) = 3x - 10$, find the element of the domain associated with each of the following functional values:

   (a) 2   (b) 8

17. Consider a function machine that accepts inputs as ordered pairs. Suppose the components of the ordered pairs are natural numbers and the first component is the length of the rectangle and the second is its width. The following machine computes the area of the rectangle. Thus for a rectangle whose length, ℓ, is 3 and whose width w, is 2, the input is (3,2) and the output is $3 \cdot 2$ or 6. Answer each of the following.

   (a) For each of the following inputs, find the corresponding outputs: (3,4), (4,3), (6,2), (1,12).
   (b) Find the set of all the inputs for which the output is 20.
   (c) What is the domain and the range of the function?

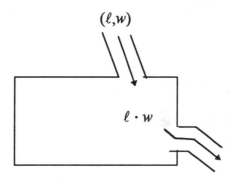

18. The following graphs show the cost and revenue functions in dollars for producing cameras. From the graphs estimate the following.

   (a) The break-even point—that is, the number of cameras that must be sold to meet expenses exactly.
   (b) The profit or loss on the first 25 cameras produced and sold.
   (c) The number of cameras that must be sold to gain a $2000 profit.

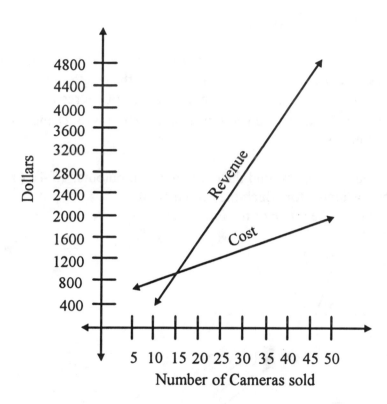

*19. Which of the following are statements?

   (a) Emily Dickinson won a Nobel Prize in physics.
   (b) How many cars does it take to create a parking lot?
   (c) It takes 3 book editors to screw in a light bulb.
   (d) $x + 3 = 15$

*20. Negate each of the following:

   (a) Butterflies are animals.
   (b) Whitney Houston always says "How de do Boo Boo."
   (c) Some umpire calls are correct.
   (d) $7 + 3 = 10$

*21. For each of the properties of sets write a corresponding property of statements.

    (a) $\overline{A \cup B \cup C} = \overline{A} \cap \overline{B} \cap \overline{C}$

    (b) $\overline{A \cap B \cap C} = \overline{A} \cup \overline{B} \cup \overline{C}$

*22. Write the converse, inverse, and contrapositive of the following. If the host was Jay Leno, the director was Doc Sevrinson.

*23. For each of the following true statements write the converse and the contrapositive of the statement and determine if the new statements are true.

    (a) If $x \in A \cap B$, then $x \in A \cup B$

    (b) If $A \subset B$, then $n(A) < n(b)$

    (c) If $A \cap B = \varnothing$, then $n(A \cup B) = n(A) + n(B)$

*24. Find a valid conclusion for the following arguments.

    (a) If I don't get an increase in salary, I will quit. I do not quit.

    (b) If the map is in the plane, it takes no more than four colors to color it. It takes more than four colors to color the map.

    (c) All women mathematicians are well known. Gloria Hewitt is a woman mathematician.

*25. Write the following argument symbolically and then determine its validity.

If a nail is lost, then a shoe is lost.
If a shoe is lost, then a horse is lost.
If a horse is lost, then a rider is lost.
If a rider is lost, then a battle is lost.
If a battle is lost, then a kingdom is lost.
Therefore, if a nail is lost, then a kingdom is lost.

*26. Determine whether or not each of the following arguments is valid.

    (a) All larch trees are conifers.
        All conifers keep their needles all year long.
        Therefore, all larch trees keep their needles all year long.

    (b) No spiders are insects.
        All insects are not arachnids.
        Therefore, no spiders are arachnids.

    (c) If a cat is spayed, then it cannot have kittens.
        My cat has kittens.
        Therefore, my cat is not spayed.

    (d) If John works in stained glass, then he makes butterflies.
        If John does not make butterflies, then he is not a glazier.
        John works in stained glass.
        Therefore, John is not a glazier.

Sample Assessment

1. Use set notation to write the months having six letters in their name.

2. Write the set $M = \{1,3,5,7,9\}$ using set-builder notation.

3. List all the nonempty proper subsets of $\{a,b,c\}$.

4. Let $U = \{x \mid x \text{ is an American}\}$
   $C = \{x \mid x \text{ is a smoker}\}$
   $D = \{x \mid x \text{ is a health problem}\}$
   $E = \{x \mid x \text{ is a male}\}$

   (i) Describe a person who is an element of each of the following sets:

   (a) $\overline{C}$ (b) $\overline{C} \cap \overline{D}$ (c) $C \cap D$
   (d) $D - C$ (e) $D \cup C$

   (ii) Use the sets above, along with the set operations to describe a set of which each of the following is a representative member.

   (a) A healthy American Male
   (b) An unhealthy male smoker
   (c) A nonsmoking healthy female
   (d) An American who is either a female or a nonsmoker.

4. Classify the following as true or false, where A and B are any two sets If false, give a counterexample.

   (a) $A \cup B = A$, then $B \subseteq A$ (b) If $A \subseteq B$, then $A \cup B = B$
   (c) $(A \cup B) \cup C = A \cup (B \cup C)$ (d) $A \cap \overline{A} = \varnothing$
   (e) $A \cup \overline{A} = \varnothing$ (f) $A - \overline{A} = \varnothing$
   (g) $A \times \overline{A} = U$ (h) $\varnothing \subset \varnothing$

6. If $U = \{q,u,e,s,t\}$, $A = \{s,e,t\}$, $B = \{s,u,e\}$, and $C = \{q,u\}$, find each of the following:

   (a) $A \cup B$ (b) $A \cap \overline{C}$
   (c) $A \cup \left(\overline{B \cap C}\right)$ (d) $\overline{A} \cap \overline{B}$
   (e) $A - B$ (f) $(A \cup B) \cap (A \cup C)$
   (g) $A \cup \overline{A}$ (h) $n(B - A)$

7. Let A = {1,2} and B = {a}. Find the following:

   (a) n(A x B)   (b) n(B x A)   (c) B x B
   (d) A x A   (e) Ø x A   (f) Is A x A a function from A to A?
   (g) Is B x B a function from B to B?   (h) n(A x Ø)

8. (a) Illustrate a one-to-one correspondence between the following sets:

$$N = \{1,2,3,4,\ldots,n,\ldots\}$$
$$F = \{4,9,14,19,24,\ldots\}$$

   (b) In your correspondence, what element of F corresponds to 57? Explain why.
   (c) In your correspondence, what element of F corresponds to n?

9. Given the function rules and domains, find the associated ranges.

   (a) $f(x) = 2x + 3$, domain = {0,1,2}
   (b) $f(x) = 0$, domain = {0,1,2}

10. Shade the Venn diagram to illustrate $\overline{A} \cup \overline{B}$.

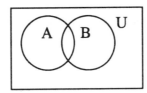

11. Describe in symbols the shaded portion Venn diagram below.

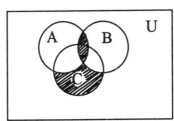

12. A survey was made of 200 students to study their use of the public library system. The findings were as follows:

   60 used the Reader's Guide.
   28 used both the card catalog and the information booth.
   68 used the information booth.
   83 did not use the library.
   43 used only the card catalog.

   Explain how the above information can be used to conclude that some students must use both the information booth and the Reader's Guide.

13. If there are 36 different flavors of ice cream and two types of cones are available, how many choice for a single scoop of ice cream on some type of cone do you have?

14. If A = {a,b,c,d} and B = {1,2,3,4}, how many different one-to-one correspondences can be made?

15. Which of the following sets are functions from the set of first components to the set of second component?

    (a)   {(1,2),(2,1)}
    (b)   {(5,10),(10,10),(15,10),(20,10)}

16. If $f(x) = x - 1$, $g(x) = x + 1$, and $N = \{1,2,3,4,\ldots\}$ is the domain of each function, find the simplest possible expression for the following.

    (a) $f(g(x))$ (b) $g(f(x))$

17. The following graphs show the cost and revenue functions in dollars for producing dishwashers. From the graphs estimate the following.

    (a)   The break-even point—that is, the number of dishwashers that must be sold to meet expenses exactly.
    (b)   The profit or loss on the first 20 dishwashers produced and sold.
    (c)   The number of units that must be sold to gain a $6000 profit.

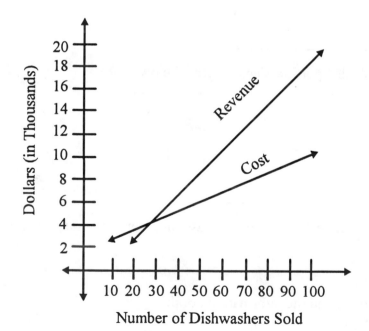

Number of Dishwashers Sold

*18. Which of the following are statements?

    (a)   Bishop Desmond Tutu won a Nobel Peace Prize for Literature.
    (b)   Is there a Nobel Prize for physics?
    (c)   All people who work for the government are bureaucrats.
    (d) $15 + x = x + 15$

*19. Negate each of the following:

    (a)   *The Valley of the Horses* was written by Jean Auel.
    (b)   All realtors get commissions on houses that they sell.
    (c)   There exists a dishonest used car salesman.
    (d) $5 - 2 \neq 3$

*20. Suppose that the property in logic that corresponds to $A \subseteq B$ is $a \rightarrow b$. For each of the following properties of sets, write a corresponding property in logic.

    (a) $A \subseteq B$ if and only if $\overline{B} \subseteq \overline{A}$
    (b)   For all sets A and B, $A \cap B \subseteq A \cup B$.

*21. For each of the following, determine if the statement is true. Write the converse and the contrapositive of the statement and determine the truth of each.

    (a)   If $A \cup B = A \cup C$, then $B = C$
    (b)   If $A \cap B = \varnothing$, then $A = \varnothing$ or $B = \varnothing$.

*22. Write the converse, inverse, and contrapositive of the following. If Michele Pfeifer is Catwoman, then she came from Gotham City.

*23. Find a valid conclusion for the following arguments.

    (a)   If you do not understand a problem, then you can solve it.
           You cannot solve a problem.
    (b)   No students like 8:00 classes.
           You like 8:00 classes.
    (c)   It always snows in Montana.
           I will go skiing if it snows in Montana.
           If I go skiing, then I will get cold.

*24. Write the following argument symbolically and then determine its validity.

If I pay attention to my job, I will get a salary increase.
If I shirk my job, then I will not get a salary increase.
I shirk my job.
Therefore, I did not pay attention to my job.

*25. Determine whether or not each of the following arguments is valid.

  (a)   If you do not understand this test, then you enjoy logic.
        You do not enjoy logic.
        Therefore, you understand this test.

  (b)   No dogs are cats.
        All cats are finicky.
        Therefore, no dogs are finicky.

  (c)   If I eat a piece of fudge, I will gain weight.
        I will not gain weight.
        Therefore, I ate a piece of fudge.

Sample Assessment

1. Convert each of the following to base ten.

   (a) MXLV   (b) 211_{four} (c) $T20_{twelve}$ (d) 101_{two}

2. Convert each of the following base ten numerals to numerals in the indicated system.

   (a) 128 to Roman   (b) 346 to base five   (c) 127 to base twelve

3. Simplify each of the following, if possible. Write your answers in the form a^b.

   (a) $3^3 \cdot 3^5 \cdot 3^5$ (b) $3^{13} \cdot 3^{13}$ (c) $4^3 + 3 \cdot 4^3$

4. For each of the following, identify the whole-number properties which are illustrated.

   (a) $2(3 + 4) = 2(4 + 3)$ (b) $5 + 7 = 7 + 5$
   (c) $1 \cdot 14 = 14 = 14 \cdot 1$ (d) $5(9 + 3) = 5 \cdot 9 + 5 \cdot 3$
   (e) $2 + (3 + 2) = (2 + 3) + 2$ (f) $5(3 \cdot 4) = (5 \cdot 3)4$

5. Using the definition of less than or greater than, prove that each of the following inequalities is true.

   (a) $5 < 7$ (b) $18 > 14$

6. Explain why the product $12 \cdot 100$ namely, 1200 has zeroes in the tens and units places

7. Use both the scratch and traditional algorithms to perform each of the following.

   (a)   542   (b) 312_{five}
         889   434_{five}
    $+$ 611 $+$ 311_{five}

8. Use both the lattice and traditional multiplication algorithms to perform each of the following.

   (a)   512   (b) 213_{six}
    $+$ 32 $+$ 52_{six}

9. Use both the repeated subtraction and the traditional algorithms to perform each of the following.

   (a) $12\overline{)312}$ (b) $101_{two}\overline{)10011_{two}}$

10. For each of the following, find all possible whole-number replacements that make the following statements true.

   (a) $5 \cdot \square + 27 < 48$ (b) $944 = \square \cdot 48 + 32$ (c) $28 - \square \geq 14$

11. Use the number line to perform each of the following operations.

(a) $10 - 3$ (b) $5 + 3$

12. Use the distributive property of multiplication over addition and addition and subtraction facts to rename each of the following, if possible.

(a) $2x + 4x + 7x + 5x$ (b) $6x^3 + 7x^3$ (c) $a(b + c + d)$

13. Joyce sold 48 student tickets to the play at $3.00 each and 37 adult tickets at $5.00 each. Expenses for the play were $300. How much money was left in the account after expenses were paid?

14. Hugo's checking account at the beginning of the month had a balance of $250. During the month he wrote five checks for $15, two checks for $12, and one check for $107. He made one deposit for $62. What is his new balance?

15. Tom, Dick, and Mary decided to share expenses for a class party. Tom bought $28 worth of pizza, Dick bought $20 worth of ice cream, and Mary bought $15 worth of soft drinks. How much should each person pay in order that each of them spend the same amount and how might they accomplish this?

16. Jim was paid $800 a month for his first 6 months of work and then received a $20 per month raise for his next 6 months. How much money did he make for the year?

17. Sue argued that $0 \div 0 = 1$ because any number divided by itself is 1. What would you tell her?

Sample Assessment

1. Convert each of the following to base ten.

    (a) $\overline{\text{MCD}}$ (b) 1413_{five} (c) $\text{T}10_{\text{twelve}}$ (d) 1011_{two}

2. Convert each of the following base ten numerals to numerals in the indicated system.

    (a)   454 to Roman   (b)   200 to base five   (c)   9 to base nine

3. Simplify each of the following, if possible. Write your answers in the form a^b.

    (a) $3^4 \cdot 3^3 \cdot 3^8 \cdot 3$ (b) $4^{14} \cdot 4^{79}$ (c) $5^6 + 4 \cdot 5^6$

4. For each of the following, identify the whole-number properties which are illustrated.

    (a) $4(6 + 7) = 4(7 + 6)$ (b) $5(7 \cdot 3) = (5 \cdot 7)3$
    (c) $5(7 + 3) = 5 \cdot 7 + 5 \cdot 3$ (d) $5 \cdot 1 = 5 = 1 \cdot 5$
    (e) $0 + 1$ is a whole number   (f) $5(7 \cdot 3) = 5(3 \cdot 7)$

5. Using the definition of less than or greater than, prove each of the following is true.

    (a) $18 < 22$ (b) $1 > 0$

6. June claims that $1 \div 0 = 1$ because one divided by nothing is still one. How would you help her?

7. Use both the scratch and traditional algorithms to perform each of the following.

    (a)   362   (b) 214_{five}
          78   232_{five}
          534              $+\ \ 223_{\text{five}}$
    $+\ \ \ \ 79$

8. Use both the lattice and traditional multiplication to perform each of the following.

    (a)   518   (b) 212_{five}
        $\times\ \ 342$ $\times\ \ \ 23_{\text{five}}$

9. Use both the repeated subtraction and the traditional algorithms to perform each of the following.

    (a) $8\overline{)3648}$ (b) $12_{\text{three}}\overline{)2021_{\text{three}}}$

10. For each of the following, find all possible whole-number replacements that make the following statements true.

    (a) $2 \cdot \square \div 15 < 27$ (b) $123 = 7 \cdot 17 + \square$

11. Use the number line to perform each of the following operations.

   (a) $2 + 4$ (b) $8 - 4$

12. Use the distributive property of multiplication over addition and addition and subtraction facts to rename each of the following, if possible.

   (a) $5x^2 + 2x^2 + 7x^2$ (b) $8x + 9x + 11x + 9x$ (c) $(a + b)(c + d)$

13. Sam's operating expenses for driving a car are $40 per week. If his expenses for driving a motorcycle for 52 weeks are $1650 how much did he save for the 52 week period?

14. Tina had $103 in her checking account. She wrote 3 checks for $5 and 2 checks for $18. She then deposited $19. What was her balance?

15. Find the missing numbers in each of the following.

   (a) _ 3 _ 5
       + 4 8 2 _
       ‾‾‾‾‾‾‾‾‾
         7 _ 89

   (b) 8 6 5 _
       − _ 2 _ 2
       ‾‾‾‾‾‾‾‾‾
         5 _ 72

16. I am thinking of a number. If I add 3, multiply the result by 15 and then subtract 25, I get 200. What is my number?

17. Why is a front-end estimate before doing the adjustment always less than the actual answer?

18. If 10 is removed from the set of whole numbers, is the set closed with respect to multiplication? Why?

Sample Assessment

1. Find the additive inverse of each of the following.

    (a) –7   (b) $2 + x$ (c) $x - y$

2. Perform the following operations:

    (a) $(-12 - -18) + 4$ (b) $-3(-2) - 2$ (c) $-12 - 3(-4) + 2(-8)$

3. For each of the following, find all integer values of x that make the equation or inequality true.

    (a) $x^2 = 9$ (b) $|-x| = 5$ (c) $4 - 3x < 2x + 84$
    (d) $|x + 2| = 7$ (e) $x + 7 = 34 - 2x$ (f) $(x - 3)^2 = 64$

4. Use a pattern approach to explain why $(-3) \cdot (4) = -12$.

5. Factor each of the following expressions.

    (a) $5x - 3x^2$ (b) $25 - x^2$

6. Evaluate the following when $x = -3$, if possible.

    (a) $-x$ (b) $|x|$ (c) $-x^2$ (d) $(-x)^2$

7. Multiply each of the following and simplify your answer.

    (a) $(b + 3d)(b - 3d)$ (b) $(-4j + 2k)(-4j - 2k)$

8. Classify each of the following as true or false, where a and b are any integers. If false, tell why.

    (a) If $ac > bc$, then $a > b$.   (b) If $-x > -7$, then $x > 7$.
    (c) $|x|$ is always equal to x.   (d) $a^2 + b^2 = (a + b)(a + b)$

9. Classify each of the following as true or false, where a and b are any integers. If false, tell why.

    (a) All whole numbers are integers.
    (b) Subtraction is commutative on the set of integers.
    (c) Multiplication is associative on the set of integers.
    (d) The set of integers is closed with respect to division.

10. What conditions must be satisfied so that the product of two integers is positive?

11. The temperature dropped 15 degrees from the high temperature to $-6°$ C. What was the high temperature?

12. The sum of two integers is 14. Their difference is 8. What are the integers?

13. Demonstrate the addition $-5 + -3 = -8$ using each of the following models:
    (a) Number line
    (b) Charged field

14. Determine all possible digits to fill in the blanks to make each of the following true.

    (a) $9 \mid 482\_\_$ (b) $6 \mid 24\_\_35$ (c) $4 \mid 63\_\_$

15. Classify each of the following as true or false, where a and b are integers. If false, give a counterexample.

    (a) If $a \neq b$, then $GCD(a, b) = 1$.
    (b) If a and b are even, then $GCD(a, b) = 2$.
    (c) If $a \mid b$, then $LCM(a, b) = a$.
    (d) If $6 \mid a$ then $12 \mid a$.

16. Find the least whole number with exactly seven positive divisors and explain why it is the least.

17. Determine whether each of the following numbers is prime or composite.

    (a) 219   (b) 791   (c) 1001

18. Find each of the following.

    (a) GCD(12, 26, 65)   (b) LCM(12, 26, 65)

19. If $a = 2^3 \cdot 3^7 \cdot 5^3 \cdot 11^4$ and $b = 2^2 \cdot 3^5 \cdot 7^2 \cdot 11 \cdot 13$, find the following. (Leave your answer written with exponents).

    (a) GCD(a, b)   (b) LCM(a,b)

20. What is the greatest prime that must be checked in order to determine if each of the following is prime?

    (a) 1317   (b) 241

21. Describe a divisibility test for 35.

22. Jane cut her cake into 6 pieces of equal size. Lori cut her cake into 8 pieces of equal size. If the cakes must now be cut so that they are identical, into how many pieces should each cake be cut?

23. In their freshman years, Jacqueline took 43 credit hours and Jean took 47 credit hours. If Jacqueline took only 5-credit courses and Jean took only 3-credit courses after their freshman years, how many credits did they have when they had the same number?

*24. Christmas falls on Monday this year. On what day will it fall next year if next year is a leap year?

*25. Find the remainder for the following: $\dfrac{7^{100}}{9}$

Sample Assessment

1. Find the additive inverse of each of the following.

   (a) 13   (b) $-3 + x$

2. Perform each of the following operations:

   (a) $(5 - -3) + 13$ (b) $6 \cdot (-8) + (-5)$ (c) $-8 + 3 \cdot (-2) - (-8) \cdot (-2)$

3. For each of the following find all integer values of x, if they exist, that make the equations true.

   (a) $-x - 3 = -8$ (b) $x^3 = -27$ (c) $|x| = 16$
   (d) $8 - 5x < 2x - 20$ (e) $|-x + 5| = 8$ (f) $(x - 2)^4 = 16$

4. Factor each of the following expressions.

   (a) $9x^2 - 3x$ (b) $4x^2 - 9$

5. (a) Show that $(x + y) \cdot (x + y) = x^2 + 2xy + y^2$
   (b) Use the result in (a) to compute $(-5 + 2a)(-5 + 2a)$

6. Evaluate the following when $x = -2$, if possible.

   (a) $-x^2$ (b) $|-x|$ (c) $-|x|$ (d) x^3

7. Classify each of the following as true or false. If false, tell why.

   (a) If $-x > 2$ then $x > -2$.   (b) If $3x = 6$ then $-6x = 12$.
   (c) $|-x|$ is always equal to $-x$. (d) $a^2 - b^2 = (a - b)(a - b)$

8. Classify each of the following as true or false. If false, tell why.

   (a) Every integer is a whole number.
   (b) Subtraction is associative on the set of integers.
   (c) Multiplication is closed on the set of integers.
   (d) Addition is commutative on the set of integers.

9. What conditions must be satisfied so that the product of two integers is negative?

10. Ann had a balance of $25 in her checking account. She wrote three checks for $5.00 each, one check for $28, and two checks for $22 each. What was her new balance?

11. The temperature dropped 37° C from the high temperature to reach a low of -8° C. What was the high temperature?

12. The difference between two integers is 22. The greater integer is equal to three times the smaller integer plus 8. What are the two integers?

13. Demonstrate $-8 + 2 = -6$ using the following models:
    (a) Number line
    (b) Charged field

14. Determine all possible digits to fill in the blanks to make each of the following true.

    (a) $9 \mid 24\_3$ (b) $6 \mid 7\_4$ (c) $5 \mid 3728\_$

15. Classify each of the following as true or false where a and b are integers. If false, give a counterexample or tell why.

    (a) GCD(a, a) = a
    (b) If LCM(a, b) = ab, then GCD(a, b) = 1.
    (c) If LCM(a, b) = 1, then a = 1 and b = 1
    (d) If $6 \mid a$ and $2 \mid a$, then $12 \mid a$

16. Find the least whole number with exactly 3 distinct prime divisors.

17. Determine whether each of the following numbers is prime or composite.

    (a) 231   (b) 393

18. Find each of the following.

    (a) GCD(156, 84, 292)   (b) LCM(156, 84, 292)

19. If $a = 5^2 \cdot 7 \cdot 11 \cdot 13$ and $b = 2^3 \cdot 5^2 \cdot 7^3 \cdot 17$, find the following. (Leave your answer written with exponents).

    (a) GCD(a, b)   (b) LCM(a,b)

20. What is the greatest prime that must be checked in order to determine if each of the following is prime?

    (a) 231   (b) 1811

21. Describe a divisibility test for 33.

22. Becky's class size will be either 16, 24, 32 students. She would like to bring exactly enough treats to have available an equal number for each student. What is the minimum number she should bring?

23. Joel's dog barks every 9 minutes. Billy's dog barks every 15 minutes. They both barked at exactly 2:00 P.M. When is the next time they will bark at the same time?

*24. Christmas is on Tuesday this year. In how many years will it be on Friday if no leap years are involved?

*25. Find the remainder for the following: $\dfrac{2^{64}}{4}$

Sample Assessment

1. For each of the following, draw a diagram illustrating the fraction.

   (a) $\dfrac{1}{6}$ (b) $\dfrac{5}{7}$

2. Write three rational numbers equal to $\dfrac{4}{5}$.

3. Reduce each of the following rational numbers to simplest form.

   (a) $\dfrac{36}{48}$ (b) $\dfrac{\left(cy^3\right)^2}{dy^2}$ (c) $\dfrac{0}{3}$ (d) $\dfrac{b^2+x}{b^3+bx}$

4. Place $>$, $<$, or $=$ between each of the following pairs to make true sentences.

   (a) $\dfrac{4}{5}$ and $\dfrac{120}{150}$ (b) $\dfrac{^-6}{5}$ and $\dfrac{^-7}{6}$ (c) $\dfrac{^-4}{20}$ and $\dfrac{4}{^-20}$

5. Perform each of the following computations. Leave your answers in simplest form.

   (a) $\dfrac{2}{3}+\dfrac{4}{5}$ (b) $\dfrac{3}{4}-\dfrac{2}{3}$

   (c) $\dfrac{5}{3}\cdot\dfrac{27}{40}$ (d) $\left(3\dfrac{1}{4}+7\dfrac{1}{8}\right)\div 8\dfrac{1}{2}$

6. Find the additive and multiplicative inverses for each of the following.

   (a) 8 (b) $3\dfrac{1}{2}$ (c) $\dfrac{^-1}{4}$ (d) $\dfrac{3}{8}$

7. The ratio of boys to girls in Mr. Joiner's class is 5 to 7. If there are 15 boys in the class, how many total students are in the class?

8. Sunflower seeds are packed in packages each weighing $3\dfrac{1}{4}$ ounces. If there is a supply of $15\dfrac{1}{2}$ pounds of sunflower seeds, how many packages of seeds can be packed? How many ounces of sunflower seeds will be left over? (16 oz. = 1 pound)

9. Estimate each of the following, indicating if the actual answer is greater than (+) or less than (−) the estimate.

   (a) $\dfrac{199}{198}+\dfrac{35}{17}$ (b) $4\dfrac{10}{11}+3\dfrac{8}{9}+\dfrac{13}{14}+\dfrac{1}{20}$ (c) $5\dfrac{19}{20}-2\dfrac{9}{10}+1\dfrac{1}{100}$

10. Estimate by rounding the fractions.

(a) $7\dfrac{8}{9} \cdot 5\dfrac{1}{13}$

(b) $\dfrac{34\dfrac{9}{10}}{4\dfrac{9}{10}}$

(c) $\dfrac{14\dfrac{19}{39}}{\dfrac{19}{39}}$

11. A plumber needs four sections of pipe $2\dfrac{7}{8}$ feet long. Can this be cut from a 12 foot section? If so, how much pipe will be left over? If not, why not?

12. Heidi's class had 17 A's out of 30 students and Barbara's class had 15 A's out of 27 students. Which class had the higher ratio of A's? Why?

13. Mable read 20 pages of a book in 15 minutes. If she continues to read at the same rate, how many pages will she read in 25 minutes?

Sample Assessment

1. Reduce each of the following rational numbers to simplest form.

   (a) $\dfrac{6^2}{48}$

   (b) $\dfrac{(xy)^2}{x^2y^2}$

   (c) $\dfrac{3x+9x^2}{x+3x^2}$

2. Perform each of the following computations.

   (a) $\dfrac{3}{8}+\dfrac{7}{12}$

   (b) $1-\dfrac{1}{2}+\dfrac{1}{3}-\dfrac{1}{4}+\dfrac{1}{5}-\dfrac{1}{6}$

   (c) $\left(5\dfrac{2}{7}+2\dfrac{3}{7}\right)\div 2\dfrac{1}{2}$

   (d) $\dfrac{3}{2}\cdot 4\dfrac{1}{3}$

3. Simplify each of the following. Write your answer in the form $\dfrac{a}{b}$, where a and b are integers and

   $\dfrac{a}{b}$ is in simplest form.

   (a) $\dfrac{\dfrac{2}{3}-\dfrac{1}{6}}{\dfrac{2}{3}+\dfrac{1}{6}}$

   (b) $\dfrac{\dfrac{2}{9}\cdot\dfrac{3}{4}}{\left(\dfrac{2}{3}\right)^2}$

4. Is the following statement true or false? (Justify your answer.) For all positive integers a, b such
   that $b \geq 2$, $\dfrac{a+1}{b-1} > \dfrac{a}{b}$.

5. A car travels 55 miles per hour and a plane travels 15 miles per minute. How far does the car travel
   when the plane travels 500 miles?

6. A $46\dfrac{5}{16}$ lb bag of nuts is packaged in $1\dfrac{3}{4}$ lb containers. The remaining nuts are given to the person
   packing the nuts. How much does the person get? Justify your answer.

7. If the ratio of boys to girls in a class is 3 to 8, will the ratios of boys to girls stay the same, become
   greater, or become smaller if 2 boys and 2 girls leave the class? Justify your answer?

8. Estimate each of the following, indicating if the actual answer is greater than (+) or less than (−) the
   estimate.

   (a) $\dfrac{29}{15}+\dfrac{198}{199}$

   (b) $5\dfrac{12}{13}+2\dfrac{9}{10}+\dfrac{19}{20}$

   (c) $10\dfrac{4}{9}-5\dfrac{1}{2}+\dfrac{99}{100}$

9. Estimate each of the following.

(a) $7\dfrac{33}{100} \cdot 3$

(b) $2\dfrac{25}{99} \cdot 8$

(c) $\dfrac{4\dfrac{10}{99}}{\dfrac{1}{10}}$

10. Place <, >, or = between each of the following pairs to make true statements.

(a) $\dfrac{11}{23}$ and $\dfrac{33}{65}$

(b) $\dfrac{7}{8}$ and $\dfrac{8}{9}$

(c) $-\dfrac{6}{7}$ and $-\dfrac{11}{33}$

11. The ratio of oranges to apples in the gift basket is 3 to 5. If there are 9 oranges, how many apples are there?

12. If $9\dfrac{1}{8}$ lb of nails cost $4.25, what is the cost of 292 lb?

13. The ratio of private school students to public school students in Adams City is 3 to 20. If there are 16,020 total students, how many are in private schools?

Sample Assessment

1. Write each of the following in simplest form with nonnegative exponents in the final answer.

   (a) $\left(\dfrac{1}{3}\right)^5 \cdot 3^{-5}$ (b) $5^4 \div 5^{-4}$ (c) $16^2 \cdot 8^{-2}$ (d) $\left(a^{-2} + b^{-2}\right)^{-1}$

2. Solve for the integer n in each of the following:

   (a) $2^n = \dfrac{1}{64}$ (b) $64^n = 32^{24}$

   (c) $24^n = 4^n \cdot 6^n$ (d) $4^n = 2^n + 2^n$

3. If $f(n) = \dfrac{3}{8} \cdot 2^n$ where n is an integer, find the following:

   (a) $f(0)$ (b) $f(-1)$ (c) $f(-3)$

   (b) the value of n for which $f(n) = \dfrac{3}{1024}$

4. Place >, <, or = between each of the following pairs to make true statements.

   (a) $2.\overline{23}$ and $\sqrt{5}$ (b) $0.\overline{3}$ and $\dfrac{1}{3}$

   (c) $0.\overline{4} \div 0.\overline{5}$ and 1 (d) $3.\overline{78}$ and $3.7\overline{8}$

5. For which values of k can $\dfrac{k}{3840}$ be written as a terminating decimal. Explain your reasoning.

6. Use fractions to justify the algorithm for the subtraction in the following.

   $8.07 - 2.3$

7. Round each of the following numbers as specified.

   (a) 508.576 to the nearest hundredth (b) 508.576 to the nearest tenth
   (c) 508.576 to the nearest hundred

8. Convert each of the following rational numbers to the form $\dfrac{a}{b}$ where a and b are integers and $b \neq 0$.

   (a) 0.27 (b) 3.104 (c) $0.2\overline{4}$ (d) 0.24

9.   Convert each of the following fractions to decimals that either terminate or repeat.

(a) $\dfrac{3}{40}$

(b) $\dfrac{3}{24}$

(c) $\dfrac{2}{13}$

10.   Find an approximation for $\sqrt{15}$ rounded to the nearest thousandth.

11.   Write each of the following in scientific notation.

(a)   5,268,000

(b)   0.000325

12.   Classify each of the following as a rational or irrational number.

(a)   6.76776777677776...

(b) $\dfrac{1}{\sqrt{15}}$

(c) $\dfrac{\sqrt{32}}{\sqrt{2}}$

13.   Without using a calculator, simplify each of the following if possible:

(a) $16^{-\frac{1}{4}}$

(b) $64^{-\frac{1}{6}}$

(c) $(-32)^{\frac{4}{5}}$

(d) $4^{\frac{1}{4}}$

14.   Solve each of the following for x, where x is a real number.

(a) $x\sqrt{3} - 2 = 5x\sqrt{3}$

(b) $0.4x - 0.68 \geq \dfrac{1}{2}(x - 3.8)$

(c) $0.\overline{9} - x = 1$

(d) $0.4 + x = 1$

(e) $5.2x - 0.01 < 0.2x + 3.6$

(f) $x^3 + \dfrac{81}{4} = \dfrac{x^3}{4}$

Sample Assessment

1. Write each of the following in simplest form with nonnegative exponents in the final answer.

    (a) $\left(\dfrac{1}{5}\right)^3 \cdot 5^{-3}$

    (b) $10^5 \div 10^{-5}$

    (c) $27^2 \cdot 9^{-3}$

    (d) $\left(1 + a^{-3}\right)^{-1}$

2. Find all integers n for which the following are true.

    (a) $4^n = \dfrac{1}{1024}$

    (b) $2^n = 3^n$

    (c) $2^n + 2^{n-1} = 3 \cdot 2^{n-1}$

    (d) $2^n > 3^n$

3. If $f(x) = 4^x$ where x is any real number, find each of the following if possible and simplify your answers. Do not use a calculator.

    (a) $f(-4)$

    (b) $f\left(\dfrac{-3}{2}\right)$

    (c) the value of x for which $f(x) = \dfrac{1}{\sqrt[5]{8^3}}$

4. Round each of the following numbers as specified.

    (a) 483.765 to the nearest hundredth
    (b) 483.765 to the nearest unit
    (c) 483.765 to the nearest hundred

5. Convert each of the following rational numbers to the form $\dfrac{a}{b}$ where a and b are integers and $b \neq 0$.

    (a) 0.38

    (b) 2.607

    (c) $0.4\overline{7}$

    (d) $0.\overline{324}$

6. Convert each of the following fractions to decimals that either terminate or repeat.

    (a) $\dfrac{7}{30}$

    (b) $\dfrac{11}{40}$

    (c) $\dfrac{5}{11}$

7. Find an approximation for $\sqrt{11}$ rounded to the nearest thousandth.

8. Place >, <, or = between each of the following pairs to make true sentences.

    (a) $4.\overline{9}$ and 5

    (b) $0.\overline{44}$ and $\dfrac{1}{25}$

    (c) $0.4\overline{6}$ and $0.4\overline{6}$

    (d) $\sqrt{3}$ and 1.7

9.   Use fractions to justify the algorithm for the subtraction in the following.

$$\begin{array}{r} 23.6 \\ -\ \underline{8.34} \end{array}$$

10.   A roll of ribbon three meters long is to be made into 16 bows of equal size. If all of the ribbon is to be used, how long is the piece of ribbon for each bow?

11.   Classify each of the following as a rational or irrational number.

(a) $\sqrt{2} + 8$ (b) $\dfrac{7}{22}$

(c) $0.\overline{23}$ (d) $3.14114111411114\ldots$

12.   Write each of the following in scientific notation.

(a)   3286   (b)   0.0000032

13.   Solve each of the following for x, if possible, where x is a real number.

(a) $5x\sqrt{2} - x\sqrt{2} = 7x\sqrt{2} + 5$ (b) $\dfrac{x}{0.4} + 80 = 0.5 + 0.8$

(c) $x^4 + 64 = \dfrac{5}{3}x^4$ (d) $0.\overline{3} + x = 0.\overline{7}$

(e) $\sqrt[3]{x^2} = 4$ (f) $x\left(1.\overline{2} - 0.\overline{2}\right) = 0.\overline{9} + 0.\overline{1}$

(g) $1.9 - x = 2$ (h) $x - \dfrac{0.5}{3} = \dfrac{1}{3}(3.7 + 2x)$

Sample Assessment

1. A loaf of whole wheat bread requires two teaspoons of salt. There are three teaspoons to a tablespoon and 16 tablespoons to a cup. How many cups of salt are required to bake L loaves of bread?

2. Solve each of the following for x and show the solution on a number line.

    (a) $\dfrac{x^2}{5} + 4 = 5$ (b) $1 - |x| > 0$

3. Solve each of the following systems of equations algebraically, if possible. Indicate whether the system has a unique solution, infinitely many solutions or no solution.

    (a) $2x + 4y = y + 12$
    $\quad\;\; y + 5 = x + 6$

    (b) $2x = 1 - 3y$
    $\quad\;\; 6y = 1 - 4x$

    (c) $2y - |x| = 3$
    $\quad\;\; 2|x| - 4y = -6$

4. A factory produces items at a cost $1.25 per item with an operational cost of $1200 (this cost is the same regardless of how many items are produced). Let $C(n)$ represent the total production cost for a production of n items.

    (a) Find an expression for $C(n)$ in terms of n.
    (b) If the manufacturer sells the items for $2.05 per item and $R(n)$ represents the revenue for a sale of n items, find $R(n)$ as a function of n.
    (c) What is the minimum number of items the manufacturer needs to sell to make a profit or break even?

5. Use mental mathematics to find the following and explain your approach.

    (a) What percent of 10,000 is 900?
    (b) 60% of 2,000.

6. Find x for the following balanced lever.

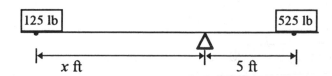

7.   If Misha receives $4\frac{1}{2}\%$ interest compounded daily on her investment, then what is her effective annual yield in a non-leap year?

8.   The figure below shows a weight of w grams (g) at a distance x cm from a fulcrum balancing a weight of 500 g at a distance of 8 cm from the fulcrum.

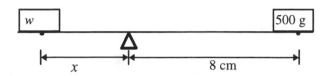

(a)   Write w as a function of x.
(b)   Sketch the graph of the function given in (a). (You may use the fact that 1000 g = 1 kg.)

9.   For each of the following, write the equation of the line determined by the given pair of points in the form $y = mx + b$ or the form $x = a$.

(a) $(-2, \frac{1}{2})$ and $(3, 5)$.

(b) $(7, 1)$ and $(0, 0)$.

(c) $(-1, \sqrt{2})$ and $(-1, 0)$.

10. Wheel's Bicycle shop advertised a bicycle for 15% off for a savings of $36. The bicycle did not sell so it was offered at a 20% discount off the sale price.

(a)   What did the bicycle sell for regularly?
(b)   What is the amount of the current discount?

11. Write each of the following as a percent.

(a)   0.1   (b) $\frac{1}{6}$ (c)   1   (d) $3\frac{3}{8}$

12. Two automobile dealers, A and B, had the same car which was listed at $18,000. Dealer A offered a $1,200 rebate and would negotiate a further 8% discount. Dealer B offered an 8% discount and would negotiate a further $1,200 rebate.

(a)   Which dealer has the lowest price?
(b)   What is the lowest price?

13. In addition to the driver, each bus may carry 20 people. If there are 93 students, four teachers, and eight parents going on a field trip to Rockaway Beach, how many buses are needed?

*14. The Cha family has decided that they need to invest some money for their daughter's college expenses. They estimate that they will need $80,000 in 16 years. If they can find an account that pays 11% interest compounded weekly, how much do they need to invest?

15. (a)   A 10 in. by 8 in. rectangular photograph is placed in a frame with a length to width ratio of 6:5 in such a way that the width of the border is the same on each side. Find the width of the border.

    (b)   Is it possible to place the photograph in part (a) in a frame with a length to width ratio of 5:4 so that the width of the border is the same on each side? Explain why or why not.

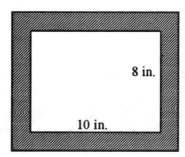

16. Paolo's ratio of free throws made to free throws attempted is 3:5. If he attempted 20 free throws, how many did he make?

17. Bashaar correctly answered 85% of the questions on his 200 question biology final. Fernando scored a 90% on his 180 question chemistry final.

    (a)   Who answered more questions correctly?
    (b)   Who answered more questions incorrectly?

18. If the length of a side of a square is s, then the area A is given by $A = s^2$ and the perimeter P is given by $P = 4s$.

    (a)   Express A as a function of P.
    (b)   Use your answer to part (a) to find the perimeter of a square whose area is 576 ft^2.
    (c)   Draw a graph of the function in part (a).

19. Jamar's car is 5 m long and 150 cm wide. If he were to build a scaled down model which was 12 cm long, how wide would it be?

*20. Rob can get $8\frac{3}{8}$% simple interest on a long-term investment. He would like to retire in 45 years as a millionaire. His investment plan allows him to invest the same amount of money every ten years for the first 40 years (Five installments). How much should Rob invest every installment to make his dream come true?

Sample Assessment

1. (a)   Mania wants to cut two strips of equal width from a rectangular piece of cardboard 20 in. by 15 in. If the length-to-width ratio of the remaining rectangle is to be 3:2 find the width of the strips if possible. If not possible, explain why not.

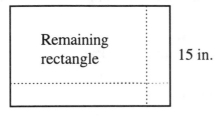

Remaining rectangle   15 in.

20 in.

   (b)   Answer the question in part (a) for the length-to-width ratio 5:4.
   (c)   Suppose the length-to-width ratio of the remaining rectangle in part (a) is r, that is, the length divided by width is some real number r. Find the width of the strips as a function of r.
   (d)   For which values of r in part (c) is it possible to cut the desired strips?

2. Solve each of the following systems, if possible. Indicate the number of solutions.

   (a) $\dfrac{1}{x} + \dfrac{1}{y} = 2$ (b) $x - 3y = 5$ (c) $2y - x^2 = 3$

   $\dfrac{1}{x} - \dfrac{1}{y} = 6$ $6y - 2x = 7$ $2x^2 - 4y + 6 = 0$

3. The Scarsdale Zoo had 12 snakes and 32 birds. In all, there were 160 animals in the zoo.

   (a)   Express the number of snakes to birds as a ratio.
   (b)   Express the number of birds to all animals at the zoo as a ratio.

4. If the length of a side of a square is s then the area A is given by $A = s^2$ and the perimeter P is given by $P = 4s$.

   (a)   Express P as a function of A.
   (b)   Produce a graph of the function given.
   (c)   What is the practical use of this function?

5. Write an expression for each of the following quantities as a function of the given variable or variables:

   (a)   the time it takes to travel a distance of x miles at a constant speed of 60 mph
   (b)   the revenue from the sale of x items at a price of $2.55 per item and y items at the price of $3.05 per item
   (c)   the sum of 101 terms in an arithmetic sequence if the fifty-first term is x
   (d)   the y-intercept of a line with slope m and x-intercept equal to -1.

6. A sale at Carney's Electronics offers a specific model of Sony radio at 20% off the regular price. If the sale price of the radios is $45, what is the regular price?

7. Assume that there were two farmers for every three people over the age of six in Ur. Further, assume that at some time, there were 4230 farmers in Ur. How many people over the age of six lived in Ur at that time?

8. Solve for x in each of the following proportions:

(a) $\dfrac{3x}{2} = \dfrac{41}{5}$

(b) $\dfrac{x+1}{8} = \dfrac{3}{4}$

9. Write each of the following as decimals.

(a) $\dfrac{1}{4}\%$

(b) 167%

10. Write each of the following equations in the form $y = mx + b$ and identify the slope and the y-intercept.

(a) $x + 2y = 3(x - 4y)$
(b) $y + 3x - 3 = x$

11. Solve each of the following for x and show the solution on a number line.

(a) $x + 6 > \sqrt{3} + 7$
(b) $|x| + 1 > 7$

12. Mary is three years older than John. John is twice as old as Una. How old is Mary if Una is y years old?

13. Find x for the following balanced lever.

14. Maan invests \$4,500 with First National Bank at $5\frac{1}{4}$ % simple interest.

    (a)   How much interest does Maan earn after one year?
    (b)   How much money did Maan have at the end of the year?
    (d)   If Maan reinvested everything for a second year, how much money would he have at the end of the second year?

*15. Sheila invests \$3,200 at 7% interest compounded quarterly.

    (a)   How much does she have after 10 years?
    (b)   20 years?
    (c)   50 years?

16. Use mental mathematics to find the following and explain your reasoning.

    (a)   40% of 50.
    (b)   What percent of 500 is 40?

17. Solve each of the following systems of equations graphically, if possible. Indicate whether the system has a unique solution, infinitely many solutions, or no solution.

    (a) $3y = x - 10$
          $y = x - 2$

    (b) $x + y = 5$
        $3x + 3y = 15$

18. Kelly counted 277 distinct beluga whales in the St. Lawrence Seaway in one week. The following week she counted 343 distinct belugas. What was the percent (to two decimal places of accuracy) of increase in the whales counted?

19. Write each of the following as a percent:

    (a) $\dfrac{1}{5}$

    (b) $\dfrac{1}{100}$

    (c)   3.042

    (d) $0.\overline{6}$

Sample Assessment

1. Suppose the names of the days of the week are placed in a hat and a name is drawn at random.

   (a) List the sample space for this experiment.
   (b) List the event consisting of the outcomes that the month drawn starts with the letter T.
   (c) What is the probably of drawing the name of a month that starts with T?

2. A fair coin was flipped three times and landed heads three times. What is the probability of a head on the next toss?

3. A bag contains five red candies, six white candies, and seven blue candies. Suppose one piece of candy is drawn at random. Find the probability for each of the following.

   (a) A white candy is drawn.
   (b) A red or blue candy is drawn.
   (c) Neither a white nor a blue candy is drawn.

4. One card is selected at random from an ordinary deck of 52 cards. Find the probability of each of the following events.

   (a) A heart is drawn.
   (b) A heart and a king are drawn.
   (c) A heart or a face card is drawn.

5. A box contains three blue cards and three white cards. If two cards are drawn one at a time, find the probability that both cards are blue if the draws are made as follows:

   (a) With replacement   (b) Without replacement

6. In a NASA rocket firing, the probability of the success of the first stage is 95%, of the second stage 97%, and of the third stage 98%. What is the probability for success for the three-stage rocket?

7. (a) If a letter is drawn from container 1, shown below, and placed in container 2, and then a letter is drawn from container 2, what is the probability that the letter is a T?

MATH	HAT
#1	#2

   (b) If a container above is selected at random, and then a letter is selected at random from the chosen container, what is the probability that the letter is a T?

8. If a couple plans to have 3 children, what is the probability of having at least 2 girls?

9. If two dice are rolled 360 times, approximately how many times should you expect the sums of 2, 3, or 12?

10. A teacher has prepared a 5-item test with the first three items being true or false and the last two items being multiple choice with four choices each. What is the probability that a students will score 100 percent if every answer is chosen at random?

11. A committee of three is selected at random from a set consisting of five Democrats, eight Republicans, and two Independents.

    (a) What is the probability that the committee consists of all Democrats?
    (b) What is the probability that the committee consists of no Republicans?

12. There were seven nominees for president and four nominees for vice president. In how many ways can the slate be chosen?

13. Compute $\dfrac{100!}{99!}$.

14. How many different two-person committees can be formed from a group of six people?

15. If automobile license plates consist of two letters followed by four digits, how many different possible license plates are possible if letters and numbers can be repeated?

16. Given the spinner below, find each of the following.

    (a) P(A)   (b) P(B)

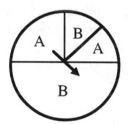

17. Find the number of ways to rearrange the letters in the word "MATHEMATICS".

18. If the odds in favor of the Rangers winning the game are 7 to 5, what is the probability that they will win?

19. Two standard dice are rolled. What are the odds in favor of rolling a sum of 10?

20. What are the odds against drawing a queen of hearts when one card is drawn from an ordinary deck of playing cards?

21. A sorority sold 132 tickets in a raffle for a $264 television set. What is the expected value of a single ticket if only one ticket wins?

22. How could picking three dates at random in the month of April be simulated using a random digit table?

Sample Assessment

1. Suppose the numbers from 1 to 26 are placed in a hat and a number is drawn at random.

    (a)   List the sample space for this experiment.
    (b)   List the event consisting of the outcomes that the number is even.
    (c)   What is the probably of drawing a number that is even?

2. What is the probability of a fair coin landing heads four times in a row?

3. A box contains four red marbles, seven white marbles, and five blue marbles. If one piece marble is drawn at random, find the probability for each of the following.

    (a)   A blue marble is drawn.
    (b)   A red or a blue marble is drawn.
    (c)   Neither a red nor a blue marble is drawn.

4. One card is drawn from an ordinary deck of 52 playing cards. Find the probability of each of the following events.

    (a)   A face card and a club is drawn.
    (b)   A face card or a club is drawn.
    (c)   A king is not drawn.

5. A box contains four red marbles, seven white marbles, and five blue marbles. If two marbles are drawn one at a time, find the probability that both marbles are white if the draws are made as follows:

    (a)   With replacement   (b)   Without replacement

6. The probability of Ann passing her math test is 90%. The probability she passes her English test is 80%. The probability she passes her Chemistry test is 70%. What is the probability she passes all three tests?

7. (a)   If a letter is drawn from container 1, shown below, and placed in container number 2, then a letter is drawn from container 2, what is the probability that the letter is a O?

LOOK   OUT

#1   #2

    (b)   If a letter is drawn from container number 1 above and then a letter is drawn from container number 2, what is the probability of the outcome OO?

8. If a couple plans to have 3 children, what is the probability of having at least 1 boy?

9. If two dice are rolled 360 times, approximately how many times should you expect a sum of 7?

10. A teacher has prepared a six-item test with the first three items being true or false and the last three items being multiple choice with four choices each. What is the probability that a students will score 0 if every answer is chosen at random?

11. A committee of two is selected at random from a set consisting of three Democrats, four Republicans, and one Independent.

   (a)   What is the probability that the committee consists of no Republicans?
   (b)   What is the probability that the committee consists of all Republicans?

12. There were eight nominees for president and three nominees for vice president. In how many ways can the slate be chosen?

13. Compute $\dfrac{26!}{24!2!}$.

14. How many different four-person committees can be formed from a group of six people?

15. If automobile license plates consist of three letters followed by three digits, how many different possible license plates are possible if letters and numbers can be repeated?

16. Given the spinner below, find each of the following.

   (a)   P(A)   (b)   P(B)

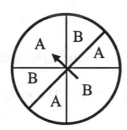

17. Find the number of ways to rearrange the letters in the word "HELLO".

18. If the odds in favor of the Tigers winning their next game are 8 to 4, what is the probability that they will win?

19. Two standard dice are rolled. What are the odds in favor of rolling a sum of 8?

20. What is the odds against drawing a queen of hearts when one card is drawn from an ordinary deck of playing cards?

21. Joe's baseball team sold 200 chances to win a $250 set of golf clubs. What is the expected value of a single chance if only one chance wins?

22. How could picking three letters of the alphabet at random be simulated using a random digit table?

Sample Assessment

1. Claude paid $38.80 for dinner for himself and two friends. If one friend's meal cost twice as much as Claude's and Claude's meal cost the same as his other friend, answer the following:

   (a) What is the mean cost of the meals?
   (b) What is the median cost of the meals?
   (c) What is the mode cost of the meals?

2. Find the following for the given scores (a) mean, (b) median, (c) mode, (d) range, (e) standard deviation.

98	98	98	98	45
84	84	52	45	37

3. The budget for the Women's Center is $1,000,000. If $500,000 is spent on advertising, $150,000 is spent on conferences, and the remainder is spent on long-term securities, draw a circle graph to indicate how the money is spent.

4. If the median is higher than the mean on a set of test scores, describe the distribution.

5. Twenty test scores are shown below.

31	30	23	27	19
26	28	38	17	29
26	34	21	32	32
22	12	26	39	25

   (a) Make a grouped frequency table for these scores, using 10 to start the first class and having interval size 5.
   (b) Draw a histogram for the grouped data.
   (c) Draw an ordered stem-and-leaf plot for the data.
   (d) Construct a box plot to illustrate the data.
   (e) Explain whether there are any outliers for the data.

6. (a) The mean age of members of a class reunion was 71.9. The next year the mean age was 71.5 years. How can the mean age decrease when all the class members are a year older?
   (b) The mean age of 10 persons in a room is 15 years. A 50-year-old person walks in. How much is the mean increased?

7. An advertisement claims "Four out of five doctors surveyed recommend Tielitnot for their patients with arthritis." State why you would or would not accept this as a valid claim to product superiority.

*8.   A standardized test has a mean of 500 with a standard deviation of 70. If 2000 students took the test and their scores approximated a normal curve, how many scores are between 360 and 640?

9.   Explain how to determine if a score is an outlier when constructing a box plot.

*10.   On a final exam the mean was 72 with a standard deviation of 15. Find the grade corresponding to a z score of -1.

Sample Assessment

1. The weights in pounds of six elementary students are: 80, 92, 71, 63, 76, and 83. Find (a) the mean (b) the median (c) the mode (d) the standard deviation to the nearest tenth of a pound.

2. The mean annual salary paid to the employees at Pay-Less Food Store was $5000. The mean annual salaries paid to female and male employees at the store were $5200 and $4200 respectively. Determine the percentages of females and males employed by the store.

3. The mean average for Joyce's 11 test scores was 62.5. How much will a score of 100 increase her mean average?

4. The scores for the winners of the British open from 1981 to 1991 are given below.

Year	Score
1981	276
1982	284
1983	275
1984	276
1985	282
1986	280
1987	279
1988	273
1989	275
1990	270
1991	272

   (a) Construct a line plot for the data.
   (b) Draw a bar graph for the data.

5. The following are the weights in pounds of 30 students at the Summer Math Camp.

146	163	142	147	135	153	140	135	128	145
146	158	140	147	136	148	152	144	156	150
168	126	138	176	163	119	154	165	142	135

   (a) Construct a frequency table for the data above with the first class starting at 115 and interval size 10.
   (b) Draw a histogram depicting the data.

*6. A principal remarked that no student from his school should have a mathematics score on a standardized test below the national mean. Comment on this.

7. The quiz scores for Mr. Read's and Miss Sol's classes are given below.

    (a) Draw a line plot for each set.
    (b) Draw a back-to-back stem and leaf plot for the two classes.
    (c) Give the interquartile range for each set of scores.
    (d) Are there any outliers for either set of data? If yes, what are they?
    (e) Draw box plots to compare the two sets of data.
    (f) What can you say about the two sets of data?

Mr. Read	Miss Sol
72	90
78	88
85	78
92	83
75	96
76	92
89	90
96	84
78	75
92	98
90	93
80	92

8. What does it mean to say that there is a positive correlation when viewing a scattergram?

* 9. Two students received z-scores of 0.8 and -0.4 respectively on a test. If their scores on the test were 88 and 64 respectively, what are the mean and standard deviation on the test?

*10. A standardized test has a mean of 200 with a standard deviation of 50. If 1000 students took the test and their scores approximated a normal curve, how many scores are between 100 and 300?

Sample Assessment

1. Sketch four lines with exactly four intersection points.

2. Sketch and name two adjacent angles that are supplementary.

3. What is the least number of vertices that a polyhedron may have?

4. Explain why a regular heptagon (7-gon) cannot be a face of a regular polyhedron.

5. Classify the following as true or false. If false, tell why.

    (a) Two distinct lines that do not intersect are parallel.
    (b) No square is a rectangle.
    (c) If a plane contains one point of a line, then it must contain the entire line.
    (d) A line separates space into three distinct sets of points.
    (e) For any two distinct points A and B, $\overleftrightarrow{AB} = \overleftrightarrow{BA}$.
    (f) A ray contains no endpoints.

6. Describe each of the following sets of points with reference to the given figure.

    (a) (plane AFP) $\cap$ (plane XYE)
    (b) (Plane XYE) $\cap \overleftrightarrow{AE}$
    (c) $\overline{BE} \cap \overline{CE}$
    (d) $\overline{CE} \cap \triangle ADF$
    (e) $\overrightarrow{AE} \cup \overleftrightarrow{DE}$
    (f) $\overrightarrow{EB} \cup \overrightarrow{EC}$
    (g) (interior $\triangle ADF$) $\cap \overleftrightarrow{AF}$

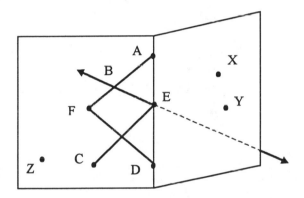

7. If the measure of an angle is 23°17′18″, what is the measure of its supplement?

8. If the non-base angle of an isosceles triangle has a measure of 70°, what is the measure of each base angle?

9. How many diagonals does a decagon have?

10. If 9x° and (5x + 8)° are the measures for complementary angles, what is the measure of each angle?

11. Is a rhombus a regular polygon? Explain your answer.

12. Given the figure shown with $\overleftrightarrow{AX} \parallel \overleftrightarrow{DY}$, find the following:

    (a)   m(∠1)
    (b)   m(∠2)
    (c)   m(∠3)
    (d)   m(∠4)
    (e)   m(∠5)

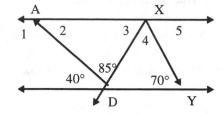

13. Complete the following table converting metric measures.

	mm	cm	m	km
(a)		5200		
(b)			260	
(c)				0.3
(d)	1,300,00			

14. In the figure, how is the measure of angle 4 related to the sum of the measures of angle 1 and angle 2. Justify your answer.

15. Which of the figures are traversable? For those that are traversable, circle all possible starting points.

    (a)   (b)   (c)

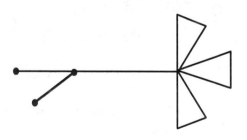

16. Draw each of the following.

    (a)   A simple closed curve that is not a polygon.
    (b)   A convex quadrilateral.

17. (a)   Show that the circumference C of a circle can be expressed as a function of its area A as
    $$C = 2\sqrt{\pi \cdot A}$$

    (b)   If the ratio between the areas of two circles is 2:1, what is the ratio between their circumferences?

Sample Assessment

1. Sketch two angles whose intersection is exactly 3 points.

2. Sketch and name two angles that have a common vertex and a common side, but are not adjacent angles.

3. What is the number of vertices in an octagonal prism?

4. If planes α and β are distinct planes having points X, Y, and Z in common, what conclusion can you make about points X, Y, and Z? Why?

5. Classify the following as true or false. If false, tell why.

    (a) For any line $\overleftrightarrow{AB}$ and point C such that $C \in \overleftrightarrow{AB}$, there is one and only one plane containing both C and $\overleftrightarrow{AB}$.
    (b) A parallelogram has four acute angles.
    (c) A line segment contains an infinite number of points.
    (d) The union of two half lines is always a line.
    (e) For any two distinct points A and B, $\overrightarrow{AB} = \overrightarrow{BA}$.
    (f) If $\overrightarrow{AB} = \overrightarrow{CB}$, then A must be a different name for C.
    (g) Every equilateral triangle is a scalene triangle.

6. Describe each of the following sets of points with reference to the given figure.

    (a) $\alpha \cap \beta$
    (b) $\triangle ADF \cap \overleftrightarrow{BE}$
    (c) $\overleftrightarrow{AF} \cap \overline{BE}$
    (d) $\angle CAF \cap \overleftrightarrow{CF}$
    (e) $\overline{AE} \cup \overleftrightarrow{FE}$
    (f) $\overrightarrow{BD} \cup \overrightarrow{BA}$
    (g) (interior $\triangle ADF$) $\cap \overleftrightarrow{AF}$
    (h) $\overline{AE} \cup \overline{EF}$

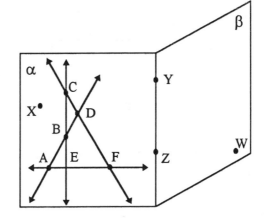

7. (a) What is the measure of each angle in a regular dodecagon?
    (b) How many diagonals does a dodecagon have?

8. Consider a circular track formed by two concentric circles (circles with a common center). Let w be the width of the track.

    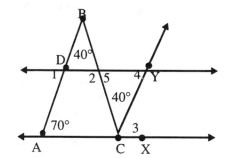

    (a) If the circumferences of the circles are 1 km and 1.013 km respectively, find the width w of the track in meters.
    (b) Suppose the circumferences of the circles are 100 km and 100.013 km respectively. How wide would the track be now?
    (c) Based on your answers to parts (a) and (b) make a conjecture concerning the width of similar tracks.
    (d) Justify your conjecture in part (c).

9. A rectangle has been defined as a parallelogram in which one of the angles is a right angle. Explain why a rectangle must have four right angles.

10. If $5x°$ and $(7x + 12)°$ are the measures for vertical angles angles formed by two intersecting lines, what is the measure of each angle?

11. (a) Find $28° \, 29' \, 46'' - 16° \, 48' \, 59''$.
    (b) Express $5.4°$ in terms of degrees, minutes, and seconds.

12. Given the figure shown with $\overset{\leftrightarrow}{AX} \, || \, \overset{\leftrightarrow}{DY}$, find the following:

    (a) $m(\angle 1)$
    (b) $m(\angle 2)$
    (c) $m(\angle 3)$
    (d) $m(\angle 4)$
    (e) $m(\angle 5)$

13. Each of the following triples are measures of three segments. Determine which can and which cannot be used to form a triangle. Justify your answers.

    (a) 10 cm, 35 cm , 20 cm
    (b) 2 m, 3 m, 50 cm
    (c) 3 ft, 5 ft, 7 yd
    (d) x cm, x cm, x cm, where x is any positive real number.

14. If $\overrightarrow{AX}$ bisects $\angle DAB$ and $\overrightarrow{AY}$ bisects $\angle BAC$, show $\overrightarrow{AX} \perp \overrightarrow{AY}$.

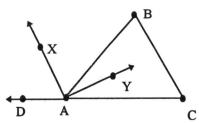

*15. Which of the figures are traversable? For those that are traversable, circle all possible starting points.

(a)   (b)   (c)

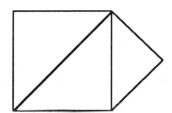   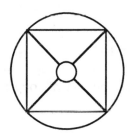   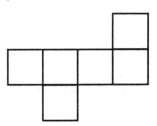

16. Draw each of the following curves.

   (a)   A closed curve that is not simple.
   (b)   A concave hexagon.

17. Complete each of the following:

   (a)   1000 m = _____ km
   (b)   25 m = _____ cm
   (c)   26,000 mm = _____ m
   (d)   0.4 mi = _____ ft
   (e)   4.8 yd = _____ ft

*18. Write a Logo procedure to construct a pair of supplementary angles given the measure of one angle, :A.

Sample Assessment

1. Given the figures, state whether the triangles are congruent based upon the given conditions. If your answer is yes, name the theorem or postulate abbreviation to justify your answer.

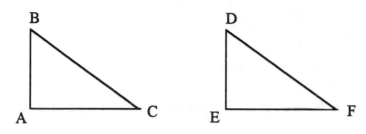

(a) $\angle A \cong \angle E$; $\angle B \cong \angle D$; $\overline{AB} \cong \overline{ED}$

(b) $\angle A$ and $\angle E$ are right angles; $\overline{BC} \cong \overline{DF}$; $\angle C \cong \angle F$.

(c) $\overline{AC} \cong \overline{EF}$; $\angle C \cong \angle F$; $\overline{BC} \cong \overline{DF}$

(d) $\overline{AC} \cong \overline{EF}$; $\overline{BC} \cong \overline{DF}$; $\overline{AB} \cong \overline{ED}$

2. In each of the parts, there is at least one pair of congruent triangles. Identify them and tell why they are congruent.

(a)

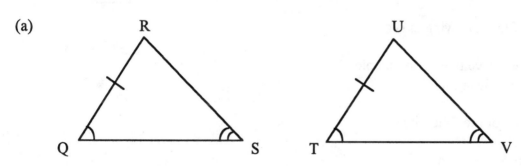

(b)

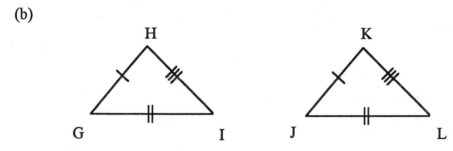

(c)

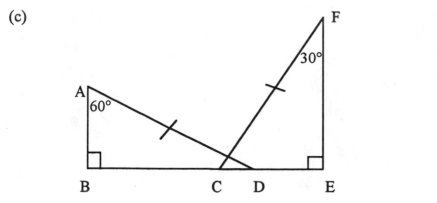

3. Construct each of the following using any tool.

(a) Angle bisector of ∠ A

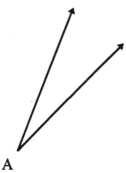

A

(b) Perpendicular bisector of $\overline{AB}$

A   B

(c) Altitude of ΔABC from A

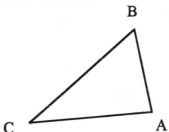

B

C   A

(d) Parallel to ℓ through *m*

• *m*

ℓ

(e) Divide the given segment into three congruent parts.

A   B

4. For each of the following pairs of similar triangles, find the missing measure.

(a)

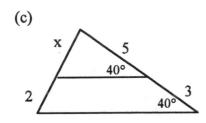

(b)

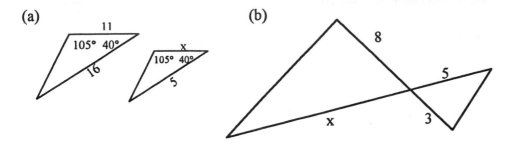

(c)

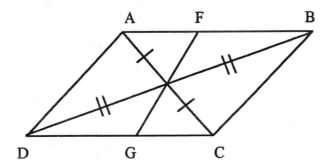

5. A person 122 cm tall casts a 37-cm shadow at the same time a tree casts a 148-cm shadow. How tall is the tree?

6. Suppose you have three straight sticks of lengths 5 cm, 12 cm, and 19 cm. Can you arrange these sticks into a triangle? If not, why not?

7. (a) What kind of figure is quadrilateral ABCD?
   (b) Is ∠GFB congruent to ∠FGC? Justify your answer.
   (c) Is ∠GFB congruent to ∠FGD? Justify your answer.

8. Give one example of information that would determine congruency for each of the following.

   (a) Two squares
   (b) Two triangles

9. $\overline{AD}$ is the perpendicular bisector of $\overline{CB}$

Construct and label three isosceles triangles that have points B and C as two of their vertices.

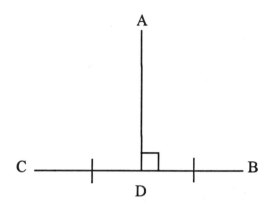

10. For each of the following, write the equation of the line determined by the given pair of points.

    (a) (3, ⁻7) and (3, ⁻27)
    (b) (⁻4, 5) and (⁻8, ⁻7)

11. Determine if the three points with coordinates given lie on the same line.
    (2, 3), (4, 6) and (6, 9)

*12. In the following, find x and y.

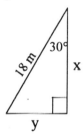

*13. If the sin θ = 0.8342, and $0 \leq \theta < 90°$, what is the cos θ?

*14. If the tan ($\angle$ABC) = 0.7002 and sin ($\angle$ABC) = 0.5736, what is the cos θ?

Sample Assessment

1. Assume that each pair of triangles is congruent and write an appropriate symbolic congruence in each case.

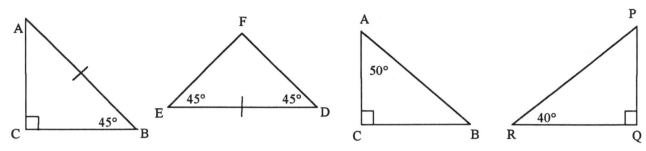

2. Using any tools to construct each of the following:

    (a)   An equilateral triangle.
    (b)   A 75° angle.
    (c)   Divide the segment $\overline{AB}$ into 3 congruent parts.

    (d)   A circle tangent to ℓ and m where $\ell \,||\, m$ that passes through P.

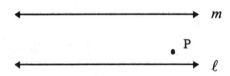

    (e)   Given △ABC below, construct a similar triangle whose sides are twice as great.

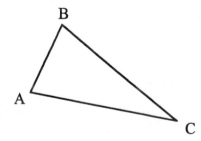

3. Given $\overline{AM} \cong \overline{MC}$ and $\overline{BM} \cong \overline{MD}$ why are the following true? Justify your answer.

    (a) $\overline{AB} \cong \overline{CD}$
    (b) $\overline{AB} \parallel \overline{CD}$

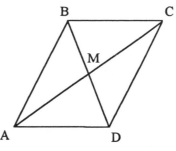

4. In each of the following find x and y if possible.

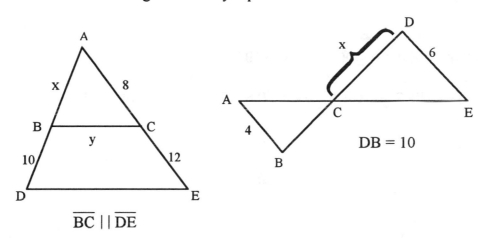

$$\overline{BC} \parallel \overline{DE}$$

5. A girl wants to calculate the height of her family's tepee. She is 112 cm tall and she finds that when she is inside and stands so that her head touches the side, her feet are 64 cm from the edge. If the tepee is a right circular cone with a diameter of 352 cm, what is its height?

6. In each of the following answer true or false. Justify your answers.

    (a)   Congruent triangles are also similar.
    (b)   Two similar triangles are also congruent triangles.
    (c)   Any two equilateral triangles are similar.
    (d)   Two isosceles triangles are similar.
    (e)   The diagonals of a trapezoid divide it into four triangles, two of which are similar.
    (f)   If three sides of one triangle are parallel, respectively, to three sides of a second triangle, then the triangles are similar.

7. Suppose you have three straight sticks of lengths 10 cm, 20 cm, and 31 cm. Can you arrange these sticks into a triangle? If not, why not?

8. Two lines are parallel if they have the same slope. Explain why the points with the following coordinates form a parallelogram.

    A(3, 4), B(5, 8), C(8, 3), D(6, ⁻1)

9.   Write the equation of $\overleftrightarrow{AB}$ from problem 9.

*10.   In the following, find x and y.

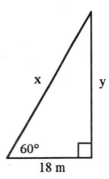

*11.   If the cos θ = 0.8342, and 0 ≤ θ ≤ 90°, what is sin θ?

*12.   If the tan (∠ABC) = 0.7002 and cos (∠ABC) = 0.8192, what is the sin ∠ABC?

Sample Assessment

1. Find the area of each of the following.

    (a)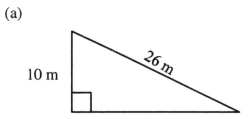

    10 m

    26 m

    (b)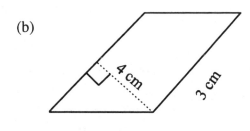

    4 cm

    3 cm

    50 mm
    parallelogram

2. Find the surface area of the square prism whose base has a side of length 5 cm and a height of 6 cm.

3. Find the area of the shaded region on the following geoboard if the unit of measurement is 1 cm^2.

4. If a square has the area 10 cm^2, what is the length of a side?

5. Explain how the formula for the area of a triangle can be determined by using the formula for the area of a parallelogram.

6. Answer the following.

    (a)   If the volume of a sphere is $\dfrac{500\pi}{3}$ m^3, what is the diameter of the sphere?

    (b)   Find the volume of a cylinder whose height is 2 m and whose base has an area of 9π m^2.

7. What is the area of the figure below? The arc shown is a semicircle.

    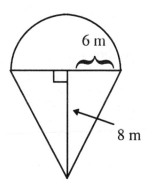

    6 m

    8 m

8. For each of the following, can the measures represent sides of a right triangle? Explain your answers.

   (a)   3 m, 4 m, 5 m

   (b) $\sqrt{2}$ cm $\sqrt{3}$ cm $\sqrt{5}$ cm

9. Complete each of the following:

   (a)   500 cm^2 = ___ m^2
   (c)   4000 g = ___ kg
   (e)   17 ha = ___ m^2
   (g)   0.027 L = ___ cm^3

   (b)   18 km = ___ m
   (d)   300 mL = ___ L
   (f)   0.027 kL = ___ mL
   (h)   4738 kL of water at 4°C has a mass of ___ kg.

10. Complete the following: (Use a calculator whenever convenient.)

   (a)   1400 ft^2 = ___ yd^2
   (c)   4.5 lb = ___ oz

   (b)   1/9 yd^3 = ___ ft^3
   (d)   32°C = ___ °F

11. (a)   Suppose one edge of a cubic tank is 8 m and the tank is filled with water at 4°C; find the volume of the tank in cubic meters.
    (b)   Find the capacity of the tank of (a) in liters.
    (c)   Find the mass of the water of (a) in kilograms.

12. Complete each of the following.

   (a)   3 dm^3 of water has a mass of ___ g.
   (b)   2 L of water has a mass of ___ g.
   (c)   13 cm^3 of water has a mass of ___ g.
   (d)   4.2 L of water has a mass of ___ g.
   (e)   3.01 L of water has a volume of ___ m^3.

13. Find the volume of a cone whose slant height is 50 cm and whose height is 40 cm.

14. If the diameter of a circle is 14 cm, find each of the following.

   (a)   the circumference of the circle
   (b)   the area of the circle
   (c)   the area of a sector of the circle that corresponds to a central angle of 18°.

15. Find the perimeter of the following if all arcs shown are semicircles.

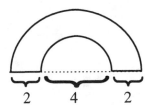

   2   4   2

Sample Assessment

1. Find the area of △ABC in each of the following.

(a)   (b)

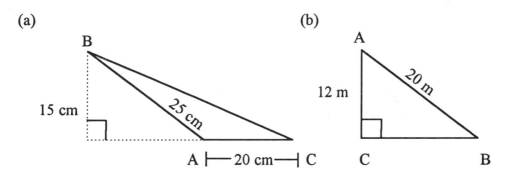

2. Assume that the only area formula you know is the formula for the area of a triangle. Explain how to derive the formula for the area of a trapezoid.

3. A toy manufacturer wants to design a wooden square pyramid whose volume is 8000 cm³.

    (a) Design such a pyramid. Make a sketch and show the dimensions of the base and the altitude.
    (b) How many such pyramids are possible? Why?

4. If each dimension of a box is quadrupled, how are the surface area and the volume affected?

5. For each of the following, can the measures represent sides of a right triangle? Explain your answers.

    (a) 30 cm   40 cm   50 cm   (b) $\sqrt{2}$ cm $\sqrt{3}$ cm $\sqrt{6}$ cm

6. A rectangular prism has dimensions 60 cm, 40 cm, 200 cm.

    (a) Find the surface area of the prism in square centimeters.
    (b) Find the volume of the prism in cubic meters.
    (c) Find the capacity of the prism in liters

7. A cone has a circular base with radius 50 cm and slant height 90 cm. Find the surface area.

8. A box-shaped container has a 2 m by 3 m rectangular base. It is partially filled with water and the height of the water is 0.5 m.

    (a) How many liters of water are in the container?
    (b) Find the mass of the water in kilograms.
    (c) If 60 L of water are added to the container, how much will the water rise?

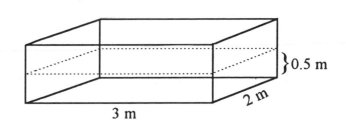

9. Find the surface area of a right circular cylinder that is 6 cm in diameter and is 12 cm in height.

10. Find x in each of the following:

(a)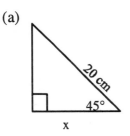

(b)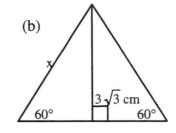

(c)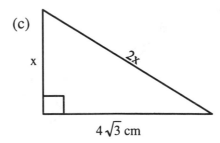

11. Complete the following: (Use a calculator whenever convenient.)

   (a) $30 \text{ m}^2 = $ ___ cm^2
   (b) $0.03 \text{ L} = $ ___ mL
   (c) $3 \text{ yd}^2 = $ ___ ft^2
   (d) $48{,}033 \text{ ft}^3 = $ ___ yd^3
   (e) $10 \text{ ha} = $ ___ m^2
* (f) $-40°\text{C} = $ ___ °F
* (g) $98.6°\text{F} = $ ___ °C

12. What happens to the surface area of a sphere if the diameter is tripled?

13. Find the volume of the figure below (assume a right circular cylinder).

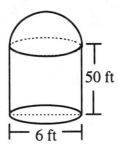

Sample Assessment

1. Complete each of the following motions.

(a)

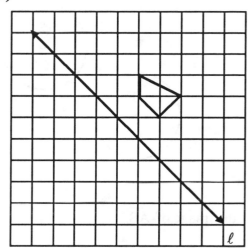

a reflection in ℓ

(b)

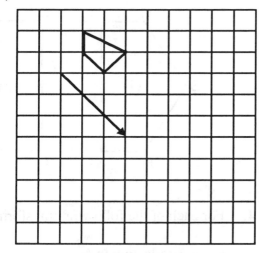

a translation as pictured

(c)

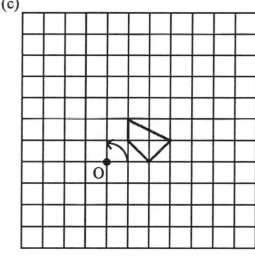

a rotation in O through
the given arc

(d)

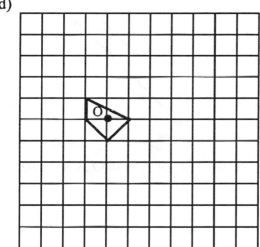

a size transformation with
center O and scale factor 2

2. How many lines of symmetry, if any, does each of the following figures have?

(a)

(b)

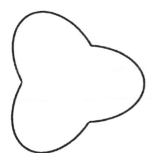

3. The following pairs of figures are congruent. Tell which transformations will take figure (1) to figure (2).

(a)

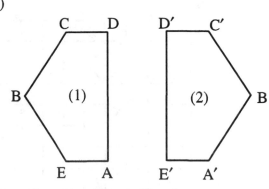

(b)

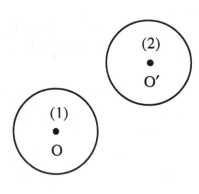

4. For each of the following transformations, construct the image of $\overline{AB}$.

(a)   A reflection in ℓ

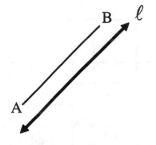

(b)   A translation which takes M to N

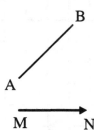

(c)   A rotation in O as indicated

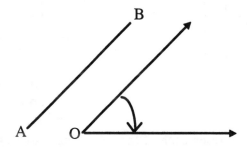

5. Describe objects which have each of the following types of symmetry.

(a)   line   (b)   point
(c)   plane   (d)   45° rotational

6. For each of the following pairs of figures, determine which transformation might take one figure to the other.

(a)

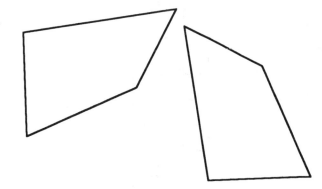

(b)

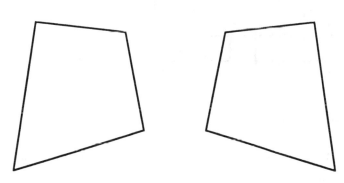

(c)

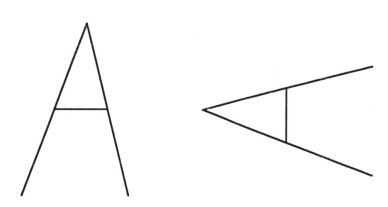

7. (a)   Draw a rectangle ABCD and then construct a line such that the image of the rectangle under reflection in the line is the original rectangle. Is there more than one line with this property?

(b)   For what kind of rectangles is it possible to find more than two lines with the property in (a). Justify your answer.

(c)   Describe all trapezoids for which it is possible to find a line ℓ such that when the trapezoid is reflected in ℓ its image is itself.

8.   (a)   Find the image of the circle with center O under a size transformation with scale factor $\frac{3}{4}$.

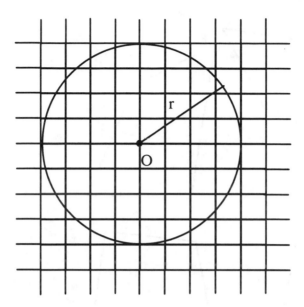

(b)   What kind of figure is the image in (a)? Why?

9.   Show that the circle with center O_1 is the image of the circle with center O under a succession of isometrics with a size transformation.

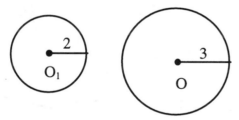

10. If possible, describe a geometric figure that can be transformed into itself by each of the following:

(a)   reflection
(b)   rotation
(c)   translation
(d)   glide reflection

11. Use a reflection to argue that the base angles of an isosceles triangle are congruent.

12. Given points A and B and ΔDEF below, find point C on ΔDEF such that ΔABC is isosceles.

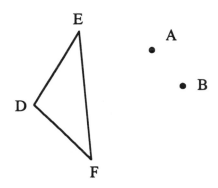

13. Let ℓ′ be the image of ℓ under a half-turn about point O. If A′ is the image of A and B′ the image of B and $\overline{OB} \perp \ell$, classify each of the following as true or false. Justify your answers.

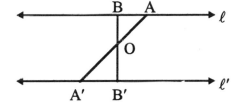

    (a)   ΔOAB ≅ ΔOA′B′
    (b)   OB′ is the distance from O to ℓ′
    (c)   ℓ||ℓ′
    (d)   The image of $\overline{AA'}$ is $\overline{BB'}$

14. A student claims that anything that can be accomplished by a translation can also be accomplished by a reflection. She claims that if A′ is the image of A under a translation, then A′ can be obtained by a reflection in the line ℓ which is the perpendicular bisector of $\overline{AA'}$. Hence, a translation and a reflection are the same. How do you respond?

15. Find the images of the points P(−3, 4) and Q(a,b) under each of the following transformations.
    (i)   Translation given by $(x,y) \rightarrow (x+3, y-4)$
    (ii)   Reflection in the line y = x
    (iii) Reflection in the line y = −x
    (iv)   Half turn about the origin
    (v)   Rotation by 90° counterclockwise about the origin.

16. Find the point whose image is (−3, 4) and the point whose image is (a, b) under each of the transformations in problem 15.

17. Given A(2, 1) and B(3, 3), find the equation of the line (in slope intercept form) through A and perpendicular to $\overleftrightarrow{AB}$.

*18. Explain why a regular pentagon cannot tessellate the plane.

*19. Write a Logo procedure called H that will draw a strip of H's similar to the one below.

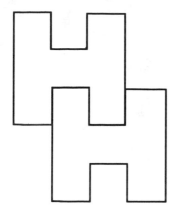

Sample Assessment

1. Complete each of the following motions.

    (a)

    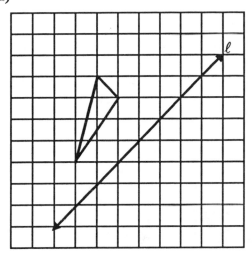

    a reflection in ℓ

    (b)

    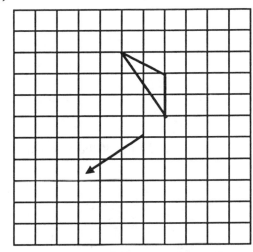

    a translation as pictured

    (c)

    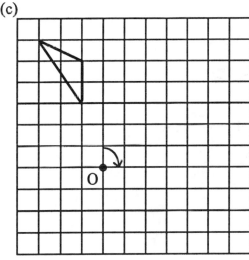

    a rotation in O through
    the given arc

    (d)

    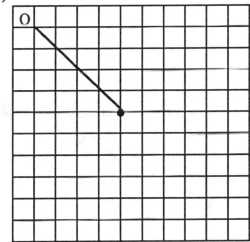

    a size transformation with
    center O and scale factor 1/2

2. For each of the following transformations construct the image of the indicated figure.

    (a)   A reflection of ΔABC in ℓ

    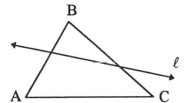

2.   (cont.)

(b)   A translation of the circle along the arrow from M to N.

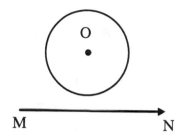

(c)   A half-turn of the line ℓ in O.

O•

(d)   A 60° rotation counterclockwise of △ABC in A.

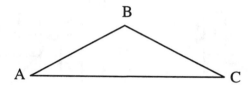

*3.   Show how to tessellate the plane with the quadrilateral given below.

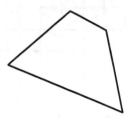

4.   How many lines of symmetry, if any, does each of the following figures have?

(a)   (b)

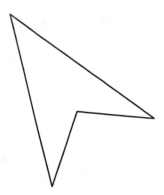   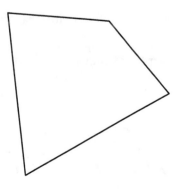

(c)   (d)

5. Describe point symmetry and rotational symmetries, if any, of the parts of Problem 4.

6. For each of the following pairs of figures, determine which transformation might take one figure to the other.

(a)   (b)

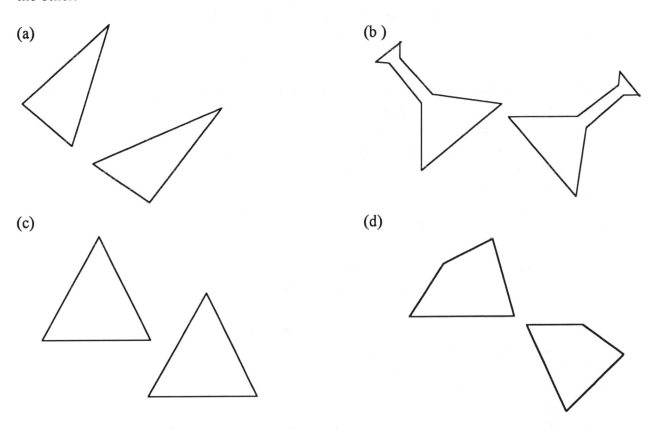

(c)   (d)

7. Find the minimum number of reflecting lines needed to accomplish the isometries in Problem 6.

8. Use a reflection to argue that the base angles of an isosceles trapezoid are congruent.

9. Show that ΔADE is the image of ΔABC under a succession of isometries with a size transformation.

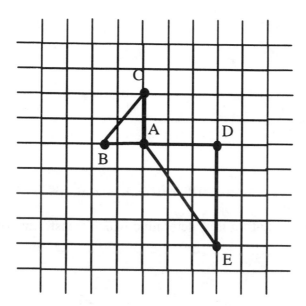

10. A student claims that anything that can be accomplished by a glide reflection can also be accomplished by a half-turn. He claims that if A′ is the image of A under a glide reflection then A′ can also be obtained by a half-turn about point O, where O is the intersection of the line of reflection with $\overline{AA'}$. Hence a glide reflection and a half-turn are the same. How do you respond?

11. A student claims that a succession of two reflections in two perpendicular lines can always be accomplished by a half-turn. Hence a secession of two reflections in two perpendicular lines is a half-turn. How do you respond?

12. Find the equation of the line (in slope intercept form) which intersects the x axis at $x = -5$ and is perpendicular to the line whose equation is $x = -2y$.

13. Find the images of the points P(2, 3) and Q(a,b) under each of the following:
    (a) Translation given by $(x,y) \rightarrow (x + 3, y + 5)$
    (b) Translation given in (a) followed by the same translation
    (c) Reflection in the line $y = 0$
    (d) Reflection in the line $x = 0$
    (e) Reflection in the line $y = 0$ followed by a reflection in line $x = 0$

14. Find the equations (in slope intercept form) of all the lines of symmetries of ΔABC if the coordinates of its vertices are A(1, 0), B(−1, 0) and C($\sqrt{3}$, 0).

*15. What regular figure can be used with a regular octagon to tessellate the plane?

*16. Write a Logo procedure called HOUSE to draw a strip of houses similar to the ones below.

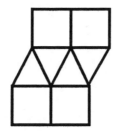

Answers to Sample Assessment

1. (a) 13, 8, 3   (b) 40, 20, 10   (c) 61, 99, 160
    (d) 128, 256, 512   (e) 4, 9, 16

2. (a) arithmetic   (b) geometric   (c) neither
    (d) geometric   (e) neither

3. (a) $6 + (n - 1)2$ or $2n + 4$ (b) $n^2 + 1$ (c) 5^n

4. (a) 5, 8, 11, 14, 17   (b) 2, 6, 12, 20, 30   (c) 8, 18, 30, 44, 60

5. 2544

6. (a) $(n + 1)$th term = nth term $+111$ (b) 11090

7. 1415

There are 9 pages with a one-digit number, 90 pages with a two-digit number, 900 pages with a three-digit number, and so on. Since $9 \cdot 1 + 90 \cdot 2 + 900 \cdot 3 = 2889$ digits, she must be past page 999. (Check that she hasn't yet reached page 9999.) She is now numbering pages with four-digit page numbers, so the number of digits she has written is:
$9 \cdot 1 + 90 \cdot 2 + 900 \cdot 3 + p \cdot 4$, or $2889 + 4 \cdot p$, where p is the number of pages past 999. Because she has written 4553 digits, $4553 = 2889 + 4 \cdot p$. Consequently:

$4553 - 2889 = 4p$
$1664 = 4p$
$p = 416$

Therefore, she has numbered 416 pages past 999 and therefore a total of 1415 pages.

8. 74 x 93

9. (a) No. The five tables in the middle of this arrangement can seat only two people. The two end tables can seat four people. Consequently, John will only be able to seat $5 \cdot 2 + 2 \cdot 4$ or 18 people with this arrangement.
    (b) Yes. The five tables in the middle of this arrangement can seat four people. The two end tables can seat five people. Consequently, John can seat $5 \cdot 4 + 2 \cdot 5$ or 30 people with this arrangement.

10. 81 rabbits

11. (a) 17 cm   (b) 46 cm

12. 49 ways if not all must be used at any given time.

13. 100 rectangles.

Answers to Sample Assessment

1. (a) 127, 107, 147   (b) 6250, 31250, 156250   (c) 43, 50, 57
    (d) 32, 0, 64   (e) 25, 29, 33

2. (a) neither   (b) geometric   (c) arithmetic
    (d) neither   (e) arithmetic

3. (a) $4 + (n - 1)5$ or $5n - 1$ (b) $6 \cdot 2^{(n-1)}$ (c) n^2

4. (a) 11, 15, 19, 23, 27   (b) 3, 8, 15, 24, 35   (c) 0, 2, 6, 12, 20

5. 1218   6.   9

7. The test tube will overflow on the 12th night. At the end of the first night the test tube contains 25 mL, but by the end of the first day it contains only 16 mL. The net gain after one night and one day is 16 mL. If the test tube has more than 175 mL at nightfall, it will over flow during the night. After the 11th night and day the test tube contains $11 \cdot 16$ or 176 mL. Therefore, it will overflow the following night.

8. 47 posts. To solve this problem, count the number of posts in each side of the rectangle, but make sure that you count each corner post only once. One of the 120 ft sides has a post every 10 ft. That means there are 13 posts on that side.

120 ft

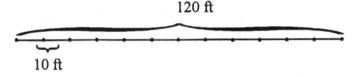

10 ft

Note that two of the thirteen posts are corner posts. Similarly, the other 120 ft side has 16 posts and the two 80 ft sides have 11 posts each. Each corner post is in two sides, so we have counted the corner posts twice. So, we need to subtract 4. Therefore, we have $13 + 16 + 11 + 11 - 4 = 47$ posts.

9. Caterina had 5 of each coin.

10. B. There are six letters that repeat. So the seventh letter in the sequence is one complete repetition plus one letter, so it is an 'A.' The 16th letter in the sequence is two complete repetitions plus four letters, so it is a 'D.' Similarly, the 200th letter in the sequence is 33 complete repetitions plus two letters, so it is a 'B.'

11. They ran 35 blocks on the 11th day.

12.   465
       x 23
      10695

13. 606

Answers to Sample Assessment

1. $V = \{x \mid x \text{ is a vowel in the name "Georg Cantor"}\}$

2. $\varnothing, \{2\}, \{o\}, \{2, o\}, \{t\}, \{2, t\}, \{o, t\}, \{2, o, t\}$

3.   (a)   x is a female who does not own a pickup.
     (b)   x is a female who either owns a pickup or a dog or both.
     (c)   x is a female mathematician who does not own a dog.
     (d)   x is a female nonmathematician who does not own a dog.
     (e)   x is a female who owns a pickup but is not a mathematician.
     (f)   x is a female nonmathematician.

4.   (a) $\{n\}$ (b) $\{u,n,i,t,e\}$ or C or U   (c) $\{n,i,t\}$ or A
     (d) $\varnothing$ (e) $\varnothing$ (f) $\{e\}$
     (g) $\{n,i,t,e\}$ (h) $\varnothing$ (i)   5
     (j)   5

5.   (a)   (b)

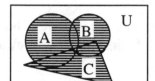

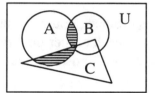

6.   15

7.   6   8.   9

9.

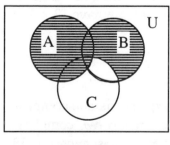

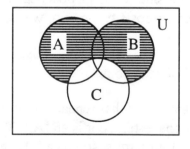

$A \cup (B - C)$ $\neq$ $(B \cup A) - C$

10.   Answers may vary. For example,

     (a) $[(A \cap B) \cup (A \cap C) \cup (B \cap C)]$
     (b) $(A \cap C) \cup (D \cap C) \cup B$

11. A x (B ∩ C) = {(o, t), (o, w), (o, o), (o, z), (o, e), (o, r), (n, t), (n, w), (n, o), (n, z), (n, e), (n, r), (e, t), (e, w), (e, o), (e, z), (e, e), (e, r)}

 (A x B) ∪ (A x C) = {(o, t), (o, w), (o, o), (n, t), (n, w), (n, o), (e, t), (e, w), (e, o), (o, z), (o, e), (o, r), (n, z), (n, e), (n, r), (e, z), (e, e), (e, r)}

12. False; Let A = {1, 2} and B = {1}.

 (a) True
 (b) True
 (c) True
 (d) False; The empty set is equivalent to itself.

13. 7

14. (a) Yes   (b) No   (c) No

15. (a) {3, 8, 13, 18, 23}
 (b) {0, 80, 15}
 (c) {3, 0, 8}

16. (a) 4   (b) 6

17. (a) Each output is 12
 (b) {(1, 20), (20, 1), (2, 10), (10, 2), (4, 5), (5, 4)}
 (c) If N is the set of Natural numbers, then the domain is N x N and the range is N.

18. (a) 15   (b) $1200   (c) 32

19. (a) Yes   (b) No   (c) Yes   (d) No

20. (a) There exists a butterfly that is not an animal.
 (b) Sometimes Whitney Houston does not say "How de do Boo Boo."
 (c) All umpire calls are incorrect.
 (d) $7 + 3 \neq 10$

21. (a) $\sim (a \vee b \vee c) \equiv (\sim a) \wedge (\sim b) \wedge (\sim c)$
 (b) $\sim (a \wedge b \wedge c) \equiv (\sim a) \vee (\sim b) \vee (\sim c)$

22. Converse: If the Director was Doc Severinson, then the host was Jay Leno.
 Inverse: If the host was not Jay Leno, then the director was not Doc Severinson.
 Contrapositive: If the Director was not Doc Severinson, then the host was not Jay Leno.

23. (a) Converse: If $x \in A \cup B$ then $x \in A \cap B$.
The statement is false.
Contrapositive: If $x \notin A \cup B$ then $x \notin A \cap B$.
The statement is true.

    (b) Converse: If $n(A) < n(B)$ then $A \subset B$.
The statement is false.
Contrapositive: If $n(A) \geq n(B)$ then $B \subseteq A$.
The statement is true.

    (c) Converse: If $n(A \cup B) = n(A) + n(B)$ then $A \cap B = \emptyset$
The statement is true.
Contrapositive: If $n(A \cup B) \neq n(A) + n(B)$ then $A \cap B = \emptyset$
This statement is true.

24. (a) I get an increase in salary.
    (b) The map is not in the plane.
    (c) Gloria Hewitt is well known.

25. Let p be the statement: A nail is lost;
q be the statement: A shoe is lost;
r be the statement: A horse is lost;
s be the statement: A rider is lost;
t be the statement: A battle is lost;
u be the statement: A kingdom is lost.

    $$[(p \rightarrow q) \wedge (q \rightarrow r) \wedge (r \rightarrow s) \wedge (s \rightarrow t) \wedge (t \rightarrow u)] \rightarrow (p \rightarrow u)$$

    The argument is valid using the Chain Rule several times.

26. (a) Valid   (b) Invalid
    (c) Valid   (d) Invalid

Answers to Sample Assessment

1. D = {August}

2. M = { x|x is an odd Natural number less than 11}

3. {a}, {b}, {c}, {a, b}, {a, c}, {b, c}

4. (a) (i)   A nonsmoking American
        (ii)   A healthy nonsmoking American
        (iii) An American smoker with a health problem
        (iv)   An American nonsmoker with a health problem
        (v)   An American who is either a smoker or unhealthy or both

    (b) (i) $\overline{D} \cap E$
        (ii) $D \cap E \cap C$
        (iii) $\overline{C} \cap \overline{D} \cap \overline{E}$
        (iv) $\overline{E} \cup \overline{C}$

5. (a) T   (b) T
    (c) T   (d) T
    (e) F. $A \cup \overline{A} = U$ (f) F. $A - \overline{A} = A$
    (g) F. Let A = {1}, and U = {1, 2}. Then $\overline{A}$ = {2} and A x $\overline{A}$ = {(1, 2)}.
    (h) F. $\varnothing \subseteq \varnothing$

6. (a) {s, u, e, t}   (b) {s,e,t}, or A
    (c) {q,e,s,t}   (d) {q}
    (e) {t}   (f) {s, u, e, t}
    (g) U   (h) 1

7. (a) 2   (b) 2
    (c) B x B = {(a, a)}   (d) A x A = {(1, 1),(1, 2),(2, 1)(2, 2)}
    (e) $\varnothing$ (f) No
    (g) Yes   (h) 0

8. (a) {1,   2,   3,   4,   ...,   n,   ...}
         $\updownarrow$ $\updownarrow$ $\updownarrow$ $\updownarrow$ $\updownarrow$ $\updownarrow$
         {4,   9,   14,   19,   ...,   5n – 1, ...}

    (b) 284, because 5 (57) – 1 = 284
    (c) 5n – 1

9. (a) {5, 7, 3}   (b) {0}

10.

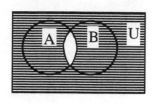

$$\overline{A} \cup \overline{B}$$

11. $(A \cap B) \cup [C - (A \cup B)]$

12. Use a Venn Diagram as shown below, where C represents card catalog users, R represents Reader's Guide users, and I represents the users of the information booth.

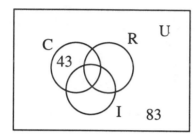

If there was no overlap between the users of the information booth and the Reader's Guide, we would have the following: n (R) + n (I) + 43 + 83 = 200. Thus, n (R) + n(I) = 74, but n(R) = 60 and n(I) = 68. Since 60 + 68 ≠ 74, there must be an overlap.

13. 72

14. $4 \cdot 3 \cdot 2 \cdot 1 = 24$

15. (a) Yes
    (b) It is a function.

16. (a) $f(g(x)) = x$ (b) $g(f(x)) = x$

17. (a) 30 (b) $2000 loss
    (c) 70 units

18. (a) Yes (b) No
    (c) Yes (d) Yes

19. (a) *Valley of the Horses* was not written by Jean Auel.
    (b) There exists a realtor who does not get a commission on a house the realtor sold.
    (c) All used car salesmen are honest.
    (d) $5 - 2 = 3$

20. (a) $a \rightarrow b$ if and only if $\sim b \rightarrow \sim a$.
    (b) For all statements a and b, $a \wedge b \rightarrow a \vee b$ is true.

21. (a) False.
    Converse: If B = C then A ∪ B = A ∪ C.
    The converse is true.
    Contrapositive: If B ≠ C then A ∪ B ≠ A ∪ C.
    The contrapositive is false.
    (b) False.
    Converse: If A = ∅ or B = ∅ then A ∩ B = ∅.
    The converse is true.
    Contrapositive: If A = ∅ or B = ∅ then A ∩ B = ∅.
    The contrapositive is false.

22. Converse: If Michelle Pfeiffer came from Gotham City, then she is Catwoman.
    Inverse: If Michelle Pfeiffer is not Catwoman, then she did not come from Gotham City.
    Contrapositive: If Michelle did not come from Gotham City, then she is not Catwoman.

23. (a) You understand the problem.
    (b) You are not a student.
    (c) I will get cold.

24. Let p be the statement: I pay attention to my job;
         q be the statement: I will get a salary increase;
         r be the statement: I shirk my job.

    Symbolically, we have $[(p \rightarrow q) \wedge (r \rightarrow \sim q) \wedge r] \rightarrow \sim p$

    It is valid.

25. (a) Valid   (b) Not valid   (c) Not valid

Answers to Sample Assessment

1. (a) 1045   (b) 37   (c) 1464   (d) 5

2. (a) CXXVIII   (b) 2341_{five} (c) $T7_{\text{twelve}}$

3. (a) 3^{13} (b) 3^{26} (c) 4^4

4. (a) Commutative Property of Addition
   (b) Commutative Property for Addition
   (c) Multiplicative Identity
   (d) Distributive Property of Multiplication over Addition
   (e) Associative Property of Addition
   (f) Associative Property for Multiplication

5. (a) Let $k = 2$. Since $2 + 5 = 7$, then $5 < 7$.
   (b) Let $k = 4$. Since $18 = 4 + 14$, then $18 > 14$.

6. Because $12 \cdot 100 = (1 \cdot 10 + 2)10^2 = 1 \cdot 10^3 + 2 \cdot 10^2 = 1 \cdot 10^3 + 2 \cdot 10^2 + 0 \cdot 10 + 0$, the tens digit and the units digit are 0.

7. (a)
```
 ¹5¹4 2        ¹5¹4 2
 8 8 9 ₁        8 8 9
   6₀1 1        6 1 1
 2 0 4 2       2 0 4 2
```

   (b)
```
 ¹3¹1 2 five      ¹3¹1 2 five
 4 3 0 1 five      4 3 4 five
   3₁1 1 five      3 1 1 five
 2 1 1 2 five     2 1 1 2 five
```

8. (a)

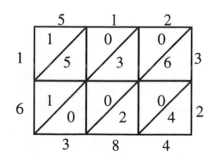

512
x 32
1024
1536
16384

Answer: 16384

8. (cont.)

(b)

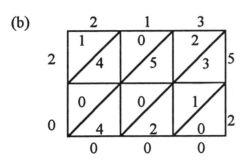

213_{six}
$\underline{\times \ 52_{six}}$
430
$\underline{1513}$
20000_{six}

Answer: 20000_{six}

9.   (a)   12 ⌐ 312
　　　　　　$\underline{-240}$ | 20 12's
　　　　　　72
　　　　　　$\underline{-72}$ | $\underline{6}$ 12's
　　　　　　0 | 26 Quotient

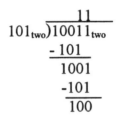

　　　　　26
12)312
　　$\underline{-24}$
　　72
　　$\underline{-72}$
　　0

(b) 101_{two} ⌐ 10011_{two}
　　　　　　$\underline{-1010}$ | 10 101's
　　　　　　1001
　　　　　　$\underline{-101}$ | $\underline{1}$ 101's
　　　　　　100 | 11 Quotient

　　　　　　11
101_{two})10011_{two}
　　$\underline{-101}$
　　1001
　　$\underline{-101}$
　　100

10. (a)   {0, 1, 2, 3, 4}　　　　(b)   {19}　　(c)   {0, 1, 2, ..., 14}

11. (a)

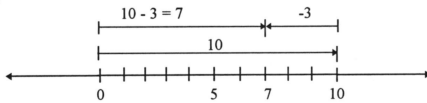

(b)

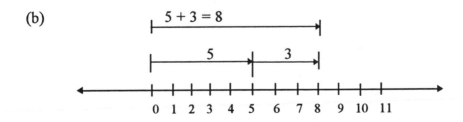

12. (a) $18x$ (b) $13x^3$ (c) $ab + ac + ad$

13. $29

14. $106

15. Dick should pay Tom $1 and Mary should pay Tom $6.

16. $10,020

17. $0 \div 0$ is equal to some unique number x such that $0 = 0 \cdot x$. Because no unique whole number exists, $0 \div 0$ is undefined.

Answers to Sample Assessment

1. (a) 1,000,400   (b) 233   (c) 1452

2. (a) CDLIV   (b) 1300_{five} (c) 10_{nine}

3. (a) 3^{15} (b) 4^{93} (c) 5^{7}

4. (a) Commutative Property of Addition
   (b) Associative Property for Multiplication
   (c) Distributive Property of Multiplication over Addition
   (d) Identity Property of Multiplication
   (e) Closure Property of Addition
   (f) Commutative Property for Multiplication

5. (a) Let $k = 4$. Since $18 + 4 = 22$, then $18 < 22$.
   (b) Let $k = 1$. Since $0 + 1 = 1$, then $1 > 0$.

6. $1 \div 0$ is equal to some unique whole number x, such that $1 = 0 \cdot x$. Because $= 0 \cdot x$ is always 0, no such number exists, and the solution is undefined. If $1 \div 0$ were equal to 1, then this implies $1 = 0 \cdot 1$ which is false.

7. (a)
$$
\begin{array}{r}
{}^2 3\,{}^2 6\,2 \\
7\,8\,0 \\
5\,3\,4 \\
7\,9\,3 \\
\hline
1\,0\,5\,3
\end{array}
\qquad
\begin{array}{r}
{}^2 3{}^2 6\,2 \\
7\,8 \\
5\,3\,4 \\
+\ \ 7\,9 \\
\hline
1\,0\,5\,3
\end{array}
$$

   (b)
$$
\begin{array}{r}
{}^1 2{}^1 1\,4_{\text{five}} \\
2\,3\,2\,1_{\text{five}} \\
2\ \ 2\,3_{\text{five}} \\
\hline
1\,2\,2\,4_{\text{five}}
\end{array}
\qquad
\begin{array}{r}
{}^1 2{}^1 1\,4_{\text{five}} \\
2\,3\,2_{\text{five}} \\
2\,2\,3_{\text{five}} \\
\hline
1\,2\,2\,4_{\text{five}}
\end{array}
$$

8. (a)

$$
\begin{array}{r}
518 \\
\times\ \ 342 \\
\hline
1036 \\
2072 \\
1554 \\
\hline
177{,}156
\end{array}
$$

Answer: 177,156

8.   (b)

	2		1		2	
1	0 / 4	0 / 2	0 / 4	2
0	1 / 1	0 / 3	1 / 1	3
	4	3	1	

$$\begin{array}{r} 212_{five} \\ \times\ 23_{five} \\ \hline 1141 \\ 424 \\ \hline 10431_{five} \end{array}$$

Answer: 10431_{five}

9.   (a)

$$\begin{array}{r|ll} 8\ \overline{)\ 3648} & & \\ -3200 & 400 & 8\text{'s} \\ \hline 448 & & \\ -\ 400 & 50 & 8\text{'s} \\ \hline 48 & & \\ -\ 48 & 6 & 8\text{'s} \\ \hline 0 & 456 & \text{Quotient} \end{array}$$

$$\begin{array}{r} 456 \\ 8\ )\overline{3648} \\ \underline{32} \\ 44 \\ \underline{-\ 40} \\ 48 \\ \underline{-\ 48} \\ 0 \end{array}$$

(b) 12_{three}

$$\begin{array}{r|ll} 12_{three}\ \overline{\big)\ 2021_{three}} & & \\ 1200 & 100 & 12\text{'s} \\ \hline 121 & & \\ 120 & 10 & 12\text{'s} \\ \hline 1 & 110_{three} & \end{array}$$

$$\begin{array}{r} 110_{three} \\ 12_{three}\ )\overline{2021_{three}} \\ \underline{12} \\ 12 \\ \underline{12} \\ 01 \\ \underline{0} \\ 1 \end{array}$$

10.   (a)   {0, 1, 2, 3, 4, 5}   (b)   4

11.   (a)

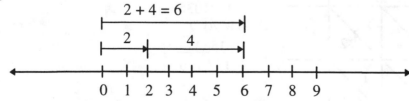

(b)

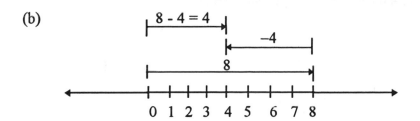

12. (a) $14x^2$ (b) $37x$ (c) $ac + ad + bc + bd$

13. $430

14. $71

15. (a)   2365   (b)   8654
          + 4824   - 3282
          ‾‾‾‾‾‾   ‾‾‾‾‾‾
            7189   5372

16. 12

17. The front-end estimate is based only on the leftmost digits that are significant. Because the remainder of the numbers are not used in the first estimate, it is less than the actual answer.

18. No, because $2 \in W$, $5 \in W$ and $2 \cdot 5$ does not have an answer in the set of whole numbers with 10 removed.

Answers to Sample Assessment

1. (a) 7   (b) -2 - x   (c) -x + y

2. (a) 10   (b) 4   (c) -16

3. (a) 3, -3   (b) 5, -5   (c) $x > -16, x \in I$
   (d) 5, -9   (e) 9   (f) 11, -5

4. $2 \cdot 4 = 8$ The first three products 8, 4, 0 are terms of an arithmetic
    $1 \cdot 4 = 4$ sequence with fixed difference -4. If the pattern continues
    $0 \cdot 4 = 0$ the next three terms are -4, -8 and -12.
    $-1 \cdot 4 = -4$
    $-2 \cdot 4 = -8$
    $-3 \cdot 4 = -12$

5. (a) $x(5 - 3x)$ (b) $(5 - x)(5 + x)$

6. (a) 3   (b) 3   (c) -9   (d) 9

7. (a) $b^2 - 9d^2$ (b) $16j^2 - 4k^2$

8. (a) F. Conterexample: $2(-1) > 7(-1)$ and $2 < 7$.
   (b) F. If $-x > -7$, then $(-1)(-x) < (-1)(-7)$, or $x < 7$.
   (c) F. Counterexample: $x = -2$
   (d) F. $(a + b)(a + b) = a^2 + 2ab + b^2$

9. (a) T   (b) F. For example, $5 - 3 \neq 3 - 5$.
   (c) T   (d) F. For example, $5 \div 3 \notin I$

10. They must be nonzero integers with like signs, that is, they must both be positive or both be negative.

11. 9°C

12. 11 and 3

13. (a)
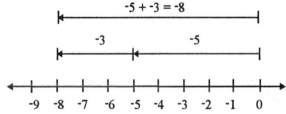

$$-9 \quad -8 \quad -7 \quad -6 \quad -5 \quad -4 \quad -3 \quad -2 \quad -1 \quad 0$$

(b)
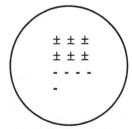 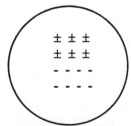

-5 charge on field   Add three negative charges;
                                  net result is -8 charge on field

14. (a) 4   (b) None   (c)   2 or 6

15. (a) F. Let a = 4 and b = 8.   (b) F. Let a = 4 and b = 8.
    (c) F. Let a = 4 and b = 8.   (d) F. Let a = 6.

16. 64 is the least whole number with exactly seven divisors because of the following:

    $64 = 2^6$

    2^6 has exactly 7 divisors: 1, 2, 4, 8, 16, 32, and 64.
    Every other positive number with 7 divisors must have some prime other than 2 in its prime factorization, and if it has a number greater than 2 in its prime factorization, then the number must be greater than 64.

17. (a) Composite   (b) Composite   (c) Composite

18. (a) 1   (b) $2^2 \cdot 3 \cdot 5 \cdot 13$ or 780

19. (a) $2^2 \cdot 3^5 \cdot 11$ (b) $2^2 \cdot 3^7 \cdot 7^2 \cdot 11^4 \cdot 13$

20. (a) 31   (b) 13

21. For a number to be divisible by 35, it must be divisible by both 5 and 7.

22. 24 pieces

23. 53

24. Wednesday

25. (a) 7   (b) 5   (c)   19

Answers to Sample Assessment

1. (a) -13   (b) 3 - x

2. (a) 21   (b) -53   (c) -30

3. (a) 5   (b) -3   (c) 16, -16
    (d) x > -4, x ∈ I   (e) -3, 13   (f) 0, 4

4. (a) 3x(3x - 1)   (b) (2x - 3)(2x + 3)

5. (a) $(x + y)(x + y) = x(x + y) + y(x + y) = x^2 + xy + yx + y^2 = x^2 + 2xy + y^2$
    (b) $(-5 + 2a)(-5 + 2a) = (-5)^2 + 2(-5)(2a) + (2a)^2 = 25 - 20a + 4a^2$

6. (a) -4   (b) 2   (c) -2   (d) -8

7. (a) F. $x < -2$ (b) F. $6x = -12$
    (c) F. $|-x| = -x$ if $x < 0$ (d)   F. $a^2 - b^2 = (a - b)(a + b)$

8. (a) F. For example, -2 is an integer but not a whole number.
    (b) F. For example, 5 - (3 - 2) ≠ (5 - 3) - 2
    (c) T
    (d) T

9. They must be nonzero integers with unlike signs.

10. -$62

11. 29°C

12. 7 and 29

13. (a)

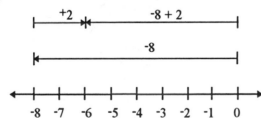

-8 -7 -6 -5 -4 -3 -2 -1 0

    (b)

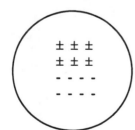

-8 charge on field

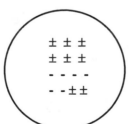

Add two positive charges;
net result is -6 charge on field

14. (a) 0,9   (b) 1, 4, 7   (c) 0, 5

15. (a)   F. If a = 0, then there is no GCD.
    (b)   T
    (c)   T
    (d)   F. Let a = 6.

16. 30

17. (a)   Composite   (b)   Composite   (c)   Prime

18. (a)   4   (b) $2^2 \cdot 3 \cdot 7 \cdot 13 \cdot 73$ or 79,716

19. (a) $5^2 \cdot 7$ (b) $2^3 \cdot 5^2 \cdot 7^3 \cdot 11 \cdot 13 \cdot 17$

20. (a)   13   (b)   41

21. For a number to be divisible by 33, it must be divisible by both 3 and 11.

22. 96

23. 2:45 P.M.

24. 3 years

25. 0

Answers to Sample Assessment

1. (a)

    (b)

2. $\dfrac{8}{10}, \dfrac{12}{15}, \dfrac{16}{20}$, and so on.

3. (a) $\dfrac{3}{4}$ (b) $\dfrac{c^2 y^4}{d}$ (c) $\dfrac{0}{1}$ (d) $\dfrac{1}{b}$

4. (a) =   (b) <   (c) =

5. (a) $\dfrac{22}{15}$ (b) $\dfrac{1}{12}$ (c) $\dfrac{9}{8}$ (d) $\dfrac{83}{68}$

6. (a) $^-8$ and $\dfrac{1}{8}$ (b) $^-3\dfrac{1}{2}$ and $\dfrac{2}{7}$ (c) $\dfrac{1}{4}$ and $\dfrac{^-4}{1}$ (d) $\dfrac{-8}{3}$ and $\dfrac{3}{8}$

7. 36

8. 76 packages, and $\dfrac{4}{13}$ oz. will be left over.

9. (a) 3+   (b) 10-   (c) 4+

10. (a) 40   (b) 7   (c) 29

11. Yes, 1/2 ft will be left.

12. Heidi's class because $\dfrac{17}{30} > \dfrac{15}{27}$.

13. $33\dfrac{1}{3}$ pages.

Answers to Sample Assessment

1. (a) $\dfrac{3}{4}$ (b) 1   (c) 3

2. (a) $\dfrac{23}{24}$ (b) $\dfrac{37}{60}$ (c) $3\dfrac{3}{35}$ (d) $\dfrac{13}{2}$ or $6\dfrac{1}{2}$

3. (a) $\dfrac{3}{5}$ (b) $\dfrac{3}{8}$

4. True. When the denominator of a fraction (whose numerator and denominator are positive) decreases, the fraction increases. When the numerator increases the fraction increases as well. A more formal approach follows: $\dfrac{a+1}{b-1} > \dfrac{a}{b}$ if and only if $ab + b > ab - a$ or $b > {}^-a$. The last inequality is true because $a > 0$ and $b \geq 2$.

5. $30\dfrac{5}{9}$ mi

6. A person gets approximately $\dfrac{13}{16}$ of a pound of nuts.

7. It will become smaller because $\dfrac{3x}{8x} > \dfrac{3x - 2}{8x - 2}$

8. (a) 3^- (b) 10^- (c) 6^-

9. (a) 22   (b) 18   (c) 41

10. (a) $<$ (b) $<$ (c) $<$

11. 15 apples

12. $136

13. Approximately 2090 students

Answers to Sample Assessment

1. (a) $\dfrac{1}{3^{10}}$ (b) 5^8 (c) 2^2 or 4 (d) $\dfrac{a^2b^2}{a^2+b^2}$

2. (a) $n=-6$ (b) $n=15$ (c) n is any integer   (d) $n=1$

3. (a) $\dfrac{3}{8}$ (b) $\dfrac{3}{16}$ (c) $\dfrac{3}{64}$ (d) $n=-7$

4. (a) $<$ (b) $=$ (c) $=$ (d) $<$

5. Because $3840 = 2^8 \cdot 3 \cdot 5$ the prime factorization of the denominator of this fraction will contain only powers of 2 and 5 if and only if k is a multiple of 3.

6.
$$
\begin{aligned}
8.07 - 2.3 &= \frac{807}{100} - \frac{23}{10} \\
&= \frac{807}{100} - \frac{230}{100} \\
&= \frac{807-230}{100} \\
&= \frac{577}{100} \\
&= 5.77
\end{aligned}
$$

7. (a) 508.58   (b) 508.6   (c) 500

8. (a) $\dfrac{27}{100}$ (b) $\dfrac{3104}{1000}$ or $\dfrac{388}{125}$ (c) $\dfrac{22}{90}$ or $\dfrac{11}{45}$ (d) $\dfrac{24}{100}$ or $\dfrac{6}{25}$

9. (a) 0.075   (b) 0.125   (c) $0.\overline{153846}$

10. 3.873

11. (a) $5.268 \cdot 10^6$ (b) $3.25 \cdot 10^{-4}$

12. (a) Irrational if pattern continues
     (b) Irrational
     (c) Rational
     (d) Rational if the repeating pattern continues.

13. (a) $\dfrac{1}{2}$ (b) $\dfrac{1}{2}$ (c) 16   (d) $\sqrt{2}$

14. (a) $\dfrac{-1}{2\sqrt{3}}$ or $\dfrac{-\sqrt{3}}{6}$ (b) $x \leq 12.2$

    (c) 0   (d) $\dfrac{5}{9}$

    (e) $x < 0.722$ (f) -3

Answers to Sample Assessment

1. (a) $\dfrac{1}{5^6}$ (b) 10^{10} (c) 1 (d) $\dfrac{a^3}{a^3+1}$

2. (a) -5 (b) 0
   (c) true for any integer (d) true for all negative integers

3. (a) $\dfrac{1}{265}$ (b) $\dfrac{1}{8}$ (c) $x = \dfrac{-9}{10}$

4. (a) 483.77 (b) 484 (c) 500

5. (a) $\dfrac{38}{100}$ or $\dfrac{19}{50}$ (b) $\dfrac{2607}{1000}$

   (c) $\dfrac{43}{90}$ (d) $\dfrac{324}{999}$ or $\dfrac{36}{111}$

6. (a) $0.2\overline{3}$ (b) 0.275 (c) $0.\overline{45}$

7. 3.317

8. (a) $=$ (b) $>$ (c) $<$ (d) $>$

9. $23.6 - 8.34 = 23.60 - 8.34$
   $$= \dfrac{2360}{100} - \dfrac{834}{100}$$
   $$= \dfrac{1526}{100}$$
   $$= 15.26$$

10. 18.75 cm

11. (a) Irrational
    (b) Rational
    (c) Rational
    (d) Irrational if pattern continues.

12. (a) $3.286 \cdot 10^3$ (b) $3.2 \cdot 10^{-6}$

13. (a) $\dfrac{-5}{3\sqrt{2}}$ or $\dfrac{-5\sqrt{2}}{6}$

    (b)   -39.6

    (c)   No such real number

    (d) $\dfrac{4}{9}$

    (e)   8

    (f) $1 \cdot \overline{1}$ or $1\dfrac{1}{9}$

    (g)   0

    (f)   4.2

Answers to Sample Assessment

1. $\dfrac{L}{24}$ cups

2. (a) $x = \sqrt{5}$ or $-\sqrt{5}$

   (b) $-1 < x < 1$

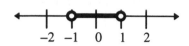

3. (a)   The unique solution is $x = 3$ and $y = 2$
   (b)   There is no solution

   (c)   There are infinitely many solutions: x is any real number and $y = \dfrac{3 + |x|}{2}$.

4. (a) $C(n) = 1.25 + 1200n + 1200$.
   (b) $R(n) = 2.05\, n$
   (c)   667

5. (a)   9%   (b)   1,200

6. 21 ft

7. 4.602%

8. (a) $w = \dfrac{4}{x}$ where w is in kg.

   (b)

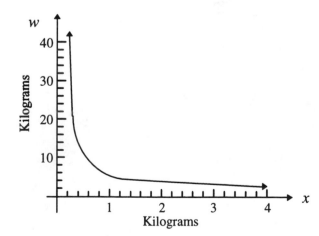

9. (a) $y = \dfrac{9}{10}x + \dfrac{23}{10}$ (b) $y = -\dfrac{1}{7}x$ (c) $x = -1$

10. (a) $240   (b) $48

11. (a) 10%   (b) $16.\overline{6}\%$ or $16\frac{2}{3}\%$ (c) 100%   (d) 337.5%

12. (a) Dealer B (b) $15,360

13. 6

14. $13,789.20

15. (a) 1 in.
    (b) The length to width ratio of the photograph is 10:8 or 5:4. The addition of the border will result in a rectangle with smaller length to width ratio since adding the same positive number to the numerator and denominator of a fraction results in a smaller fraction. Hence it is not possible to place the photograph as required. If we attempt to solve the problem algebraically denoting the width of the border by x we need to solve the equation $\dfrac{10+2x}{8+2x} = \dfrac{5}{4}$. This equation is equivalent to $40 + 8x = 40 + 10x$ or $2x = 0$. Hence $x = 0$ and the placement of the photograph is impossible.

16. 12

17. (a) Bashaar
    (b) Bashaar

18. (a) $A = \dfrac{p^2}{16}$ (b) $p = 96$ ft
    (c)

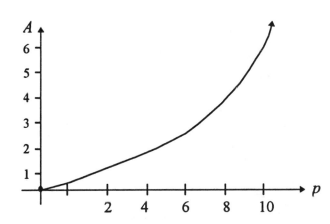

19. 3.6 cm

20. $15,081.6

Answers to Sample Assessment

1. (a) 5 in.

   (b) It is impossible to obtain such a ratio. If x is the width then the equation $\dfrac{20-x}{15-x} = \dfrac{5}{4}$ has the

   solution $x = -5$ which is not meaningful because x must be positive. This happens because for

   $x > 0$, $\dfrac{20-x}{15-x} > \dfrac{20}{15} > \dfrac{5}{4}$.

   (c) $\dfrac{5(3r-4)}{r-1}$

   (d) $r > \dfrac{4}{3}$

2. (a) $x = \dfrac{1}{4}$, $y = \dfrac{1}{2}$. One solution

   (b) No solution; that is, 0 solutions.

   (c) Infinitely many solutions: x is any real number and $y = \dfrac{3+x^2}{2}$

3. (a) $\dfrac{12}{32}$ or $\dfrac{3}{8}$

   (b) $\dfrac{32}{100}$ or $\dfrac{1}{5}$

4. (a) $p = 4\sqrt{A}$

   (b) The following is the graph for $0 \le A \le 5000$. (Students may choose to draw the graph for smaller values of A.)

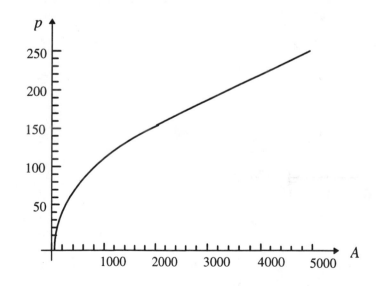

   (c) The function allow us to determine the perimeter of a square knowing only its area.

5. (a) $\dfrac{x}{60}$ (in hours)   (b) $2.55x + 3.05y$ (in dollars)

    (c) $101x$ (d) y intercept is m

6. \$56.25

7. 6,345

8. (a) 16.4   (b) 5

9. (a) 0.0025   (b) 1.67

10. (a) $y = \dfrac{1}{14}x;$ slope $\dfrac{1}{14};$ y intercept 0.

    (b) $y = 2x + 3;$ slope $-2;$ y intercept 3.

11. (a) $x > \sqrt{3} + 1$

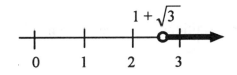

    (b) $x < = 6$ or $x > 6$

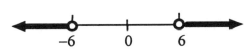

12. Mary's age is $2y + 3$

13. 50 lb

14. (a) \$236.25
    (b) \$4,736.25
    (c) \$4,984.90

*15. (a) \$6,405.11
     (b) \$12,820.45,
     (c) \$102,809.57

16. (a) 20. Explanation: Methods vary, one approach is to find 10% of 50 which is \$5. Then 40% of 50 is 4 times 5 or \$20.
    (b) 8%. Explanation: Methods vary, one approach is to find 1% of 500 which is 5. Because $40 = 8 \cdot 5$, 8% of 500 is 40.

17. (a)   The unique solution is $x = -2, y = -4$.

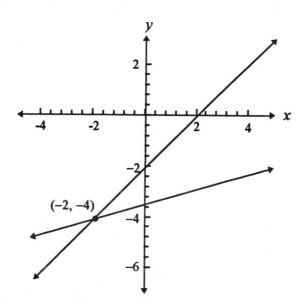

(b)   There are infinitely many solutions. If x is any real number then $y = -x + 5$.

18. 23.83%

19. (a)   20%
    (b)   1%
    (c)   304.2%

(d) $66.\overline{6}$ % or $66\dfrac{3}{8}$ %

Answers to Sample Assessment

1. (a) {Sunday, Monday, Tuesday, Wednesday, Thursday, Friday, Saturday}
   (b) {Tuesday, Thursday}
   (c) $\dfrac{2}{7}$

2. $\dfrac{1}{2}$

3. (a) $\dfrac{6}{18}$ or $\dfrac{1}{3}$ (b) $\dfrac{12}{18}$ or $\dfrac{2}{3}$ (c) $\dfrac{5}{18}$

4. (a) $\dfrac{13}{52}$ or $\dfrac{1}{4}$ (b) $\dfrac{1}{52}$ (c) $\dfrac{22}{52}$ or $\dfrac{11}{26}$

5. (a) $\dfrac{9}{36}$ or $\dfrac{1}{4}$ (b) $\dfrac{6}{30}$ or $\dfrac{1}{5}$

6. 0.90307 or approximately 0.9

7. (a) $\dfrac{5}{16}$ (b) $\dfrac{7}{24}$ 8. $\dfrac{1}{2}$

9. 40   10. $\dfrac{1}{128}$

11. (a) $\dfrac{60}{2730}$ or $\dfrac{2}{91}$ (b) $\dfrac{210}{2330}$ or $\dfrac{1}{13}$

12. 28 ways   13. 100

14. 15   15. 6,760,000

16. (a) $P(A) = \dfrac{3}{8}$ (b) $P(B) = \dfrac{5}{8}$ 17. $\dfrac{11!}{2!\,2!\,2!}$ or 4,989,600

18. $\dfrac{7}{12}$ 19. $\dfrac{3}{33}$ or $\dfrac{1}{11}$

20. 51 to 1   21. $2.00

22. Answers vary, for example, let the numbers 01, 02, 03, 04, 05, . . ., 29, 30 represent the dates of the month. Pick a starting place and mark off blocks of two until three of the blocks are obtained.

Answers to Sample Assessment

1. (a) $\{1, 2, 3, \ldots, 26\}$
   (b) $\{2, 4, 6, \ldots, 26\}$
   (c) $\dfrac{1}{2}$

2. $\dfrac{1}{16}$

3. (a) $\dfrac{5}{16}$ (b) $\dfrac{9}{16}$ (c) $\dfrac{7}{16}$

4. (a) $\dfrac{3}{52}$ (b) $\dfrac{22}{52}$ or $\dfrac{11}{26}$ (c) $\dfrac{48}{52}$ or $\dfrac{12}{13}$

5. (a) $\dfrac{49}{256}$ (b) $\dfrac{42}{240}$ or $\dfrac{7}{40}$

6. 0.504

7. (a) $\dfrac{6}{16}$ or $\dfrac{3}{8}$ (b) $\dfrac{1}{6}$

8. $\dfrac{7}{8}$ 9. 60

10. $\dfrac{27}{512}$ 11. $\dfrac{12}{56}$ or $\dfrac{3}{14}$

12. 24 ways   13. 325

14. 15   15. $26^3 \cdot 10^3$ or 17,576,000

16. (a) $P(A) = \dfrac{1}{2}$ (b) $P(B) = \dfrac{1}{2}$

17. 60   18. $\dfrac{4}{12}$ or $\dfrac{1}{3}$

19. 5 to 31   20. $1.25

21. Answers may very, for example, mark of the digits in blocks of two. Let the numbers 01, 02, 03, 04, 05, . . ., 25, 26 represent the consecutive letters of the alphabet. Disregard blocks of two not in this range.

Answers to Sample Assessment

1. (a) Approximately $12.93
    (b) $9.70
    (c) $9.70

2. (a) Mean, 73.9;
    (b) Median, 84;
    (c) Mode, 98;
    (d) Range, 61
    (e) Approximately 24.57

3.

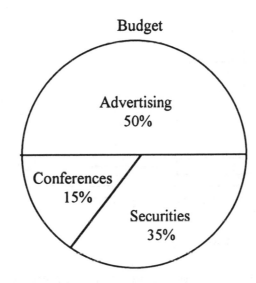

4. There are more high scores than low ones, but the low ones lower the mean.

5. (a)

Class	Frequency
10-14	1
15-19	2
20-24	3
25-29	7
30-34	5
35-39	2
Total	20

5. (cont.)

(b)

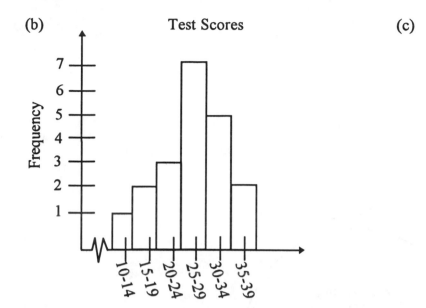

(c)

Test Scores	
1	279
2	1235666789
3	0122489

2|1 represents a score of 21

(d)

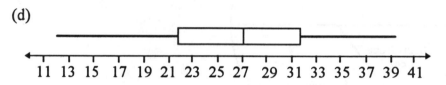

(e)   There are none that fit the definition.

6. (a)   More of the older members have died or did not attend or a greater number of younger members attended.

   (b)   Approximately 3.18 years.

7. You do not know who was surveyed, how many were surveyed, or what types of questions were asked. The claim should not be taken at face value without more information.

*8. 1900 students

9. The outlier is any score that is more than 1.5 interquartile ranges above the upper quartile or more than 1.5 interquartile ranges below the lower quartile.

*10. 57

Answers to Sample Assessment

1. (a) 77.5   (b)   78   (c)   no mode   (d)   Approximately 9.14

2. 80% females and 20% males

3. 3.125

4. (a)

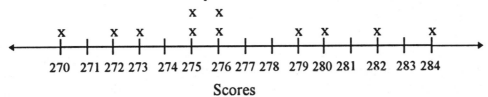

British Open Scores - 1981 - 1991

Scores

(b)

British Open Scores - 1981 - 1991

Year

5. (a)

Class of Weights	Frequency
115-124	1
125-134	2
135-144	10
145-154	10
155-164	4
165-174	2
175-184	1
Total	30

5. (cont.)
   (b)   Class Weights of Huntsville Space Camp

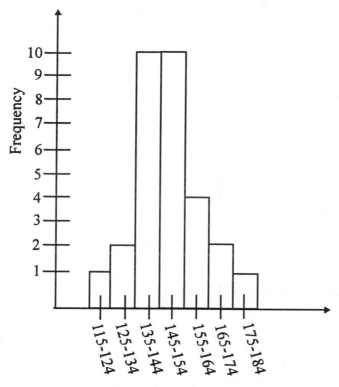

Class Weight (in Pounds)

*6. On a standardized test, or on any test, there should be students that score below the mean. Without more information, there is no reason to believe that every student in any given school should score above the national mean on a test. Although possible, this is highly unlikely.

7. (a)

Mr. Read's Class Scores

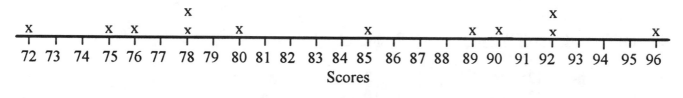

Scores

Miss Sol's Class Scores

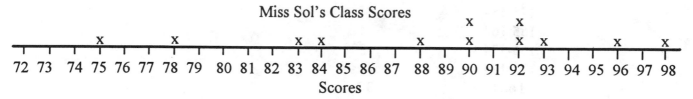

Scores

7. (cont.)
   (b)

TEST SCORES

Miss Sol's Class		Mr. Read's Class	
85	7	25688	
843	8	059	9|8 = 98
86332200	9	0226	

(c) The IQR for Mr. Read is 14. The IQR for Miss Sol is 9.

(d) There are no outliers for either set of data.

(e)

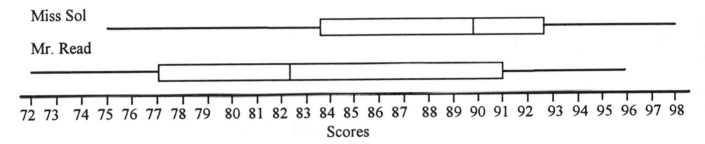

(f) Miss Sol's class did better on the quiz than Mr. Read's class. 75% of Miss Sol's class scored above the median for Mr. Read's class.

8. A positive correlation means that the points fell near a trend line and the trend line slopes up from left to right. This implies that the data on the two axes are related and given one value we can make predictions about the other.

*9. Mean, 72. Standard deviation, 20.

*10. 950

Answers to Sample Assessment

1. Answers may vary. For example,

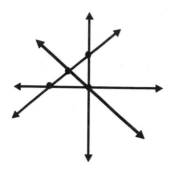

2. Answers may vary. For example,

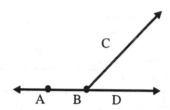

    ∠ABC and ∠CBD are supplementary.

3. 4

4. At least three figures must fit together at the vertex to make a polyhedron. If three angles of a regular heptagon were together at one vertex, then the sum of the measures of these angles would be $3 \cdot \left(\dfrac{900}{7} \right)^\circ$ which is greater than 360°.

5. (a) False, they could be skew.
    (b) False, all squares are rectangles.
    (c) False, the line can pass through the plane and intersect in 1 point.
    (d) False, it takes a plane to separate space.
    (e) True.
    (f) False, it has one end point.

6. (a) $\overleftrightarrow{AD}$
    (b) $\overleftrightarrow{AE}$
    (c) Point E
    (d) Points P and E
    (e) $\overleftrightarrow{AE}$
    (f) ∠BEC
    (g) ∅

7. 156° 42′ 42″

8. 55°

9. 35

10. 63° and 27°

11. No, to be a regular polygon all sides and all angles must be congruent. The angles of a rhombus are not necessarily congruent.

12. (a) 140°   (b) 40°   (c) 55°
    (d) 55°   (e) 70°

13.

	mm	cm	m	km
(a)	52,000	5,200	52	0.052
(b)	260,000	26,000	260	0.260
(c)	300,000	30,000	300	0.3
(d)	1,300,000	130,000	1,300	1.3

14. The measure of angle 4 is equal to the sum of the measures of angles 1 and 2. A justification follows.

$m(\angle 3) + m(\angle 4) = 180°$
$m(\angle 1) + m(\angle 2) + m(\angle 3) = 180°$
Therefore $m(\angle 3) + m(\angle 4) = m(\angle 1) + m(\angle 2) + m(\angle 3)$ which implies
$m(\angle 4) = m(\angle 1) + m(\angle 2)$.

15. (a) Traversable

(b)

(c) Not traversable

16. (a)   For example,

(b)

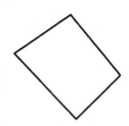

17. (a) $A = \pi r^2$. Hence $r^2 = \dfrac{A}{\pi}$. Now:

$$C^2 = (2\pi r)^2 = 4\pi^2 r^2 = 4\pi^2 \cdot \frac{A}{\pi} = 4\pi A.$$

Hence $C = 2\sqrt{\pi \cdot A}$

(b) $\dfrac{C_1}{C_2} = \dfrac{2\sqrt{\pi A_1}}{2\sqrt{\pi A_2}} = \sqrt{\dfrac{A_1}{A_2}} = \sqrt{2}$.

Answers to Sample Assessment

1.

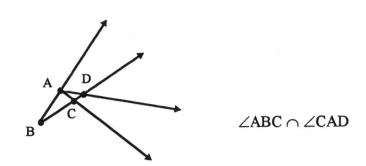

$\angle ABC \cap \angle CAD$

2.

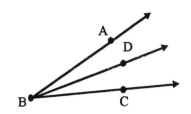

$\angle ABC$ and $\angle DBC$

3. 16

4. X, Y, and Z are collinear because if two distinct planes intersect, they intersect in a line.

5. (a)   False, there are an infinite number of planes containing a line.
    (b)   False, the sum of the four interior angles in a parallelogram must be 360°. With four acute angles this cannot happen.
    (c)   True
    (d)   False, for example in the figure below $\overset{\bullet\rightarrow}{BA} \cup \overset{\bullet\rightarrow}{CD}$ is not a line.

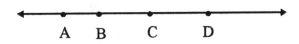

    (e)   False, one ray starts at A and goes in the B direction and one ray starts at B and goes in the A direction.
    (f)   True.
    (g)   False, in an equilateral triangle at least 2 sides are congruent.

6. (a) $\overset{\leftrightarrow}{YZ}$ (b)   Points B and E   (c)   Point E
    (d)   Points B and E   (e) $\overset{\leftrightarrow}{FE}$ (f) $\overset{\leftrightarrow}{AB}$
    (g) $\varnothing$ (h) $\overline{AF}$

7. (a)   150°
    (b)   54

8. (a) Approximately 2.07 m
   (b) Same as in part (a)
   (c) If the difference between the circumferences of the concentric circles is constant, then regardless of the size of the circles the width of the tracks is always the same. In particular if the difference is 13 m, the width will always be $\dfrac{13}{2\pi}$ or approximately 2.07 m.
   (d) Let r_1 and r_2 be the radii of the circles and d the difference between the circumferences. (In parts (a) and (b), d = 13 m.) Then:

   $$2\pi r_1 - 2\pi r_2 = d,$$
   $$2\pi(r_1 - r_2) = d$$
   $$r_1 - r_2 = \frac{d}{2\pi}.$$

   Because $w = r_1 - r_2$ we have $w = \dfrac{d}{2\pi}$. Because d is constant, w will always be the same.

9. Let ABCD be the rectangle shown, with ∠A as a right angle.

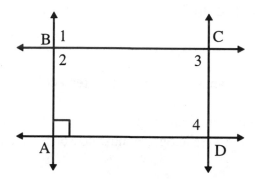

   Because rectangle ABCD is a parallelogram, $\overleftrightarrow{BC} \parallel \overleftrightarrow{AD}$ and $\overleftrightarrow{AB} \parallel \overleftrightarrow{DC}$. Corresponding angles, ∠BAD and ∠1 are congruent, and thus ∠1 is a right angle. Because ∠1 and ∠2 are supplementary, ∠2 is a right angle. Similarly, it can be proved that ∠3 and ∠4 are right angles.

10. 30°

11. (a) 11° 40′ 47″
    (b) 5° 24′ 0″

12. (a) 70°   (b) 70°   (c) 70°
    (d) 110°   (e) 70°

13. (a) Points A and C are outside, but point B is inside.
    (b) Points A and B are inside, and point C is outside.
    In parts (a) and (b) you could choose a point that is on the outside and draw a segment to the indicated points. An odd number of intersection points indicates an interior point.

14. $\overrightarrow{AX}$ bisects $\angle DAB$, so $\angle DAX \cong \angle XAB$. $\overrightarrow{AY}$ bisects $\angle BAC$, so $\angle BAY \cong \angle YAC$.
m($\angle DAX$) + m($\angle XAB$) + m($\angle BAY$) + m($\angle YAC$) = 180°
Hence, 2m($\angle XAB$) + 2m($\angle BAY$) = 180° and m($\angle XAB$) + m($\angle BAY$) = 90°

Therefore, $\angle XAY$ is a right angle. Hence $\overrightarrow{AX} \perp \overrightarrow{AY}$.

15. (a)   Traversable

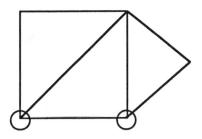

    (b)   Not traversable
    (c)   Not traversable

16. (a)   For example,   (b)

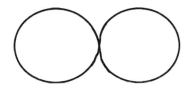   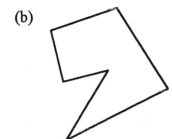

17. We use the triangle inequality to determine and justify the answers.

    (a)   Because 20 + 10 < 35, a triangle cannot be formed.
    (b)   Because 50 cm = 0.5 m, 2 + 3 > 0.5, 2 + 0.5 > 3 and 3 + 0.5 > 2, a triangle can be formed.
    (c)   Because 7 yd = 21 ft and 3 + 5 < 21, a triangle cannot be formed.
    (d)   Because x + x > x for x > 0, a triangle can be formed.

18.   TO SUPP.ANGLES :A
           FE 100
           BK 50
           RT :A
           FD 50
           BK 50
           RT 180–:A
           LT 180
           BK 50
       END

Answers to Sample Assessment

1. (a)   Yes. ASA   (b)   Yes. AAS   (c)   Yes. SAS   (d)   Yes. SSS

2. (a) $\triangle QRS \cong \triangle TUV$ by AAS.
    (b) $\triangle GHI \cong \triangle JKL$ by SSS.
    (c) $\triangle ABD \cong \triangle CEF$ by ASA. (It must first be determined that m($\angle FCE$) is 60°.)

3. Constructions.

4. (a) $\dfrac{55}{16}$ (b) $\dfrac{40}{3}$ (c) $\dfrac{10}{3}$

5. 488 cm

6. No, the length of any side of a triangle must be less than the sum of the lengths of the other two
    sides. Note that $19 > 5 + 12$.

7. (a)   ABCD is a parallelogram.
    (b)   No, these two angles are supplementary, but not necessarily congruent.
    (c)   Yes, these two angles are congruent because they are alternate interior angles of parallel lines.

8. Answers may vary.

    (a)   A side on one square is congruent to a side on the other square.
    (b)   SAS.

9. Any triangle with its third vertex on $\overleftrightarrow{AD}$ is isosceles.

10. (a) $x = 3$ (b) $y = 3x - 16$

11. The points are all on the same line with slope $\dfrac{3}{2}$.

*12. $x \doteq 15.6$ m; $y = 9$ m

*13. $\theta \doteq 56.6°$

*14. m($\angle ABC$) = 35° so $\cos 35° \doteq 0.8192$

Answers to Sample Assessment

1. (a) $\triangle ABC \cong \triangle EDF$ (b) $\triangle ABC \cong \triangle PRQ$

2.   Constructions.

   (d)   Hint: If the distance between the lines is d, the radius of the required circle is d/2. The center of the circle is on the line k parallel to m and at the distance d/2 from m and from ℓ. To locate the center, draw an arc with center at P and radius d/2; the points of intersection of arc width k are the possible centers of the required circle. There are two such circles.

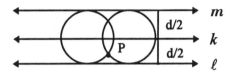

3. (a)   Follows from $\triangle AMB \cong \triangle CMD$ which are congruent by SAS.

   (b)   From $\triangle AMB \cong \triangle CMB$ it follows that $\angle BAM \cong \angle DCM$ and hence that $\overline{AB} \parallel \overline{CD}$.

4. (a) $x = \dfrac{20}{3}$; y cannot be determined from the given data.

   (b) $x = 6$

5.   308 cm

6. (a)   True by AA.
   (b)   False. In similar triangles the ratio between corresponding sides does not have to be 1.
   (c)   True by AA since all the angles have measure 60°.
   (d)   False. Two isosceles triangles may have noncongruent base angles.
   (e)   True. $\triangle BCE \sim \triangle DAE$ by AA; $\angle CBE \cong \angle EDA$ as they are alternate interior angles between the parallels $\overleftrightarrow{BC}$ and $\overleftrightarrow{AD}$ and the transversal $\overleftrightarrow{BD}$, and the angles at E are congruent as vertical angles.

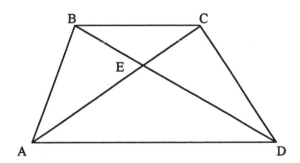

   (f)   True. If two sides of one angle are parallel respectively to two sides of a second angle, the angles must be congruent. (If a proof is desired extend two non-parallel sides of the angles and use corresponding angles to show that the angles are congruent.)
   Consequently the statement follows by AA.

7.   No, the length of any side of a triangle must be less than the sum of the lengths of the other two sides. Note that $31 > 10 + 20$.

8. The slope of $\overleftrightarrow{AB}$ is 2; the slope of $\overleftrightarrow{BC}$ is $\dfrac{-5}{3}$; the slope of $\overleftrightarrow{DC}$ is 2; and the slope of $\overleftrightarrow{AD}$ is $\dfrac{-5}{3}$. Thus, $\overleftrightarrow{AB} \mid\mid \overleftrightarrow{CD}$ and $\overleftrightarrow{BC} \mid\mid \overleftrightarrow{AD}$. Therefore ABCD is a parallelogram.

9. $y = 2x - 2$.

*10. $x = 36$; $y \doteq 15.59$

*11. $\sin \theta \doteq 0.5515$

*12. $\sin(\angle ABC) \doteq 0.5736$.

Answers to Sample Assessment

1. (a) 120 m^2 (b) 12 cm^2

2. 170 cm^2 3. 8 cm^2

4. $\sqrt{10}$ cm

5. Given any triangle ABC as shown, another triangle A′B′C′ can be constructed and placed to
    form parallelogram ABA′C. The area of parallelogram ABA′C is bh. Thus, the area of ΔABC is
    $\dfrac{1}{2}$ bh.

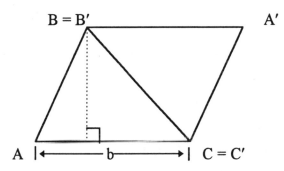

6. (a)   10 m   (b) $18\pi \text{ m}^3$

7. $(48 + 18\pi) \text{ m}^2$

8. (a)   Yes. $3^2 + 4^2 = 5^2$

    (b)   Yes. $\left(\sqrt{2}\right)^2 + \left(\sqrt{3}\right)^2 = \left(\sqrt{5}\right)^2$

9. (a)   0.05   (b)   18,000   (c)   4
    (d)   0.3   (e)   170,000   (f)   27,000
    (g)   27   (h)   4,738,000

10. (a) $155.\overline{5}$ (b)   3   (c)   72   (d)   89.6

11. (a) 512 m^3 (b)   512,000 L   (c)   512,000 kg

12. (a)   3000   (b)   2000   13. $12,000\pi \text{ cm}^3$
    (c)   13   (d)   4200
    (e)   0.00301

14. (a) 14π cm   (b) $49\pi \text{ cm}^2$ (c) $(40/20) \pi \text{ cm}^2$ or $2.45\pi \text{ cm}^2$

15. $6\pi + 4$

Answers to Sample Assessment

1. (a)   150 cm^2 (b)   96 m^2

2. Use a diagonal of a trapezoid to divide it into two triangles as shown below. The height of each triangle is the same. The area of one triangle is $\frac{1}{2}$ b_1h and area of the other triangle is $\frac{1}{2}$ b_2h.

   Hence the area of the trapezoid is $\frac{1}{2}$ $h(b_1 + b_2)$.

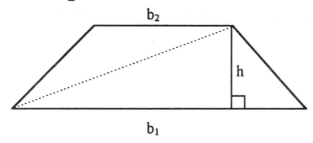

3. (a)

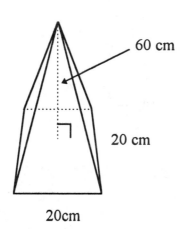

60 cm

20 cm

20cm

   (b)   There are infinitely many possible pyramids. If a is the length of the side of the base and h the height of the pyramid, then the volume of the pyramid is $(1/3)a^2h$. We have $(1/3)a^2h = 8000$ or $h = 24,000/a^2$. Thus we may assign a arbitrary value for a and obtain a corresponding value for h.

4. The surface area is 16 times as great; the volume is 64 times as great.

5. (a)   Yes. $50^2 = 30^2 + 40^2$ (b)   No. $\left(\sqrt{6}\right)^2 \pm \left(\sqrt{2}\right)^2 + \left(\sqrt{3}\right)^2$

6. (a)   44,800 cm^2 (b) 0.48 m^3 (c)   480 L

7. S.A. = 7000π cm^2

8. (a)   3000 L   (b)   3000 kg   (c)   1 cm or 0.01 m

9. 90π cm^2 or 282.7 cm^2

10. (a) $10\sqrt{2}$ cm or 14.14.cm   (b)   6 cm   (c)   4 cm

11. (a)   300,000   (b)   30   (c)   27
    (d)   1779   (e)   100,000   (f) $^-$40
    (g)   37

12. It is nine times greater.

13. 468π ft^3 or 1470.3 ft^3

Answers to Sample Assessment

1.   (a)

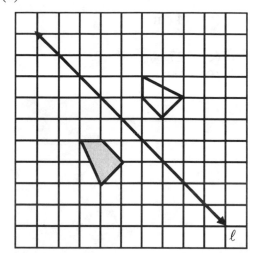

(b)

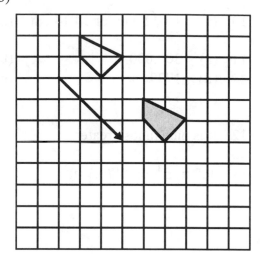

(c)

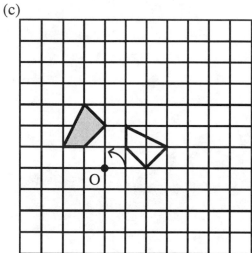

(d)

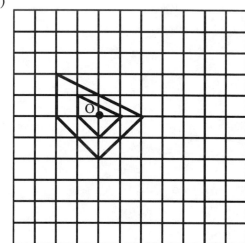

2.   (a)   6   (b)   3

3.   (a)   Reflection or half turn
     (b)   Slide, reflection, or half turn

4.   (a)   (b)   (c)

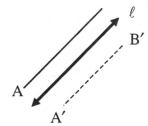

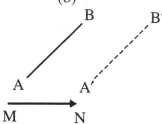

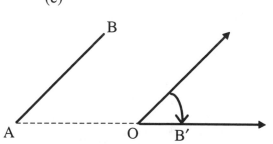

5.   Answers may vary.

6.   (a)   Rotation   (b)   Reflection   (c)   Rotation

7. (a) A line which is the perpendicular bisector of any pair of opposite sides has the property.
   (b) For squares. Because the diagonals of a square are perpendicular bisectors of each other, the lines containing the diagonals have the required property. Hence a square has four such lines.
   (c) Isosceles trapezoids.

8. (a)

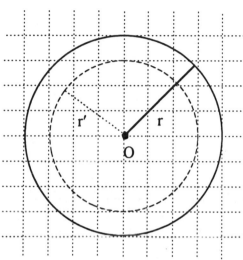

   (b) The figure is a circle with center O and radius $\frac{3}{4}$r because the image of every point is a point which is $\frac{3}{4}$r away from O.

9. One way is to apply the following transformations in succession; a translation from O to O_1, and a size transformation with center O_1 and scale factor $\frac{2}{3}$.

10. Answers may vary.

11. Hint: Use the angle bisector of the non-base angle as a reflecting line.

12. Hint: Use the perpendicular bisector of $\overline{AB}$.

13. (a) True. $\triangle OAB \cong \triangle OA'B'$ by SAS since $\overline{OA} \cong \overline{OA'}$, $\overline{OB} \cong \overline{OB'}$ and the angles at O are vertical angles.
   (b) True. From (a) by CPCTC $\angle B' \cong \angle B$ and hence $\angle B'$ is a right angle. Because $OB \cong \overline{OB'}$ and $\overline{OB'} \perp \ell'$, OB' is the distance from O to ℓ'.
   (c) True. The angles at B are alternate interior angles between ℓ and ℓ' and the transversal $\overleftrightarrow{BB'}$
   (d) False. The Image of $\overleftrightarrow{AA'}$ is $\overleftrightarrow{AA'}$.

14. What the student says is true for a single point, but not for the entire plane. For example, if B is on ℓ, then B', the image of B under the translation, is not the reflection of B in ℓ.

15. (a)   P′(0, 0) , Q′ (a + 3, b − 4)

    (b)   P′(4, −3) , Q′ (b, a)

    (c)   P′(−4, 3) , Q′ (−b, −a)

    (d)   P′(3, −4) , Q′ (−a, −b)

    (e)   P′(−4, −3) , Q′(−b, a)

16. (a)   (−6, 8) , (a − 3, b + 4)

    (b)   (4, −3) , (b, a)

    (c)   (−4, 3) , (−b, −a)

    (d)   (3, −4) , (−a, −b)

    (e)   (4, 3) , (b, −a)

17. $y = -\dfrac{1}{2}x + 2$

*18. The measure of each interior angle in a regular pentagon is $\dfrac{3 \cdot 180°}{5}$ or 108°. Because 360 is not divisible by 108 a regular pentagon cannot tessellate the plane.

19. TO H :S
    IF YCOR > 80 TOPLEVEL
    HE :S
    FORWARD 2∗ :S
    LEFT 90
    FORWARD :S
    RIGHT 90
    H :S
    END
    TO HE :S
    FORWARD 3∗ :S

    RIGHT 90
    FORWARD :S
    RIGHT 90
    FORWARD :S
    LEFT 90 FORWARD :S
    LEFT 90 FORWARD :S
    RIGHT 90 FORWARD S RIGHT 90
    FORWARD 3∗ :S

    RIGHT 90 FORWARD :S
    RIGHT 90 FORWARD :S
    LEFT 90 FORWARD :S
    LEFT 90 FORWARD :S
    RIGHT 90 FORWARD S RIGHT 90
    END

Answers to Sample Assessment

1. (a)

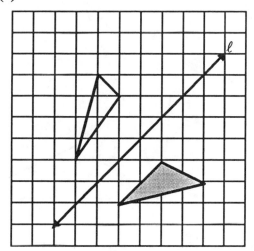

(b)

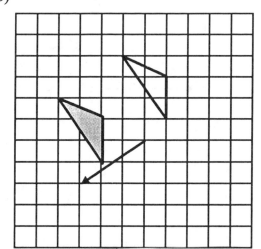

(c)

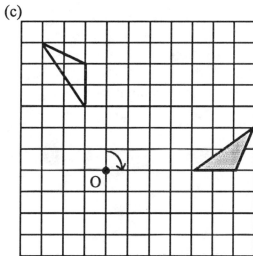

(d)

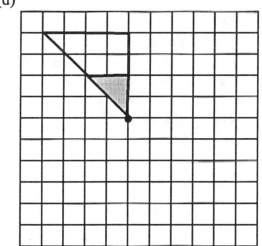

2. (a)

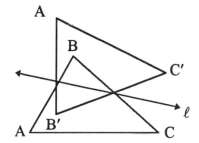

(b)

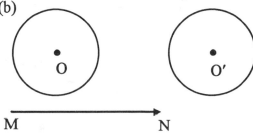

2.   (cont.)

(c)

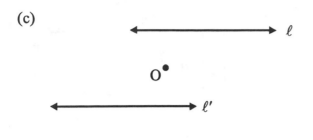

(d)

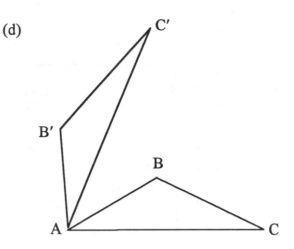

3. Hint: Try half-turns of the figure about midpoints of the sides.

4. (a)   1   (b)   1   (c)   5   (d)   6

5. (a)   Neither
    (b)   Neither
    (c)   Rotational symmetries of 72°, 144°, 216°, 288°
    (d)   Rotational symmetries of 60°, 120°, 180°, 240°, 300°; also has point symmetry

6. (a)   Reflection   (b)   Reflection
    (c)   Translation   (d)   Rotation

7. (a)   1   (b)   1   (c)   2   (d)   2

8. Hint: Use the line through the midpoints of parallel sides.

9. Find the image of ΔABC under a translation from B to A. Then apply to this image a reflection in
    the line $\overleftrightarrow{BA}$. Finally apply a size transformation with center A and a scale factor of 2.

10. What the student says is true for a single point, but not for the entire plane, or even two points. If
    B′ is the image of B(B ≠ A) under the same glide reflection, then the intersection of the line of the
    reflection with $\overline{BB'}$ is different than O.

11. The student is correct. The half-turn is about the point of intersection of the perpendicular lines ℓ
    and *m*. If the lines intersect at O, then A′ is the reflection of A in ℓ, A″ is the reflection of A′ in m,
    and A‴ is the reflection of A″ in ℓ. Then A, A′, A″ and A‴ are vertices of a rectangle. Because the
    diagonals of a rectangle bisect each other at O, A″ is the image of A under a half-turn in O.

11. (cont.)

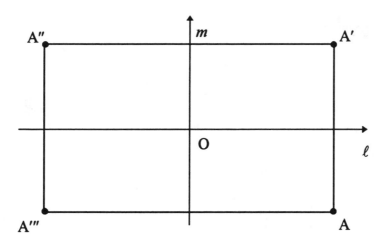

12. $y = 2x + 10$

15. (a) $P'(5, 8)$, $Q'(a + 3, b + 5)$
    (b) $P''(8, 13)$, $Q''(a + 6, b + 10)$
    (c) $P'(2, -3)$, $Q'(a, -b)$
    (d) $P'(-2, 3)$, $Q'(-a, b)$
    (e) $P'(-2, -3)$, $Q'(-a, -b)$

14. $y = 0$ or $y = 0 \cdot x + 0$, $y = -\dfrac{1}{\sqrt{3}}x + \dfrac{1}{\sqrt{3}}$, $y = \dfrac{1}{\sqrt{3}}x + \dfrac{1}{\sqrt{3}}$

15. A square with a side the same length as a side of the octagon.

```
*16.  TO HOUSE :S
         IF XCOR > 90 TOPLEVEL
         HOUSE :S
         SETUP1 :S
         HOUSE :S
         SETUP2 :S
         HOUSE :S
      END

      TO HOUSE :S
         SQUARE :S
         FD :S   RT 30
         TRIANGLE :S
      END

      TO TRIANGLE :S
         REPEAT 3[FD :S  RT 90]
      END

      TO SETUP1 :S
         REPEAT 2[FD :S RT 90]
      END

      TO SETUP2 :S
      FD :S LT 30
      FD :S RT 180
      END
```

1. $n^{50} > 2^n$ is not true for $n = 1$ because $1^{50} = 1$ and $2^1 = 2$, but $1 \not> 2$. Hence, the statement is not true for all values of n. Even though the statement is true for $n = 2, 3, \ldots, 50$ we could not conclude that it is true for all values of n greater than 1 because inductive reasoning does not assure the truth of a general statement. In fact, it can be shown that for $n \geq 439$ the statement is false.

2. Since the population is increasing, the ratio of the geometric sequence is greater than 1. Because the terms of such a geometric sequence increase faster than the terms of any arithmetic sequence, it is possible to show that given any increasing geometric sequence and any arithmetic sequence, for some n the nth term of the geometric sequence will be greater than the corresponding terms of the arithmetic sequence.

3. In the first case, the calculator multiplies the terminating decimal 0.3333333 by 3 to yield the answer 0.9999999 which is also a terminating decimal. In the second case, $1 \div 3 = 0.\overline{3}$. The calculator stores more than the 8 digits which appear in the display and when it multiplies by 3 it rounds the answer to 1.

4. Students still need to learn their basic facts. Without the basic facts, students cannot do the mental math and estimation that are so important in mathematics and are called for in the *Standards*. For example, if a student does not know that $9 + 6 = 15$, then the student would have trouble recognizing that $937 + 654 = 1291$ could not be correct. Basic facts are needed because it is becoming even more important to recognize whether computed results are reasonable. Many studies have shown that using calculators enhances young children's ability to learn basic facts.

5. The sequence can be thought of as having first term 6 and the fixed difference 0. We can get from one term to the next by adding the same fixed number, namely 0. Therefore this sequence satisfies the definition of an arithmetic sequence.

6. Two terms can lead to more than one sequence. For example, the terms 3, 6, . . . could lead to 3, 6, 9, 12, . . . which is an arithmetic sequence with fixed difference 3. It might also lead to 3, 6, 9, 15, 24, 39, . . . in which each successive term is obtained by adding the two previous terms. Another sequence is 3, 6, 10, 15, 21, . . . in which the rule is add 3 to the first term, then add 4 to the second term, then add 5 to the third term, and so on. From these examples, we can see that two terms are not enough to determine any sequence.

1. One way to designate the empty set is { }. Anything we enclose in the braces is an element of the set. Thus, {∅} is a set having one element, so it is not empty. The difficulty usually arises from the reluctance to consider the empty set as an element.

2. In fact it is true that $A \cup B = \{a,b,c,d,c,d\}$; however, because the agreement is not to list any element in a set more than once, $\{a,b,c,d,c,d\} = \{a,b,c,d\}$.

3. The student is right. To show that the hypothesis implies $B = C$ we show that $B \subseteq C$ and $C \subseteq B$. To show that $B \subseteq C$ let $x \in B$, then $x \in A \cup B$ and because $A \cup B = A \cup C$, $x \in A \cup C$. Consequently $x \in A$ or $x \in C$. If $x \in C$ then $B \subseteq C$. If $x \in A$ then since we started with $x \in B$ it follows that $x \in A \cap B$. Because $A \cap B = A \cap C$ we conclude that $x \in A \cap C$ and therefore $x \in C$. Thus $B \subseteq C$. Similarly starting with $x \in C$ it can be shown that $x \in B$ and hence that $C \subseteq B$.

4. No. For example, the set of all rational numbers greater than or equal to 0 and less than or equal to 1 is an infinite set whose greatest element is 1.

5. The student is incorrect. The student is distributing the complement bar over A and B. The student should be encouraged to check the assertion $\overline{A \cap B} = \overline{A} \cap \overline{B}$ with an example and with a Venn diagram.

6. What the student said is true if $B \subseteq A$ or $B = \emptyset$. However, in general, $\overline{A} \cap \overline{B} \neq \overline{A}$. Consider $U = \{1,2,3,4\}$, $A = \{1\}$, and $B = \{2\}$. Here $\overline{A} = \{2,3,4\}$ and $\overline{A} \cap \overline{B} = \{3,4\} \neq \overline{A}$.

7. Since "formula" is not defined, it is really impossible to answer the question. Most likely, students view a formula as a single equation. If this is the case, the concepts are not the same. Students are usually misled by the fact that many functions which appear in mathematical applications are given by equations. However, not every equation represents a function; for example, let $x = y^2$. For every $x \neq 0$, there are two corresponding values of y, and hence the equation does not define a function.

8. The student is wrong. If for example, $A = \{1, 2, 3\}$ and $B = \{2, 3, 4\}$, then neither $A \subseteq B$ nor $B \subseteq A$.

9. Even though the Cartesian product of sets includes all pairings in which each element of the first set is the first component in a pair with each element of the second set, this is not necessarily a one-to-one correspondence. A one-to-one correspondence implies that there must be the same number of elements in each set. This is not the case in Cartesian product. For example, consider sets $A = \{1\}$ and $B = \{a,b\}$.

10. Let $A = \{1, 2, 3\}$ and $B = \{4, 5, 6\}$. The set $\{(1, 4), (2, 5), (3, 6)\}$ is a function from A to B and it is a subset of A x B. However not every subset of A x B is a function from A to B. For example $\{(1, 4), (1, 5), (2, 5), (3, 6)\}$ is a subset of A x B but it is not a function because two different ordered pairs with the same first component are in the set. In general a function from A to B is a subset of A x B but not every subset of A x B is a function from A to B.

11. The student is wrong. The ordered pair (x,y) is considered a single input. If x and y are in N then (x,y) is an element in N x N and hence the domain of the function is N x N.

1. The expressions are not equal because $2(3 \cdot 4) = 24$ and $(2 \cdot 3)(2 \cdot 4) = 6 \cdot 8 = 48$. There is not distributive property of multiplication over multiplication.

2. No. The first equation is true because $39 + 41 = 39 + (1 + 40) = (39 + 1) + 40 = 40 + 40$. Now, $39 \cdot 41 = (40 - 1)(40 + 1) = (40 - 1) 40 + (40 - 1)1 = 40^2 - 40 + 40 - 1 = 40^2 - 1$, and $40^2 - 1 \neq 40^2$.

3. Yes. If $a < b$, we can write $a = bq + r$ where $q = 0$ and $r = a$. Notice that in this case, we still have $0 \leq r < b$. For example, if $a = 3$ and $b = 5$, then $3 = 0 \cdot 5 + 3$.

4. They are equal in value because multiplication is commutative; 5 times 4 means $5 \cdot 4$; 5 multiplied by 4 is $4 \cdot 5$; and $5 \cdot 4 = 4 \cdot 5$.

5. $0 \div 0 = x$ if and only if $0 = 0 \cdot x$. Any number x solves the last equation, and consequently $0 \div 0$ does not have a unique value. Suppose $0 \div 0 = 1$. Because $0 = 0 \cdot 2$, if we divide both sides of the equation by 0, then $1 = 1 \cdot 2$ or $1 = 2$. Thus, $0 \div 0 = 1$ leads to a contradiction, and consequently it cannot be defined as 1.

6. Evidently the student does not understand the process of long division. The repeated subtraction method should help in understanding the above mistake.

```
6│ 36
   6│ 1 six
  ───
   30
   30│ 5 sixes
    │ 6 sixes
```

Instead of adding 1 and 5, the student wrote 15.

7. It is correct. Because M is a special symbol for 1000, it is preferable to write MI for 1001 rather than $\overline{\text{II}}$. Romans usually reserved the bar for numbers greater than 4000.

8. The following should be discussed. $(2^3)^2 = 2^3 \cdot 2^3 = 2^6$. On the other hand $2^{(3^2)} = 2^9$.

9. In general, $a \div (b - c) \neq (a \div b) - (a \div c)$. For example, $100 \div (25 - 5) \neq (100 \div 25) - (100 \div 5)$. In fact the right-hand side is $4 - 20$, which is not defined in the set of whole numbers. However, the right distributive property of division over subtraction does hold provided each expression is defined in the set of whole numbers; that is $(b - c) \div a = (b \div a) - (c \div a)$.

10. The student probably has in mind the fact that if $a \in W$, $a - 0 = a$. It should be pointed out that 0 would be the identity for subtraction if $0 - a = a$ was also true. Since $0 - a$ is not defined in the set of whole numbers $0 - a \neq a$ and therefore 0 is not the identity for subtraction.

11. Any number can be represented by a directed arrow of a given length. In this case, the directed arrow represents 3 units. Any arrow 3 units in length can be used to represent 3, regardless of its starting point.

12. The teacher should copy parts of the NCTM *Standards* for both the student and the class to read. This gives the mathematics educators' organization point of view about the use of calculators.

13. To show the parent a current view about the use of manipulatives in the classroom, the NCTM *Standards* can be used to show a professional opinion about their use. Possibly the parent went to school in an era when the use of counting on fingers was discouraged.

14. The teacher should agree with the parent. Writing in mathematics is one of the more important pieces of meta-mathematics to learn. The ability to communicate what one knows in a subject is not restricted only to finding answers but in being able to share with others the process by which those answers arrived and how they fit the original problem. Being able to write mathematics is one way to do that.

1. The algorithm is correct, and the student should be congratulated for finding it. One way to encourage such creative behavior is to name and refer to the procedure after the student who invented it, for example, "David's subtraction method." In fourth grade the technique can be explained by using a money model. Suppose you have $4 in one checking account and $80 in another, for a total of $84. You spent $27 by withdrawing $7 from the first account and $20 from the second. The first checking account is overdrawn by $3; that is, the balance is -$3. The balance is the second account is $60. After transferring $3 from the second account to the first, the balance in the first account is $0 and in the second $57; that is, the total balance is $57.

2. The student is correct that a debt of $5 is greater than a debt of $2. However, what this means is that on a number line $^-5$ is farther to the left than is $^-2$. The fact that $^-5$ is farther to the left than $^-2$ on a number line implies that $^-5 < {^-2}$.

3. The student does not complete the argument in detail. Indeed $a - b = a + {^-b}$. However, $b - a = b + {^-a}$. In general, $a + {^-b} \neq b + {^-a}$. For example, $5 + {^-2} \neq 2 + {^-5}$.

4. The students does not fully understand the order of operations. The teacher should emphasize that in order to avoid ambiguity, mathematicians agree that multiplication is performed before addition or subtraction. A few simpler examples like $10 - 2 \cdot 3$ should be helpful.

5. The procedure can be justified as follows. Since for all integers c, $^-c = (-1)c$, the effect of performing the opposite of an algebraic expression is the same as multiplying the expression by $^-1$. However, in the expression $x - (2x - 3)$, the "$-$" is used to denote subtraction, not simply finding the opposite. If the expression is first rewritten as $x + {^-(2x + {^-3})}$, then it is the case that $^-(2x + {^-3}) = {^-1}(2x + {^-3})$, or $^-2x + 3$. Now the expression can be rewritten as $x + {^-2x} + 3$, which a student might obtain from the father's rule.

6. It is quite possible that the student has used a circular argument in this proof. The teacher would need to know how the cancellation property of multiplication involving integers was proved. Most likely, the proof used the fact that $(-1)(-1) = 1$. If so, then there is an error in the reasoning.

7. The picture is supposed to illustrate the fact that an integer and its opposite are mirror images of each other. Because a could be negative, the picture is correct. For example, possible values for a and ^-a are $a = {^-1}$, $^-a = 1$ and $a = {^-7}$, $^-a = 7$. At this point, the teacher could remind the students that the "$-$" sign in ^-a does not mean that ^-a is negative. If a is positive, ^-a is negative, but if a is negative, ^-a is positive.

8. Yes. The students' conclusion is that $a \mid 0$ and this is true because $a \cdot 0 = 0$.

9. The student is generalizing the statement "if $d \mid a$ and $d \mid b$, then $d \mid (a + b)$" to the corresponding statement for "does not divide." (Generalizations have to be checked carefully.) The statement the student wrote is false; for example, $3 \nmid 7$ and $3 \nmid 2$, but $3 \mid (7 + 2)$.

10. It has been shown that any four-digit number n can be written in the form $n = a \cdot 10^3 + b \cdot 10^2 + c \cdot 10 + d = (a \cdot 999 + b \cdot 99 + c \cdot 9) + (a + b + c + d)$. The test for divisibility by some number g will depend on the sum of the digits $a + b + c + d$ if, and only if, $g \mid (a \cdot 999 + b \cdot 99 + c \cdot 9)$ regardless of the values of a, b, and c. Since the only numbers greater than 1 that divide 9, 99, and 999 are 3 and 9, the test for divisibility by dividing the sum of the digits by the number works only for 3 and 9. A similar argument works for any n-digit number.

11. The student is wrong. For example, 1029 is divisible by 7, but neither 29 nor 10 is divisible by 7. However, it is true that a number with an even number of digits is divisible by 7 if each of the numbers formed by pairing the digits into groups of two is divisible by 7. The proof for any six-digit number follows. (The proof for any number with an even number of digits is similar.) Let $= a \cdot 10^5 + b \cdot 10^4 + c \cdot 10^3 + d \cdot 10^2 + e \cdot 10 + f$ be any six-digit number such that 7 divides each of the two-digit numbers $a \cdot 10 + b$, $c \cdot 10 + d$, and $e \cdot 10 + f$. The number, n, can be written as follows: $n = a \cdot 10^5 + b \cdot 10^4 + c \cdot 10^3 + d \cdot 10^2 + e + 10 + f = (a \cdot 10 + b)10^4 + (c \cdot 10 + d)10^2 + (e \cdot 10 + f)$. Since 7 divides $(e \cdot 10 + f)$, $(c \cdot 10 + d)$, and $(a \cdot 10 + b)$, it follows from the basic properties of divisibility that $7 \mid [(a \cdot 10 + b)10^4 + (c \cdot 10 + d)10^2 + (e \cdot 10 + f)]$.

12. It is very hard to refute the student's claim, because there are infinitely many primes. We can say that unlike when finding successive counting numbers, where it is possible to produce the next number by adding one, there is no known way to produce the next prime from a given prime number.

13. It is true that a number is divisible by 21 if, and only if, it is divisible by 3 and by 7. However, the general statement is false. For example, 12 is divisible by 4 and by 6 but not by $4 \cdot 6$ or 24. One part of the statement is true, that is, "if a number is divisible by $a \cdot b$, then it is divisible by a and b." The statement "if a number is divisible by a and by b, it is divisible by ab" it is true if a and b are relatively prime. To see why this is true, suppose GCD $(a, b) = 1$ and m is an integer such that $a \mid m$ and $b \mid m$. Since $a \mid m$, $m = ka$ for some integer k. Now $b \mid m$ implies that $b \mid ka$ for some integer k. Since a and b are relatively prime, it follows from the Fundamental Theorem of Arithmetic and the fact that $b \mid ka$ that $b \mid k$ (why?), and therefore $k = jb$, for some integer j. Substituting $k = jb$ in $m = ka$, we obtain $m = jba$, and consequently $ab \mid m$.

14. The student is partially correct. If a and b are distinct natural numbers, then the student is correct. By definition, $a \leq$ LCM(a, b); $b \leq$ LCM(a, b). Also GCD$(a, b) \leq a$ and GCD$(a, b) \leq b$. Hence, GCD$(a,b) \leq$ LCM(a, b). However, the equality holds if $a = b$.

15. $x = 3k$, $y = 4k$, $z = 5k$ satisfies the equation for any integer k. Hence the student is right.

16. The number 1 is not a prime because it does not have exactly two divisors; it has only one.

17. In finding the least common demoninator of fractions, one must find the LCM of the denominators. Thus the LCM of a set of denominators is the least common denominator.

1. 0/6 is not in simplest form. A fraction a/b is in simplest form if and only if GCD(a,b)=1; however GCD$(0,6) = 6$. The simplest form of 0/6 is 0/1.

2. Let the number be a. One half of a is $(1/2)(a) = a/2$. Dividing a by 1/2 yields $2a$. Consequently the student is incorrect.

3. The first student's approach is correct. What the second student has done is to treat the problem as if it had been $(1/5)(5/3)=1/3$, when in reality, the problem is 15/53. Writing the problem as $(10 + 5)/(50 + 3)$ may help.

4. No. Because $2/3 - 1/2 = 1/6$ and $3/4 - 2/3 = 1/12$, there is no fixed number that can be added to each term in order to obtain the next term.

5. Yes. The student is correct. Suppose that the fractions are positive and $a/b < c/d$. This inequality is equivalent to $ad < bc$. The student claims that $a/b < (a + c)/(b + d) < c/d$. This is equivalent to $a(b + d) < b (a + c)$ and $(a + c)d < c(b + d)$. However, each of the last inequalities is equivalent to $ad < bc$.

6. Yes, the student is correct. Let $a/b = c/d = r$. Then $a = br$, $c = dr$, and therefore $(a + c)/(b + d) = (br + dr)/(b + d) = r(b + d)/(b + d) = r = a/b = c/d$.

7. The student is generalizing the distributive property of multiplication over addition to the distributive property of multiplication over multiplication. The latter does not hold.

8. The student is wrong unless $n = 0$ or $p = m$.

9. The student was probably thinking that more pieces meant more pizza. A pizza (or circle) could be cut into 6 pieces, then each piece could be cut into 2 pieces. This shows the amount of pizza did not change from these last cuts, only the number of pieces changed.

10. The student is incorrect but has an idea about finding the limit of $(a + x)/(b + x)$ when x is very large. The limit of that expression as x becomes very large is 1.

1. (a) No. Because $1.01 - 1.1 = -0.09$ and $1.001 - 1.01 = 0.009$, there is no fixed number that can be added to each term in order to obtain the next term. In fact this is a geometric sequence because each term can be multiplied by 0.1 to obtain the next term.

    (b) No. The difference between each term (starting from the second term) and the preceding term is not fixed. The sequence is a geometric sequence with ratio $\left(\dfrac{1}{2}\right)^{-3}$ or 8.

2. The principal square root of 25, written $\sqrt{25}$, is defined to be the nonnegative number whose square is 25. Consequently, $\sqrt{25} = 5$.

3. The principal square root of a^2 is always nonnegative. Hence, $\sqrt{a^2} = a$ if $a > 0$. If $a < 0$, then $-a$ is positive, and hence $\sqrt{a^2} = -a$. For example, if $a = -5$, then $\sqrt{(-5)^2} = {}^-(-5) = 5$. Consequently the student is wrong.

4. All properties of integral exponents do not automatically extend to rational exponents. The corresponding properties for rational exponents have to be justified. The property $\left(a^m\right)^n = a^{mn}$ is true when a is nonnegative and m and n are rational numbers. For $a < 0$, m an even integer and $n = 1/m$, the property is false. For example, $\left((-5)^2\right)^{1/2} \neq -5$.

5. Most likely, the student thinks that $-x$ is a negative number. This is wrong. Depending upon the value of x, $-x$ can be positive, negative, or 0. If $x < 0$, then $-x > 0$. In fact, $x = -9$ is the solution of the given equation.

6. Scientific notation is typically used for very large numbers or very small numbers (numbers close to 0). In scientific notation, a number N is written in the form $N = A \cdot 10^n$ where $1 \leq A < 10$. Thus, negative numbers are not considered in this definition. If this notation is to be used with negative numbers, we can work with the number as if it were a positive number and then annex a negative sign at the end, for example, $-2,390,000$ could be written as $-2.39 \cdot 10^6$.

7. In the second method, the student did not use the distributive property correctly. Notice that $(8 + 1/2)(6 + 1/2) = (8 + 1/2)6 + (8 + 1/2)(1/2)$. Because $(8 + 1/2)6 = 8 \cdot 6 + (1/2)6 = 48 + 3$, the 3 is missing in the student's example. Adding 3 to the student's answer results in the correct answer of 55 1/4.

8. 0.36 can be written as 36/100 and 0.9 can be written as 9/10. Comparing the numerators of the fractions will not determine which fraction is larger because the denominators are different. To compare the fractions, they need to have the same denominator. Because $0.9 = 0.90 = 90/100$ and 90 is greater than 36, $0.9 > 0.36$.

9. Be definition, $\sqrt{5}$ is the principal square root of 5, and has one value, the nonnegative number b such that $b^2 = 5$. The solutions of $x^2 = 5$ are $\sqrt{5}$ and its opposite $\sqrt{5}$. Both solutions are written as

$\pm\sqrt{5}$.

10. It is evident what happens when 0.5 is raised to large powers. Because $\left(\frac{1}{2}\right)^{10} = \frac{1}{1024}$ and

$\frac{1}{2^{20}} = \left[\left(\frac{1}{2}\right)^{10}\right]^2 = \frac{1}{1,048,576}$, it is clear that $\frac{1}{2}$ raised to a positive integer, gets quickly close to 0.

In fact any number between 0 and 1 when raised to a sufficiently large exponent will get as close to 0 as we wish. At the level of this course it may be sufficient to use a calculator to see what happens when 0.999 is raised to large powers. Using the $\boxed{x^2}$ key repeatedly we get: 0.9841194, 0.9684911, 0.937975, 0.879797, 0.7740428, 0.5991423, 0.3589715, ... which are the approximate values of 0.999^2, 0.999^4, 0.999^8, 0.999^{16}, ..., 0.999^{1024}. We see that the tenth term in the sequence is less than 0.5 and hence further squaring should quickly result in numbers closer and closer to 0.

11. (a) The calculator does not carry the decimals out far enough to compare the two numbers.

(b) $\frac{9444}{9445} - \frac{9443}{9444} > 0$,

$\frac{9444^2 - 9443 \cdot 9445}{9444} > 0$

The last inequality is true if and only if the numerator of the fraction is positive. Using a calculator we find that $9444^2 - 9443 \cdot 9445 = 1$ and hence that

$\frac{9444}{9445} > \frac{9443}{9444}$

It is possible to determine which fraction is greater with fewer calculations as follows.

$\frac{9443}{9444} = \frac{9444-1}{9444} = 1 - \frac{1}{9444}$ and $\frac{9444}{9445} = \frac{9445-1}{9445} = 1 - \frac{1}{9445}$.

Because $\frac{1}{9445} < \frac{1}{9444}$, $\frac{-1}{9445} > \frac{-1}{9444}$ and hence, $1 - \frac{1}{9445} > 1 - \frac{1}{9444}$.

Yet another approach is to multiply each decimal equivalent by 10. Because $\frac{9444}{9445} \cdot 10$ is displayed as 9.998412 and $\frac{9443}{9444} \cdot 10$ as 9.89411, the first fraction is the greater one. However this approach will not work to show that $\frac{94444}{94445} > \frac{94443}{94444}$.

1. The teacher was right. Nat obtained the correct answer by using an incorrect method because in general $a + b(x + c) \neq (a + b)(x + c)$. Some advanced students could be encouraged to find other equations for which a similar mistake will produce a correct answer. This will happen if the equations $a + b(x + c) = x + d$ and $(a + b)(x + c) = x + d$ have the same solution. This can be shown to happen if and only if $d = a + b + c - 1$. Consequently a, b and c can be chosen at will but d is determined by the above equation.

2. Yes, the student is correct. Let $\dfrac{a}{b} = \dfrac{c}{d} = r$. Then $a = br$, $c = dr$, and therefore $\dfrac{a+c}{b+d} = \dfrac{br+dr}{b+d} = \dfrac{r(b+d)}{b+d} = r = \dfrac{a}{b} = \dfrac{c}{d}$.

3. The rule is always true because we can add the same number to each side of an equation or inequality. Thus if $x + a = c$ then $x + a + (-a) = c + (-a)$ and hence $x = c + (-a)$. A similar argument holds for inequalities.

4. No. The check only shows that the equations are correctly solved. It is possible that the equations were not set up correctly; that is, that they do not represent the information given in the word problem. In such a case, without following the written information, it would be impossible to detect the error.

5. $3\,1/4\% = 3\% + 1/4\% = 3/100 + (1/4)/100 = 0.03 + 0.0025 = 0.0325$. Knowing that $1/4 = 0.25$, the student incorrectly wrote $1/4\% = 0.25$.

6. It is possible to mark up the price of a product 150%. For example, if a product sells for $10, then a 150% markup is $1.5(\$10) = \$15$. Thus, the product would sell for $25.

7. Let s denote the amount of salary. After $p\%$ increase, the new salary is $s(1 + p/100)$. When this amount is decreased by $q\%$, the result is $s(1 + p/100)(1 - q/100)$. Similarly if the initial salary is first decreased by $q\%$ and then the new amount is raised by $p\%$, the final salary is $s(1 - q/100)(1 + p/100)$. Because the two expressions are equal, the student is right.

8. By definition $p\% = p/100$ where p is any real number. Hence $0.01\% = 0.01/100$. Because $0.01/100 \neq 0.01$, the student is wrong.

9. (a)   If $y = kx$ and $x = cz$ then $y = k(cz) = (kc)z$ and hence y is directly proportional to z.

    (b)   If $y = k/x$ and $x = c/z$ then $y = k/(c/z) = (k/c)z$. Hence y is also directly proportional to z.

1. Each toss of a fair coin is independent of the previous one. Hence the probability of a tail on each toss is $\frac{1}{2}$ regardless of how many tails appeared in previous tosses.

2. If the four areas corresponding to the colors were equal in size, the events of the spinner landing on each of the colors would be equally likely, and the student would be correct. However, since the four areas are different in size, the events are not equally likely, and the student is wrong.

3. Tossing three heads on the first three tosses of a coin does not imply the coin is unfair. Only when a fair coin is tossed a much greater number of times can expect to get approximately equal numbers of tails and heads. The probability of three heads in three tosses is $\frac{1}{8}$.

4. The student is wrong. The sample space for this event is not {HH, HT, TT}, but rather {HH, HT, TH, TT}. Consequently the probability of HH is $\frac{1}{4}$.

5. The student is not correct. The confusion probably lies in the fact that the student thinks that probabilities are additive. The student does not understand the Multiplication Rule for Probabilities. A tree diagram for the experiment could possibly help. A partial tree diagram is given below

$$\xrightarrow{\frac{1}{6}} 5 \xrightarrow{\frac{1}{6}} 5$$

Thus $P(5,5) = \frac{1}{6} \cdot \frac{1}{6} = \frac{1}{36}$

6. For an experiment with sample space S with equally likely outcomes, the probability of an event A is given by $P(A) = \frac{n(A)}{n(S)}$. Because an event A must be a subset of S, the smallest that n(A) could be is 0. This occurs when $A = \emptyset$. Because n(S) is never negative and n(A) is never negative, then the P(A) can never be negative.

7. The probability of an event is a ratio and does not necessarily reflect the number of elements in the event or in the sample space. For example, if n(S) = 20 and n(A) = 12, then $P(A) = \frac{12}{20}$ which could also be reported as $P(A) = \frac{3}{5}$.

8. The student is confused about choosing four objects none at a time. In any set of choices, there is always the option of choosing nothing, and there is one way to choose nothing. Therefore, we say $_4P_0 = 1$.

9. We define 0! as 1 because it fits the formula for combinations. It is also consistent with the rest of mathematics. To define 1/0 as 1 would cause many inconsistencies. If $1/0 = 1$ and $1/1 = 1$, then $1/0 = 1/1$ which should imply that $0 = 1$. This is not true.

10. For all multistage experiments, the probability of the outcome along any path in a tree diagram is equal to the product of the probabilities along the path. The sum of the probabilities on all the branches from any point is always 1 and the sum of the probabilities for all the possible outcomes is always 1. The probability of an event is the sum of the probabilities of the elements in the event.

1. The new mean is $\dfrac{9(10,000) + 20,000}{10} = 11,000$. Consequently the new mean has increased by $1000. The median and mode may be changed in special cases, for example, if the scores were 2000, 8000, 8000, 8000, 9000, 10,000, 12,000, 12,000, 13,000, and 18,000, then the median and mode change.

2. A first discussion might include asking what the student means by the "best average." If the student is thinking of choosing from the mean, median, or mode, then we need to discuss which is the most appropriate. The mode is used if it is desirable to know which value occurs most often in the distribution. For example, if a store wants to know which size pants is most frequently sold, the mode is the most appropriate average to use.

3. The student is not correct. The stem and leaf plot is very useful when trying to organize information that will later be used to make a bar graph or a frequency polygon. It is not the most useful plot when trying to depict information that will be organized into a circle graph for example.

4. Since the median is 90, at least half of the class had grades of 90 or more. Since Tom scored 80, he did not do better than half of the class.

5. A graph displays the data in a way that is possible to see at a glance how parts of the data compare to each other. One of the disadvantages of graphical representation is that it is not always possible to obtain accurate readings from graphs.

6. In a grouped frequency table, the precise value of the raw data is not displayed, and hence it is impossible to conclude from the table which value occurs most often. Consequently it is impossible to find the exact mode from the information given in a grouped frequency table. In this situation the mode is usually given as a class interval.

7. If the mean is less than the median, then one can be certain that there were more scores above the mean than below it. The low scores tend to be further from the mean than the high scores.

8. No, it is not possible to have a standard deviation of -5. By definition, the standard deviation is the positive square root of the variance.

9. Mel did not really miss the cut-off by a single point. He would have had to increase his score on each of the 10 tests by a single point to reach an average of 90 or increase his total score for the 10 tests by 10 points to reach an average of 90.

10. Bar graphs are typically used to display data that is not continuous, for example, the number of students in each sixth grade class at Washington School. They are used when data falls into distinct categories and we want to compare the totals. The line graph is more appropriate when we want to emphasize trends in data that change continuously over time.

11. The student is not correct. The data could consist of many data points, all of which have the same numerical value. In that case, the mean, median, and all data points have the same value.

12. The answer is probably "Yes." A manufacturer should be able to ensure with some degree of accuracy that his product is the "same" all the time. In order to do that, then tools should be calibrated with a small standard deviation.

13. An average deviation is sometimes used, but most people use the standard deviation. To find the average deviation, one would start the process like finding the standard deviation by finding the difference of a data value and the mean. One would then sum all the differences and find their mean. The average deviation may be misleading; you can have an average deviation of 0 when the standard deviation is nowhere close to 0.

1. From the Denseness Property, we know that for any two points we can always find a point between them. Since this is true for any two points we see that there are an infinite number of points in a segment.

2. The distinct lines are parallel if they do not intersect and are contained in a single plane. Lines which do not intersect and are not contained in any single plane are called skew lines. Many of the properties of parallel lines depend upon the fact that they are contained in a single plane and therefore do not share these properties with skew lines.

3. The measure of an angle has nothing to do with the fact that rays cannot be measured. The measure of an angle in degrees is based on constructing a circle with center at the vertex of the angle and dividing the circle into 360 congruent parts. The number of parts in the arc that the angle intercepts is the measure of the given angle in degrees. The number of parts in the intercepted arc is the same regardless of the size of the circle (or protractor).

4. Extending the rays does not change the angle measure.

5. A regular polygon is a polygon in which all the angles are congruent and all the sides are congruent. In general neither condition implies the other, and hence neither is sufficient to describe a regular polygon. For example, a rhombus that is not a square has all sides congruent, but all its angles are not congruent. A rectangle that is not a square has all its angles congruent, but not all its sides congruent.

6. Let n be the number of sides of a regular polygon, all of whose angles measure 90 degrees. The sum of the measures of all the interior angles is $n \cdot 90 = (n - 2)180$. This equation has the solution $n = 4$. Thus the polygon must have 4 sides, and therefore it is necessarily a square.

7. If two parallel lines are defined as lines which are in the same plane and do not intersect, then two identical lines cannot be parallel, because their intersection is nonempty. It is possible to define two identical lines as parallel or non parallel. Some books define it one way; other books the other way.

8. For line segments in the same plane to be parallel, they must be on parallel lines.

9. Vertical angles are formed by two intersecting lines. In this case angle 1 is formed by a line and a ray.

10. Cut the cylinder open along any line perpendicular to the base. The shortest path between A and B is the segment connecting A and B. Now fold the rectangle back into the cylinder; the path will appear on the cylinder.

11. Since an angle is a set of points determined by two rays with the same endpoint, to say that two angles are equal implies that the two sets of points determining the angels are equal. The only way this can happen is if the two angles are actually the same angle. To say that two angles are congruent is to say that the angles have the same size or measure.

12. The student is incorrect. While the degree is the basic unit of angle measure, it can be further subdivided. This in itself would prove that the student is incorrect. However, many geometry books also consider a Protractor Postulate which puts all the rays in a half-line emanating from a point in a one-to-one correspondence with the real numbers greater than or equal to 0 and less than 180. This would allow infinitely many rays emanating from one point.

13. A square is a particular kind of rectangle in which all sides have equal measures. All squares are rectangles.

14. To be regular, all sides must be congruent but also all angles must be congruent. All angles are not congruent unless the rhombus is a square.

1. The symbol $\cong$ used only for congruent parts. Because AB and CD designate length of segments and not the segments themselves, it is not true that AB $\cong$ CD. Notice that if segments are congruent, then they are of the same length; hence it is correct to write AB = CD.

2. Some of the constructions that cannot be done using a compass and straightedge are angle trisection, duplication of a cube, and squaring the circle. Given any angle, it is impossible with only a compass and straightedge to find two rays which divide the angle into three congruent angles. Some angles, but not all, can be trisected with straightedge and compass. For example, a right angle can be trisected. The duplication of a cube involves constructing the edge of a cube whose volume is twice the volume of a given cube. Squaring a circle involves constructing a square which has the same area as a given circle. For over 2000 years mathematicians tried to perform these three constructions. In the nineteenth century it was finally proved that these constructions cannot be done with straightedge and compass alone. A clear exposition of these proofs can be found in the book by Courant and Robbins, *What Is Mathematics?* (London: Oxford University Press, 1941 and 1969, pp. 117-140).

3. Perhaps the "best" definition relies on transformational geometry discussed in Chapter 12. Two figures can be defined to be congruent if and only if one figure can be mapped onto the other by successively applying translation, reflection, rotation, or glide reflection. For similarity add a size transformation.

4. For a detailed discussion of the trisection problem, see *The Trisection Problem*, by Robert Yates (Washington, D. C.: NCTM Publications, 1971).

5. The student is wrong. $\angle 1 \cong \angle 2$ implies that $\overline{AD}$ and $\overline{BC}$ are parallel, but does not imply that the other two sides are parallel.

6. This is false. Consider, for example, a rectangle which is not a square. The polygon resulting from connecting the midpoints of the sides of the rectangle is a rhombus with no right angles. Such a rhombus is not similar to the rectangle.

7. The symbol = is used for identical objects. Two triangles are equal if they represent the same set of points. Congruent triangles are not necessarily identical because their positions may be different.

8. The student is wrong. The student is forgetting that when we say $\triangle ABC$ is congruent to $\triangle BCA$, this means that there is a one-to-one correspondence set up among the vertices so that corresponding sides are congruent. If $\triangle ABC$ is congruent to $\triangle BCA$, then $\overline{AB} \cong \overline{BC}$, $\overline{AC} \cong \overline{BA}$, and $\overline{BC} \cong \overline{CA}$. This is not true in a general triangle.

9. The answer is no. For example a square and a rectangle do not have to be congruent though both have all 90° angles.

10. The student is correct. All *n*-gons for the same *n* have the same shape.

11. The student is correct. All circles have the same shape.

1. The units have to be the same because volume is measured in cubic units. A cubic unit is the volume of a cube having all its dimensions measured in the same units.

2. Yes, the same type of relationship does hold. For a proof and discussion, see G. Polya, *Mathematics and Plausible Reasoning*, Vol. 1 (Princeton, N.J.: Princeton University Press, 1954, pp. 15-17).

3. No. An angle is a union of two rays. The student probably means the area of the interior of an angle. However, because the interior of an angle occupies an infinite part of a plane, it does not have a measurable area.

4. The area of the interior of any simple closed curve can be described as the sum of the areas of the finitely many nonoverlapping parts into which it can be divided. In the student's case, the square is divided into <u>infinitely</u> many parts, and hence the above property does not apply.

5. Consider a cube with side 6 cm. The volume is 216 cm^3 and its surface area is 216 cm^2.

6. The metric system is much simpler than the English system of measurement. For example, converting from one unit to another within the metric system requires only multiplication or division by a power of 10. Almost all the countries in the world are using the metric system. In order for the United States to be able to trade effectively with other countries, it is essential that it uses the same system as everybody else.

7. Using the student's reasoning, in a right isosceles triangle, the side opposite the 90° angle should be twice as long as the side opposite the 45° angle. We know that the hypotenuse, c, is $\sqrt{2}$ times the length of a leg.

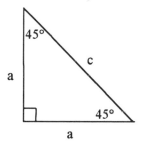

8. The given box has a volume of 125 cm^3 and not 5 cm^3. The student most likely thinks of 5 cm^3 as (5 cm)^3.

9. We use square centimeters or square inches to indicate the area of a square 1 cm or 1 in. on a side. However, we cannot have a square with 1 are or 1 hectare on a side because are and hectare are not linear measures. The area of a square 10 m on a side is 1 a, and 1 ha is the area of a square 100 m on a side.

10. Many areas cannot be found by the use of formulas, but that does not keep the area from existing. The argument is analogous to saying electricity does not exist because it cannot be seen.

11. The argument is no different here than for the area of a circle. A circle has curves and its area is in square units. All area is in square units. With a cylinder it is easy to see the lateral surface area if the cylinder is cut along an edge and opened up. The area is the same as a rectangle which has width equal to the height of the cylinder and length equal to the circumference of the circular base. Because this rectangle has area in square units, it makes sense that the lateral surface area is in square units.

1. The answer is no. If you are given only a single point and its image, then either a translation, rotation, reflection, or glide reflection could be used. It takes three noncollinear points to determine the isometry.

2. Again, having only a segment and its image is not enough to determine the transformation. It requires three noncollinear points. For a further examination of this problem, see *Transformational Geometry*, by Richard Brown (Palo Alto, CA: Dale Seymour Publications, 1989).

3. A kite always has one line of symmetry. This line of symmetry contains one of the diagonals. It is the diagonal through the vertices of the angles of the kite which are not necessarily congruent.

4. The student is wrong. One counterexample is a right triangular prism whose bases are scalene triangles.

5. We do have a function that is sometimes called a point transformation. Since it is not a one-to-one mapping of the plane to the plane, it is not a true transformation. The student is correct.

6. Let the translation on the grid be a translation from A to B. Let C be the vertex of a right $\triangle ABC$ where $\overline{AC}$ is in the horizontal direction. Then the translation from A to B can be accomplished by a translation from A to C followed by a translation from C to B.

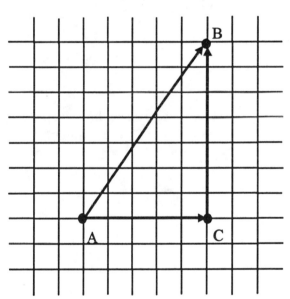

7. Construct $\triangle ACB$ so that $\overline{AC}$ is on one of the lines and $\overline{CB}$ on the other. The image of $\triangle ACB$ under a size transformation is a similar triangle. Hence an angle and its image are congruent. Consequently the image of $\angle ACB$ is a right angle and the image lines are perpendicular.

1-1 (a)   Answers vary, for example, the next three terms could be Δ, Δ, O. The rule for the pattern could be one circle, two triangles, one circle, two triangels, and so on in this manner.

(b)   The rule could be the first letter of the days of the week:
<u>f</u>riday, <u>s</u>aturday, <u>s</u>unday, <u>m</u>onday, <u>t</u>uesday, <u>w</u>ednesday so the pattern is **f, s, s, m, t, w**.
The rule might be the first letter of the numbers:
<u>f</u>ive, <u>s</u>ix, <u>s</u>even, <u>e</u>ight, <u>n</u>ine, <u>t</u>en, so the pattern is **f, s, s, e, n, t**.

1-2   No, if 621 is the number of toothpicks then 3n + 1 must be equal to 621, where n must be a natural number. However, if $3n + 1 = 621$, then $3n = 620$ and n would have to be 206 2/3 which is impossible because we have to have a natural number of toothpicks.

1-3   Because the 2nd term is 11, then $11 = a + d$. Because the 5th term is 23, then $23 = a + 4d$. Solving both equations for a and setting them equal, we have $11 - d = 23 - 4d$ which implies that $d = 4$. To find the 100th term, we substitute in $a + (n - 1)d$ and the 100th term is
$7 + (100 - 1) \cdot 4 = 7 + 99 \cdot 4 = 403$.

1-4 (a)   After 10 hours, there are $2 \cdot 3^{10} = 18,098$ bacteria and after n hours there are $2 \cdot 3^n$ bacteria.

(b)   After 10 hours, there are $2 + 10 \cdot 3 = 32$ bacteria and after n hours there are $2 + n \cdot 3$ bacteria. We can see after only 10 hours that geometric growth is much faster than arithmetic growth. In this case 18,098 vs. 32.

1-5   The possibilities are given below.

ℓ	w	P
1	120	242
2	60	124
3	40	86
4	30	68
5	24	58
6	20	52
8	15	46
10	12	44

Therefore we see the least perimeter is obtained from the 10 x 12 (or 12 x 10) frame.

1-6   No, she can seat $2 + 2 \cdot 25 = 52$ people this way. She can seat 20 people using a big square.

1-7   Answers may vary. For example, because each person owes $13 Al could pay $4.25 to Betty and $4 to Carl and Dani could pay $7 to Carl and everyone would be even.

1-8   She needs $1 + 2 + 3 + ... + 33 = 33(34)/2 = 561$ cubes.

1-9   The building has 23 floors.

1-10 (a)   20, 13   (b)   0.75, 0.375   (c)   16, 16

Puzzle Problem Answers

1. None, there is no dirt in a hole.

2. A quarter and a nickel. (One coin is not a nickel, but the other one is.)

3. 4

4. 3

5.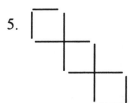

6.

3	5	
0	5	(fill 5)
3	2	(empty 5 into 3)
0	2	(empty 3)
2	0	(pour 2 into 3)
2	5	(fill 5)
3	④	(empty 5 into 3)

7. 25

8. There is no extra dollar. There is no reason that the second column should sum to $50.

9. $63

10. They didn't play each other.

11. None, Noah took animals on the ark, not Adam.

12. 5 in.

2-1 (a) & (b) Number the swimming lanes 1, 2, 3, 4 and name the people A, B, C, D. Then we represent the correspondence:

$$
\begin{array}{ccc}
1 & \leftrightarrow & A \\
2 & \leftrightarrow & B \\
3 & \leftrightarrow & C \\
4 & \leftrightarrow & D \\
\end{array}
\qquad \text{as} \qquad
\begin{array}{cccc}
1 & 2 & 3 & 4 \\
A & B & C & D \\
\end{array}
$$

The 24 one-to-one correspondences are listed below:

1 2 3 4	1 2 3 4	1 2 3 4	1 2 3 4
A B C D	B A C D	C A B D	D A B C
A B D C	B A D C	C A D B	D A C B
A C B D	B C A D	C B A D	D B A C
A C D B	B C D A	D B D A	D B C A
A D B C	B D A C	C D A B	D C A B
A D C B	B D C A	C D B A	D C B A

(c)   We notice that:

$$24 = 4 \cdot 3 \cdot 2 = 4 \cdot 3 \cdot 2 \cdot 1 = 4!.$$

We also notice that we had four choices for people to swim in lane 1. After making a choice, we see that we had three choices to swim in lane 2, leaving us with two choices for lane 3 and finally, one choice for lane 4. Extrapolating from this, we conjecture that there are

$$5! = 5 \cdot 4 \cdot 3 \cdot 2 \cdot 1 = 120$$

distinct one-to-one correspondences between a pair of five-element sets.

2-2 If event M can occur in m ways and, after it has occurred, event N can occur in n ways and, after it has occurred, event P can occur in p ways, then event M followed by event N followed by event P can occur in $m \cdot n \cdot p$ ways.

2-3 No, two sets may be equivalent without being equal. To see this consider the following example:

$$A = \{a,b,c\}$$
$$B = \{1,2,3\}.$$

Then:

$$a \leftrightarrow 1$$
$$b \leftrightarrow 2$$
$$c \leftrightarrow 3$$

is a one-to-one correspondence between A and B, and therefore A ~ B. However, A ≠ B.

2-4 If $n(A) = n(B)$, then A and B have the same number of elements. Denote the number of elements in each set by m. Let

$$A = \{a_1, a_2, \ldots, a_m\}$$
$$B = \{b_1, b_2, \ldots, b_m\}.$$

Then we may give a one-to-one correspondence between these sets by matching pairs of elements as follows:

$$a_1 \leftrightarrow b_1$$
$$a_2 \leftrightarrow b_2$$
$$\vdots \quad \vdots \quad \vdots$$
$$a_m \leftrightarrow b_m$$

Because the elements of B can be different from the elements of A, A is not necessarily equal to B.

2-5 (a)   Yes, from the definitions, $A \subseteq B$ means that every element of A is an element of B. Similarly, $A \subset B$ means that every element of A is an element of B but there exists an element in B which is not an element of A. Hence, if $A \subset B$, it is true that every element of A is in B. Consequently, $A \subseteq B$. Notice that if the more stringent condition $A \subset B$ is satisfied, then the weaker condition $A \subseteq B$ must necessarily be satisfied as well.

   (b)   No. To see this, consider the following counterexample:

$$A = \{a,b,c\}$$
$$B = \{a,b,c\}.$$

Then , $A \subseteq B$. Notice that $A \not\subset B$ since $A = B$.

2-6 (a)   Assuming that a simple majority forms a winning coalition, we see that any subset consisting of three or more senators is a winning coalition. There are 16 such subsets. To see this, let {A,B,C,D,E} be the set of five senators on the committee. Then the following are all possible winning coalitions:

{A,B,C}	{A,B,D}	{A,B,E}	{A,C,D}
{A,C,E}	{A,D,E}	{B,C,D}	{B,C,E}
{B,D,E}	{C,D,E}	{A,B,C,D}	{A,B,C,E}
{A,B,D,E}	{A,C,D,E}	{B,C,D,E}	{A,B,C,D,E}

(b)   From the list in part (a), we see that there are five subsets containing exactly four members. We also see that there are five senators on the committee. To understand why these numbers are the same, notice that creating a four-element subset is equivalent to deleting a single element from the total set. That is, we can give a one-to-one correspondence between the set of four-element subsets of {A,B,C,D,E} and the set of senators by corresponding to each four-element subset the senator who is not in that subset as shown:

$$\{A,B,C,D\} \longleftrightarrow E$$
$$\{A,B,C,E\} \longleftrightarrow D$$
$$\{A,B,D,E\} \longleftrightarrow C$$
$$\{A,C,D,E\} \longleftrightarrow B$$
$$\{B,C,D,E\} \longleftrightarrow A$$

We can give a one-to-one correspondence between the three-element subsets and the two-element subsets of {A,B,C,D,E} by matching each three-element subset with the unique two-element subset which contains the senators on the committee, but not in the subset. For example: {A,B,C} ↔ {D,E}.

From part (a), we know that there are exactly 10 three-element subsets of the committee, hence, there must be 10 two-element subsets of the committee.

2-7   The formula is: $n(A \cup B) = n(A) + n(B) - n(A \cap B)$

To justify this formula, notice that in $n(A \cup B)$, the elements of $A \cap B$ are counted only once. In $n(A) + n(B)$, the elements of $A \cap B$ are counted twice; once in A and once in B. Thus, subtracting $n(A \cap B)$ from $n(A) + n(B)$ makes the number equal to $n(A \cup B)$.

For example: If $A = \{a,b,c\}$ and $B = \{c,d\}$ then $A \cup B = \{a,b,c,d\}$ and $n(A \cup B) = 4$. However, $n(A) + n(B) = 3 + 2 = 5$ since c is counted twice. Because $A \cap B = \{c\}$, $n(A \cap B) = 1$ and $n(A) + n(B) - n(A \cap B) = 4$.

2-8   (a)   It is always true that:

$$A \cap (B \cap C) = (A \cap B) \cap C.$$

The following figure gives Venn diagrams of each side of the above equation.   Because the Venn diagrams result in the same set, the equation is always true.

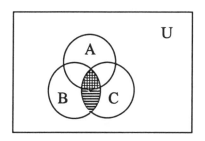
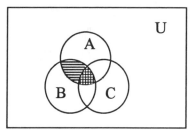

(b)   It is always true that:

$$A \cup (B \cup C) = (A \cup B) \cup C.$$

The following Venn diagrams justify this statement.

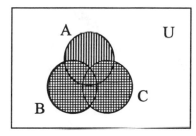
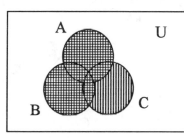

(c)   In general:

$$A - (B - C) \neq (A - B) - C.$$

To see this, consider the following counterexample.

$$A = \{1,2,3,4,5\}$$
$$B = \{1,2,3\}$$
$$C = \{3,4\}$$

Then

$$A - (B - C) = A - \{1,2\} = \{3,4,5\}.$$

But

$$(A - B) - C = \{4,5\} - C = \{5\}.$$

Thus for the above choice of A, B and C, we have that $A - (B - C) \neq (A - B) - C$

2-9   The following Venn diagrams show

$$A \cup (B \cap C) = (A \cup B) \cap (A \cup C).$$

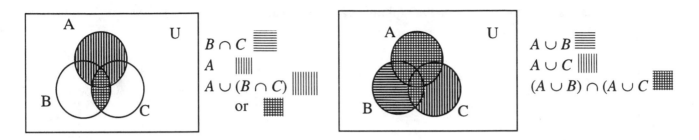

2-10   The following figure shows a Venn diagram for three sets A, B and C in universe U showing the eight non-overlapping regions numbered $R_1, R_2, \ldots, R_8$.

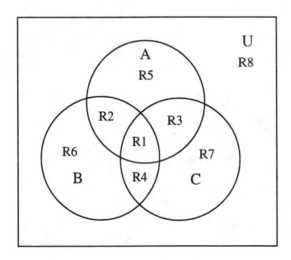

2-11   No. To see why, notice that

$$C(10.5) = 27 \cdot 10.5 = 283.5 \text{ cents} \doteq 284 \text{ cents} = \$2.84.$$

But, as explained in the text, the telepone company will charge

$$27 \cdot 11 = 297 \text{ cents} = \$2.97$$

The 13 cent discrepancy arises from the fact that a customer is charged for each whole minute and for an extra full minute, for any part of a minute which was started but not finished. Notice that the cost function $C = 27t$ is only valid for natural numbers t.

2-12 The following are some properties of sets and the corresponding properties of statements.

$$A \cap (B \cup C) = (A \cap B) \cup (A \cap C) \leftrightarrow a \wedge (b \vee c) \equiv (a \wedge b) \vee (a \wedge c)$$
$$A \cup (B \cap C) = (A \cup B) \cap (A \cup C) \leftrightarrow a \vee (b \wedge c) \equiv (a \vee b) \wedge (a \vee c)$$
$$A \cup (B \cup C) = (A \cup B) \cup C \leftrightarrow a \vee (b \vee c) \equiv (a \vee b) \vee c$$
$$A \cap (B \cap C) = (A \cap B) \cap C \leftrightarrow a \wedge (b \wedge c) \equiv (a \wedge b) \wedge c$$
$$\overline{A \cup B} = \overline{A} \cap \overline{B} \leftrightarrow \sim (a \vee b) \equiv \sim a \wedge \sim b$$
$$\overline{A \cap B} = \overline{A} \cup \overline{B} \leftrightarrow \sim (a \wedge b) \equiv \sim a \vee \sim b$$
$$\overline{A} \cap (B \cup C) = (\overline{A} \cap B) \cup (\overline{A} \cap C) \leftrightarrow \sim a \wedge (b \vee c) \equiv (\sim a \wedge b) \vee (\sim a \wedge c)$$

Of course, many other identities and correspondences exist.

3-1 Student answers may vary. Sample response: Each portion of the little finger of the left hand represents a digit from 1 to 9. The comparable sections of the ring finger represent tens from 10 to 90; of the middle finger represent hundreds from 100 to 900; of the pointer thousands from 1000 to 9000; and the thumb ten thousands from 10,000 to 90,000.

3-2 The illustration indicates successive divisions by 5's. This shows that there are 164 fives in 824 with 4 as a remainder. Next there are 32 fives in 164 with 4 fives as a remainder. Equivalently we could say that there are 25 fives in 824 with 4 fives and 4 units as a remainder. This process continues until we see that there is 1 625 in 824 with 1 125; 2 25's; 4 5's; and 4 units in 824.

3-3 For example, if the sets of elements are {a, b, c} and {a, d}, then the union of the sets of elements is {a, b, c, d}. The union has only 4 elements while the original sets have 3 and 2 respectively. The sum of 3 and 2 is 5 not 4, the number of elements in the set union.

3-4 Multiplication of whole numbers can be defined as a binary operation as addition of whole numbers was. An illustration of how ordered pairs of whole numbers are mapped to their product follows:

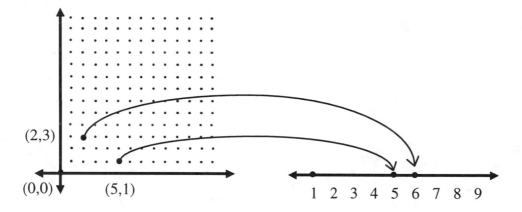

3-5 To use a number line for addition in base 5, a student will need to mark the line using base 5 numbers. For example, the line will need to be marked as shown below.

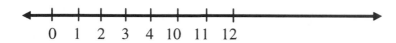

With such a number line as pictured, the addition is similar to addition in base 10 on a number line.

4-1 (a) $22 \cdot 18 = (20 + 2)(20 - 2) = 20^2 - 2^2 = 400 - 4 = 396$
(b) $24 \cdot 36 = (30 - 6)(30 + 6) = 30^2 - 6^2 = 900 - 36 = 864$
(c) $998 \cdot 1002 = (1000 - 2)(1000 + 2) = 1000^2 - 2^2 = 1,000,000 - 4 = 999,996$

4-2 Yes, it is true. If $3 \mid x$, then 3 divides any numbers times x and in particular $3 \mid xy$.

4-3 $1 + 2 + 5 + 0 + 6 + 5 = 19$, so we must find numbers x and y such that $9 \mid 19 + (x + y)$. Any two numbers that sum to 8 or 17 will satisfy this. Therefore the blanks could be filled with 8 and 9, or 9 and 8, or 0 and 8, or 8 and 0.

4-4 (a) Answers vary. For example, only square numbers are listed in Column 3, 2 is the only even number that will ever be in Column 2; and Column 2 contains prime numbers. The powers of 2 appear in successive columns.
(b) There will never be other entries in Column 1 because 1 is the only number with one factor. Other numbers have at least the number itself and 1.
(c) 49, 121, 169
(d) 64
(e) The square numbers have an odd number of factors. Factors occur in pairs; for example, for 16 we have 1 and 16, 2 and 8, and 4 and 4. When we list the factors, we list only the distinct factors, so 4 is not listed twice, thereby making the number of factors of 16 an odd number. Similar reasoning holds for all square numbers.

4-5 (a) 1, 2, 3, 6, 9
(b) 1, 2, 3, 4, 6, 8
(c) Only white rods can be used to form one-color trains for prime numbers if two or more rods must be used.
(d) 8. The number must have at least factors of 1, 2, 3, 5, 6, 10, 15, and 30.

4-6 (a) No, because the multiples of 2 have 2 as a factor.
(b) The mutiples of 3 (3, 6, 9, 12, 15, . . .)
(c) The mutiples of 5 (5, 10, 15, 20, . . .)
(d) The multiples of 7(7, 14, 21, . . .)
(e) We have to check only divisibility by 2, 3, 5, and 7.

4-7 (a) Answers vary. For example, 2 is the only even prime, so after 2 is circled, all the columns beginning with an even number can be crossed out.
(b) 2; no, because consecutive numbers after 2, 3 would consist of an even and an odd number and all the even numbers have 2 as a factor.
(c) 7, with the numbers 90–96. Yes, the string could get as long as we wanted it to be.

4-8 The 1, 2, 3, and 6 rods can all be used to build both the 24 and 30 train. The greatest of these is 6, so GCD (24, 30) = 6.

4-9   We use the 8 rod and the 10 rod and start building trains. We stop the first time the trains are the same length. This happens when we use five of the 8 rods and four of the 10 rods. Therefore the LCM is the length of the train, which is 40.

4-10 (a)   Yes
       (b)   Yes
       (c)   Yes, 0 is the identity
       (d)   Yes

5-1 (a)   Every integer can be represented as a rational number by making the denominator be 1. For example, an integer such as -5 can be represented as $-5/1$.

(b)   A Venn diagram depicting the relationship among Natural numbers, Integers and Rational numbers follows:

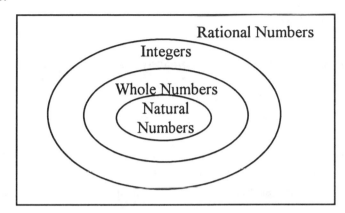

5-2   Theorem 5-1 states that if a, b, and c are integers and $b > 0$, then $a/b > c/b$ if and only if $a > c$. The question is to investigate if the theorem is true if $b < 0$. Consider $2 > 1$ and $-1 < 0$.

Now $2/(-1) < 1/(-1)$ which contradicts an expanded theorem when $b < 0$.

5-3 (a) $\dfrac{2}{15} + \dfrac{4}{21} = \dfrac{2 \cdot 21 + 15 \cdot 4}{15 \cdot 21} = \dfrac{42 + 60}{315} = \dfrac{102}{315} = \dfrac{34}{105}$

(b)   The least common multiple of 4, 5 and 6 is 60. Thus,

$$\left(\frac{3}{4} + \frac{1}{5}\right) + \frac{1}{6} = \left(\frac{45}{60} + \frac{12}{60}\right) + \frac{10}{60} = \frac{67}{60}$$

5-4   To determine how many $2/3$'s in 6, consider the following diagram representing 6 units with $2/3$ of each unit shaded.

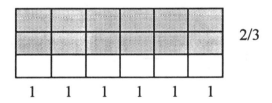

There are six $2/3$'s shaded and three others that could be placed in the unshaded portion giving a total of nine $2/3$'s in six units.

6-1   (a)   The next five ratios accurate to seven digits after the decimal point are:

1.625,   1.6153846,   1.6190476,   1.6176471,   1.6181818.

The ratios seem to get closer and closer to a single number which starts with 1.61.

(b)   The eleventh ratio is $\dfrac{144}{89}$ or approximately 1.6179775. Thus the ratio seem to get closer and closer to 1.617. Consequently from the tenth term on the Fibonacci sequence behaves approximately like a geometric sequence with ratio 1.617.

(c)   The eleventh term of the Fibonacci sequence is 89. If the sequence from the eleventh term on behaves approximately like a geometric sequence with ratio $r = 1.617$ then from the eleventh term on, the Fibonacci sequence can be approximated by the following geometric sequence:

$$89,\ 89r,\ 89r^2,\ 89r^3,\ 89r^4,\ \dots$$

Because the first 10 terms of the Fibonacci sequence are not listed in that sequence, the fiftieth term of the Fibonacci sequence is the 50–10 or fortieth term in the above geometric sequence. The fortieth term of the geometric sequence is $89 \cdot r^{40-1}$ or $89 \cdot (1.617)^{39}$. Using a calculator we find that this number is approximately $1.22766 \cdot 10^{10}$. Thus the fiftieth term of the Fibonacci sequence is approximately $1.22766 \cdot 10^{10}$.

6-2   (a) $0.\overline{7} = 0 \cdot \overline{1} \cdot 7 = \dfrac{1}{9} \cdot 7 = \dfrac{7}{9}$

(b) $0.\overline{07} = 0.\overline{01} \cdot 7 = \dfrac{1}{99} \cdot 7 = \dfrac{7}{99}$

(c) $0.\overline{49} = 49 \cdot 0.\overline{01} = 49 \cdot \dfrac{1}{99} = \dfrac{49}{99}$

(d) $0.\overline{345} = 345 \cdot 0.\overline{001} = 345 \cdot \dfrac{1}{999} = \dfrac{345}{999}$

6-3   (a)   The approach works because $\sqrt{\sqrt{\sqrt{a}}} = \left(\left(a^{\frac{1}{2}}\right)^{\frac{1}{2}}\right)^{\frac{1}{2}} = \left(a^{\frac{1}{4}}\right)^{\frac{1}{2}}$

$$= a^{\frac{1}{8}}$$

$$= \sqrt[8]{a}$$

(b)   For $n = 2^k$, where k is a positive integer. As shown in part (a), repeatedly applying the square

root function to a we get $a^{\overbrace{\frac{1}{2} \cdot \frac{1}{2} \cdot \frac{1}{2} \cdots \frac{1}{2}}^{k \text{ times}}}$ or $a^{\frac{1}{2^k}} = \sqrt[2^k]{a}$.

7-1

Property	Equality	Inequality (>)
Subtraction	a = b implies a − c = b − c	a > b implies a − c > b − c
Division	a = b and c ≠ 0 implies a/c = b/c	a > b and c > 0 implies a/c > b/c a > b and c < 0 implies a/c < b/c
Cancellation for Subtraction	a − c = b − c implies a = b	a − c > b − c implies a > b
Cancellation for Division	a/c = b/c implies a = b if c ≠ 0	a/c > b/c and c < 0 implies a < b a/c > b/c and c > 0 implies a > b

7-2   We know that with $\frac{1}{3}$ of a certain amount of money Debbie bought presents and was left with $48.

Hence she was left with $\frac{2}{3}$ of that amount or $48. Thus $\frac{1}{3}$ of the amount is $24 and $3 \cdot \frac{1}{3}$ of the

amount is $3 \cdot \$24$ or $72. Because she spent $\frac{2}{5}$ of previous amount on books she was left with $\frac{3}{5}$ of

the amount or $72. Thus $\frac{1}{3}$ of the amount is $72 ÷ 3 or $24 and $5 \cdot \frac{1}{3}$ of the amount is

$5 \cdot \$24$ or $120. After spending $150, she had $120. Thus her original earnings were $120 + $50 or
$170.

7-3   If we graph the equation y = mx for small values of m like m = 0.1 and m = 0.01 we see that when m
gets close to 0, the line gets closer to the x-axis.

If we graph the equation y = mx for large values of x like m = 100 and m = 1000 we see that when m
continues to increase the line gets closer to the y-axis.

7-3   23 persons per square mile means that on average in an area of one square mile there are 23 people.
On the other hand the fact that there are 23 square miles per person tells us that on average in an area
of 23 square miles there is one person. Notice that the first information implies that in 23 square
miles there are 23 · 23 or 529 people.

8-1 (a)   1

(b)   1

(c)   Yes, they always sum to 1 which is the sum of the probabilities of all the different elements in the sample space.

8-2 (a) $\dfrac{6}{15} + \dfrac{4}{15} = \dfrac{10}{15}$ or $\dfrac{4}{9}$

(b) $\dfrac{4}{15} + \dfrac{1}{15} = \dfrac{5}{15}$ or $\dfrac{1}{3}$

(c) $\dfrac{4}{15} + \dfrac{4}{15} = \dfrac{8}{15}$

8-3 (a)   Answers vary.

(b) $\dfrac{3}{8}$

(c)   No, simulations will not always result in the same probability as the theoretical probability. However, if the experiment is repeated a great number of times, the simulated probability should approach the theoretical probability.

8-4 (b)   There is one way to toss a head and one way of not tossing a head, so the odds in favor are 1:1.

(c)   There are four ways to draw an ace and 48 ways of not drawing an ace, so the odds in favor are 4:48 or 1:12.

(d)   There are 13 ways of drawing a heart and 39 ways of not drawing a heart, so the odds in favor are 13:39 or 1:3.

8-5   The number of permutations on n things taken r at a time is given by $n!/(n-r)!$. Therefore, to find $_{16}P_8$ we could use the calculator to find 16! and then divide it by 8!.

9-1 A student might decide that the fifth period class did somewhat better than did the second period class. The fifth period class has more students scoring higher than does the second period class. In the fifth period class, the most common score is 89 while the most common score for the second period class is 79.

9-2 One probably would not expect any outliers, because the outliers were on the lower end of the scale and the lower end of the data was dropped. One would expect all the five-number summary points to increase. There will probably little noticeable difference in the story the data tells.

10-1 (a)   Consider four collinear points {D, A, B, C}. Then $\overrightarrow{AB}$ is shown in Figure (i) and $\overrightarrow{BA}$ in Figure (ii). Notice that D $\notin \overrightarrow{AB}$ but D $\in \overrightarrow{BA}$. Hence $\overrightarrow{AB} \neq \overrightarrow{BA}$.

    D A B C   D A B C

       (i)   (ii)

(b)   Because two points determine a unique line it is always true that $\overleftrightarrow{AB} = \overleftrightarrow{BA}$.

(c) $\overline{AB} = \overline{BA}$ because $\overline{AB}$ is the segment whose endpoints are A and B and $\overline{BA}$ is the segment whose endpoints are B and A.

10-2 There are infinitely many planes containing three given collinear points. Pages in an open book illustrate the answer. (See Figure 10-6 (b)).

10-3 Because three noncollinear points determine a plane, four planes can be formed. These are the planes containing the four faces of the tetrahedron. Notice that the number of such planes is the number of three-element subsets of {D, E, F, G}, that is, the number of combinations of four objects taken three at a time. The number of such combinations is $_4C_3 = 4$. (See chapter 8).

10-4 Let O be the center of the globe. First consider two points A and B on the globe which are the endpoints of a diameter, that is, A, O, and B are collinear. It follows from Investigation 10-2 that there are infinitely many planes containing A and B and hence the center of the globe, O. Each of these planes intersects the globe in a "great" circle. Consequently if A, O, B are collinear, there is no unique "line" through A and B.

If A and B are on the globe so that A, O, and B are not collinear, then A, O, and B determine a unique plane. The intersection of this plane with the globe is the unique "great" circle containing A and B.

10-5 One approach to this problem is to start shading the area surrounding point X. If we stay between the lines, we should be able to decide whether the shaded area is inside our outside the curve.

The shaded part of the figure below indicates that point X is located outside the curve.

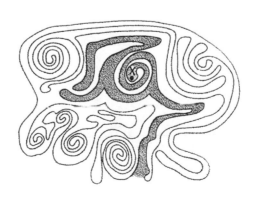

10-6 (1)   True. From the definition (Table 10-5) we know that an equilateral triangle has three congruent angles. Therefore it has at least two congruent sides and hence it is isosceles.

(2)   True. By definition, a regular quadrilateral is a four-sided figure which is both, equilateral and equiangular. A square has four sides of equal length and four right angles—so a square is a regular quadrilateral.

(3)   True. Because a rhombus is a parallelogram and a rectangle is a parallelogram with a right angle, if one angle of a rhombus is a right angle then all of its angles are right.

(4)   True; follows from part (3).

(5)   True, because a rectangle is a parallelogram and if one angle of a parallelogram is a right angle all its angles are right angles.

(6)   True. A rectangle is a trapezoid since it is a quadrilateral with at least one pair of parallel sides.

(7)   True. A square is a rectangle which is an isosceles trapezoid. Also a square is a kite. Hence there are isosceles trapezoids which are kites.

(8)   False as shown in the figure below.

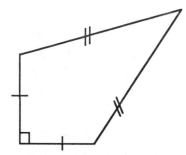

10-7 $m(\angle AQC) = x_1 + x_2 = 50 + 40 = 90°$ because
$x_1 = m(\angle QAB)$ (alternate interior angles) and

$x_2 = m(\angle QCE)$ (alternate interior angles since $\overleftrightarrow{PQ} \parallel \overleftrightarrow{CE}$).

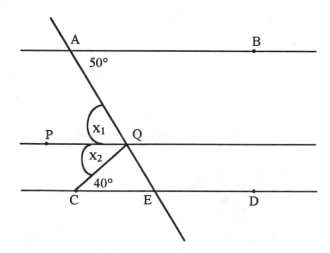

10-8 (a)   Infinitely many. Any plane containing the North and South Poles intersects the globe in a great circle.

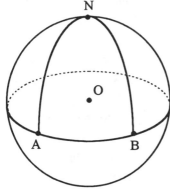

(b)   Consider the arc $\overset{\frown}{AB}$ which is the minor arc connecting two points A and B on the equator. Let $\overset{\frown}{NA}$ and $\overset{\frown}{NB}$ be the minor arcs which are arcs of the great circles resulting from the intersection of planes ANO and BNO with the globe correspondingly. $\overset{\frown}{AN} \cup \overset{\frown}{NB} \cup \overset{\frown}{AB}$ is a required spherical triangle.

(c)   Yes. A spherical triangle in part (b) can be chosen so that each of the angles is a right angle. This will happen if $\angle AOB$ is a right angle.

(d)   The sum is greater than 180°.

10-9   Given a convex octagon we can construct all the diagonals from a single vertex. The diagonals create 6 or 8-2 triangles. In general for an n-gon there will be n-2 triangles. The sum of the measures of all the angles in the triangles is (n-2)180° which is the sum of the measures of the angles of the n-gon.

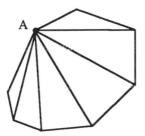

10-10 (a) $V + F - E = 2$

(b) In case of the pentagonal pyramid in Figure 10-55
$V = 6$, $F = 6$, $E = 10$, and $V + F - E = 12 - 10 = 2$.

10-11 (a) No. If a network is traversable, only the starting and stopping vertices can be odd. Any other vertex must be even because each time we enter the vertex we need to leave it.

(b) No.

11-1   Any two segments are similar because regardless of length, they have the same shape. The same is true of angles with the same measures. Remember that the shape of an angle is not determined by the length of the rays determining the angles.

11-2   There are only three possible ways to write the congruence with triangle ABC paired with A′B′C′, triangle ACA paired with B′C′A′ and triangle CAB paired with C′A′B′.

11-3 (a)   In order to construct a triangle from three lengths of straws, the length of one piece must be greater than the lengths of the other two pieces.
   (b)   The triangle would be equilateral and equiangular.
   (c)   There can be no triangle constructed. The three pieces would lie along a segment.
   (d)   Yes. See the answer to part a.
   (e)   Yes.

11-4 (a)   The triangles do not have to be congruent. An example is seen in the following drawing.

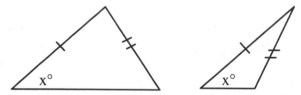

   (b)   If the non-included angle is a right angle, the triangles are congruent.

11-5   The triangles are not congruent but should be similar.

11-6   The way to accomplish the construction is to place one leg of the right triangle on the given line and to construct a perpendicular to the line through the given point P. Then use the right triangle to construct a perpendicular to the one just constructed at point P.

11-7   The triangles formed can be proved congruent and then corresponding parts of congruent triangles are congruent can be used to show that the angles are congruent. Thus the angle is bisected and the point is on the angle bisector. You may need to use the measurement tool to convince yourself that the angle measures are the same.

11-8   The statement is not true for polygons. For example a rectangle and a square have congruent angles but do not have to be congruent.

11-9   The triangles formed are similar and one would expect the segments cut by the parallel segments to have proportional lengths. They do not. Thus, there is the possibility for a misleading graph.

11-9   Hint: Draw an altitude of the equilateral triangle; sin 30° is 1/2; cos 30° is approximately 0.866, and tan 30° is approximately 0.577.

11-10 Because the sum of the measures of the angles in the right triangle is 180°, the other acute angle has measure $180° - 90° - 70° = 20°$. Thus $\sin 20° = x/3.2$, or x is approximately 1.1 cm.

11-11 (a) The following is true as long as the $\cos (\angle ABC)$ is not equal to 0.

$$\tan(\angle ABC) = \frac{\sin(\angle ABC)}{\cos(\angle ABC)}$$

(b) The value of the sum is 1.

12-1 (a)   12   (b)   6   (c)   4

12-2 Approximately 259 cm^2

12-3 (a)   The areas of the parallelogram and the rectangle are the same because they are composed of the same two pieces and the area of the figures is the sum of the areas of the two pieces.

   (b)   The formula for the area of a rectangle is $A = \ell w$. The length of the new rectangle is just base b of the parallelogram and the width of the rectangle is just the height of the parallelogram. Therefore, the formula for the area of the parallelogram is $A = bh$.

12-4 Two triangles are congruent so the areas are equal. The area of the parallelogram is equal to twice the area of one of the triangles formed by cutting along a diagonal. This is consistent with what we have done since the formula for the area of one of the triangles is $A = 1/2(bh)$ and so multiplying this by 2 we have the formula for the area of a parallelogram.

12-5 If we rotate the trapezoid 180 degrees about M, the figure formed by the original and the new figure is a parallelogram with base $(b_1 + b_2)$ and height h where b_1 and b_2 are the bases of the original trapezoid. The area of the parallelogram is $A = h(b_1 + b_2)$. Because this is twice the area of the original trapezoid, we divide by 2 to obtain $A = h/2(b_1 + b_2)$ which is the formula for the area of the original trapezoid.

12-6 The square on one leg that is labeled 1 could be cut off and placed in the dashed space on the square of the hypotenuse. Then pieces 2, 3, 4, and 5 could be cut off and placed around piece 1 so that the square on the hypotenuse is filled exactly with the 5 pieces. This shows that the sum of the areas of the squares on the two legs of a right triangle is equal to the area on the square of the hypotenuse.

12-7 (a)   You could build the triangle and then measure the angles to see if there was a right angle. If there was, then the triangle is a right triangle. You could measure the three sides and use the Converse of the Pythagorean Theorem to see if a right triangle is formed.

   (b)   If the three lengths of a right triangle are multiplied by a fixed number, then the resulting lengths determine a right triangle, for example, if the right triangle lengths are 3-4-5, and the fixed number is 5, then 15-20-25 is a right triangle.

   (c)   If the three lengths of a right triangle are multiplied by a fixed number, then the resulting numbers determine a right triangle.

12-8 It makes no difference in the Distance Formula if $(x_1 - x_2)$ and $(y_1 - y_2)$ are used instead of $(x_1 - x_2)$ and $(y_1 - y_2)$ respectively. Because both quantities in the formula are squared, the result is the same whether the difference is positive or negative.

12-9 Because we want the surface area of a right prism, we must include the top and bottom so we need the $2B$ (where B is the area of the base which is the same as the area of the top) in the formula $S.A. = ph + 2B$. From the net, we see that the lateral surface area opens up into a rectangle that has width equal to the height, h. The length of the rectangle is equal to the sum of the lengths of the sides of the base which is the perimeter of the base. Therefore the area of the rectangle (lateral surface area of the prism) is $A = \ell w = ph$. Hence the surface area for any right prism is given by $S.A. = ph + 2B$.

12-10 The two figures have bases in the same plane and the figures have the same height. Figure 12-61 shows that if a plane parallel to the base is passed through the figures, then equal areas are obtained. By Cavalieri's Principle these two figures have equal volumes.

12-11 (a) By Cavalieri's Principle the volumes are the same.
(b) By Cavalieri's Principle the volumes are the same.
(c) The volume of any prism or cylinder that has area of the base B and height h has volume,
$V = Bh$.

12-12 (a) 1 g   (b) 1 kg   (c) 1 dm^3 (d) 1 mL   (e) 1 g   (f) 1 kL   (g) 1 t

13-1   Yes. The slide arrow is from P to P'. Using the Pythagorean Theorem $(PP')^2 = 3^2 + 2^2$. Hence $PP' = \sqrt{13}$.

13-2   With P as center draw an arc which intersects m at two points A and B. Without changing the opening of the compass draw two arcs, one centered at A and the other at B. Their intersection is the required point P'. (Notice that by construction $PAP'B$ is a rhombus and the diagonals of a rhombus are perpendicular bisectors of each other.)

13-3 α and β are each complements of measures of congruent angles.

Answers Appendix I

A1-1   TO CIRCLE
                REPEAT 360[FD 1 RT 1]
        END

Answers Appendix II

1. (a)   The values displayed using $\boxed{\text{TRACE}}$ are the exact values in L1 and L2.
   (b)   Only points are displayed because this is the graph of the ordered pairs where the x-value comes from L1 and the y-value is the corresponding value from L2.
   (c)   A linear pattern is shown on the graph, that is, all the points fall along a line.
   (d)   The $\boxed{\text{TRACE}}$ function cannot be used to find the prince of 12 CD's. The cost can be estimated by extending the pattern along the line.

2. (a)   The graph of the line $y = 12.95x + 5$ contains all the points in Plot 1. The graph obtained by graphing Plot 1 are the large points along the line. Plot 1 is graphed only for integer values $x = 1$ to 10, whereas $y = 12.92x + 5$ is graphed for all real values of x. Plot 1 is a subset of $y = 12.95x + 5$.
   (b)   Depending on the window, the cost of 12 CD's can be obtained from the graph of $y = 12.95x + 5$ by using the $\boxed{\text{TRACE}}$ feature.

Answers to Problems

CHAPTER 1

ONGOING ASSESSMENT 1-1

1. (a)   (c)

   (b) (d)
2. (a) 11, 13, 15 arithmetic (b) 250, 300, 350 arithmetic
(c) 96, 192, 384 geometric (d) $10^6, 10^7, 10^8$, geometric
(e) 33, 37, 41 arithmetic (f) $6^3, 7^3, 8^3$ neither
3. (a) 199, $2n - 1$ (b) 4950, $50(n - 1)$ (c) $3 \cdot 2^{99}, 3 \cdot 2^{n-1}$
(d) $10^{100}, 10^n$ (e) 405, $5 + 4n$ or $9 + 4(n - 1)$ (f) $100^3 =$
1,000,000, n^3
4. 2, 7, 12
5. (a) Answers vary, for example, one possibility is to notice
that the sum of the first n odd numbers is given by n^2; that is,
$1 + 3 + 5 + 7 = 4^2 = 16$. Others might notice that to find the
sum you could square the sum of the average of the first and
last term; that is, $1 + 3 + 5 + 7 = [(1 + 7)/2]^2 = 4^2 = 16$.
(b) 324
6. 10 white and 55 black
7. (a) 12, 14 (b) 18, 21
8. (a) 30, 42, 56 (b) 10,100 (c) $n(n+1)$ or $n^2 + n$
9. (a) 51 (b) $6 + (n - 1)5$ or $5n + 1$
10. (a) 41 (b) $4n + 1$ or $5 + (n - 1) - 4$.
11. (a) 10,000 (b) n^2
12. (a) 42 (b) $4n + 2$
13. 1200 students
14. 15 liters
15. $1225
16. (a) $1660 (b) $7500 (c) 103 months
17. 19
18. 23rd year
19. (a) 3, 5, 9, 15, 23, 33 (b) 4, 6, 10, 16, 24, 34 (c) 15, 17,
21, 27, 35, 45
20. (a) 299, 447, 644 (b) 56, 72, 90 (c) 108, 190, 304
21. (a) 101 (b) 61 (c) 200 (d) 87 (e) 11
22. (a) 3, 6, 11, 18, 27 (b) 4, 9, 14, 19, 24 (c) 9, 99, 999,
9999, 99999 (d) 5, 8, 11, 14, 17

23. (a) 1, 1, 2, 3, 5, 8, 13, 21, 34, 55, 89, 144, ... (b) Yes; the
sum of the first four terms equals the sixth term − 1. The sum
of the first five terms equals the seventh term − 1. The sum of
the first six terms equals the eighth term − 1. (c) 143 (d) The
sum of the first n terms equals the (n+2)th term − 1.
24. (a) 2, 4, 6, 10, 16, 26, 42, 68, 110, 178, 288, 466, ...
(b) The sum of the first three terms is 4 less than the fifth term.
The sum of the first four terms is 4 less than the sixth term. The
sum of the first five terms is 4 less than the seventh term. The
sum of the first six terms is 4 less than the eighth term.
(c) 462 (d) The sum of the first n terms equals the (n+2)th
term −4.
25. The sequence in (b) becomes greater than the sequence in
(a) on the 12th term.
26. (a) 1, 5, 9, 13, 17, 21, ... (b) $4n - 3$
27. 64, 128, 256
28. 6, 5, 4, 6, 5, 4, 6, 5, 4, 6, 5

Communication
29. (a) You must produce at least one rectangle that does not
have diagonals that are perpendicular. Any non-square
rectangle will do. (b) You must produce two even numbers
whose sum is not divisible by 4. For example $2 + 4 = 6$, and 6
is not divisible by 4.
30. You must produce at least one Montana university student
who does not wear cowboy boots.
31. Answers vary, for example, if the sky has dark clouds, then
you expect it to rain. This expectation is based on observations
you have made.

No, a conclusion based on inductive reasoning is not
certain. The conclusion is based on observation or experimentation and is not necessarily true, as can be seen in the
example above. It may happen that dark clouds form and it
does not rain.
32. (a) Yes. The difference between terms in the new sequence
is the same as in the old sequence because a fixed number was
added to each number in the sequence. (b) Yes. If the fixed
number is k, the difference between terms of the second
sequence is k times the difference between terms of the first
sequence.

Open-ended
33. Answers vary, for example, two more patterns follow.

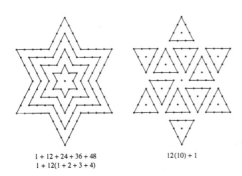

$1 + 12 + 24 + 36 + 48$
$1 + 12(1 + 2 + 3 + 4)$

$12(10) + 1$

34. Answers vary, for example, the following is an array of pentagonal numbers.

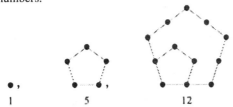

The pattern for the number of dots is 1, 5, 12, 22, 35, 51, ... The number of additional dots for each pentagon forms an arithmetic sequence with 1st term 1 and difference 3. For the 100th pentagonal number we would have $1 + 4 + 7 + 10 + 13 + 16 + ... + 298$ additional dots, where $298 = 1 + (100 - 1)3$. Therefore, the 100th pentagonal number is $100/2(1 + 298) = 14,950$.

35. (a) No matter what numbers are chosen, the result is always 2.
(b) Answers vary depending on whether only results from the group were used or it was proven to be true for all numbers.
(c) Answers vary, for example:

	Explanation
Pick a number	n
Multiply by 3	3n
Add 51	$3n + 51$
Divide by 3	$(3n + 51)/3 = n + 17$
Subtract your original number.	$(n + 17) - n = 17$
The answer is 17.	

(d) Answers vary.

36. (a) 81 (b) 40 (c) 3^n (d) $1 + 3 + 3^2 + 3^3 + ... + 3^{n-1}$

Technology Corner (p. 18)
The rules for the columns are given below.

Column	Rule
B	$x + y$
C	$y - x$
D	$x \cdot y$
E	$2(x + 3)$
F	$2x + y$
G	$xy + 1$

Brain Teaser (p. 15)
(a) N, T, E (Rule: <u>O</u>ne, <u>T</u>wo, <u>T</u>hree, <u>F</u>our, <u>F</u>ive, <u>S</u>ix, <u>S</u>even, <u>E</u>ight, <u>N</u>ine, <u>T</u>en, <u>E</u>leven) (b) Letters composed of only line segments go above the line. Letters with curves go below the line.

ONGOING ASSESSMENT 1-2
1. (a) 4950 (b) n(n + 1)/2 (c) 251,001
2. (a) 4 (b) 5 (c) n - 1
3. 112
4. 12
5. 160 miles
6. Dandy, Cory, Alababa, Bubba
7. 45
8. 18
9. $1.19
10. 12
11. 12
12. 10 boys, 12 dogs
13. $2.45
14. 16 days
15. (a) 42, 55, 68, 81, 94, 107, 120, 133, 146, 159, 172, 185, 198 (b) 13
16. (i) 10,500 squares (ii) $n^2 + 5n$ squares
17. (a) 11 (b) 63
18. width = 230 ft, length = 310 ft
19.

17	7	9
3	11	19
13	15	5

20. 170
21. Yes; she can use the 8 1/2-inch side twice to get 17 inches and then use the 11-inch side to get back to 6 inches.
22. (a) 260,610 (b) 100,701 (c) 20,503
23. (a) 204 squares (b) The number of different squares is more than doubled. It is now 1496.
24. (a) If both numbers were less than or equal to 9, then their product would be less than or equal to $9 \cdot 9 = 81$ which is not greater than 82. (b) Follow the same argument as in (a): 81 is not greater than 81.

Communication
25. Answers vary, for example, the discussion could be about designing a course and work schedule, or working out a budget.
26. Answers vary, but the discussion should include the points that at the 5-8 level a variety of strategies should be used with the emphasis on multistep and nonroutine problems. Also, at the 5-8 level students should be able to generalize solutions and strategies to new problem situations. Otherwise the standard for problem solving is almost the same.
27. Answers vary, but the discussion should point out that the two methods give the same answer and that the advantage of this method is that it works with an even or odd number of terms.
28. Answers vary, for example, if these nine numbers are to be used in a magic square, then the sum in each of the three columns must be the same and must be a natural number. The natural number must be 1/3 of the sum of all nine numbers. However $1 + 3 + 4 + 5 + 6 + 7 + 8 + 9 + 10 = 53$ and $53/3 = 17 \, 2/3$ which is not a natural number. Therefore these numbers cannot be used for a magic square.
29. (a) Answers vary, for example, we could weigh 4 marbles against 4 marbles and then pick the heavier side. We could then weigh 2 marbles against 2 marbles and pick the heavier side. Finally we could weigh 1 marble against 1 marble and the heavier one is the one we are looking for. (b) We could divide the marbles into groups of 3, 3, and 2 and weigh 3 marbles against 3 marbles. If they balance, only one more weighing is necessary to determine the heavier of the two that

were not weighed. If they do not balance, select any two from the heavier side and weigh one against one. If they balance, the heavy one is the one that was not weighed. If they do not balance, the heavy one is the one that goes down.

Open-ended
30. The answers will vary but should include some way to measure the number of breaths in a minute and then multiply the number by 60, then by 24, and then by 365.
31. Answers vary depending on the textbook series chosen.
32. Answers vary, for example, any of the investigation problems in this section are examples of problems that the discussed strategy could be used with.
33. Answers vary, for example, in this section see the extension of Problem 2 in the Looking Back portion of the problem.

Cooperative Learning
34. The problem could be solved by reducing the problem to simpler cases and looking for a pattern or with other strategies. The final order is 1, 6, 2, 10, 3, 7, 4, 9, 5, 8.
35. 35 moves. This can be solved using the strategy of examining simpler cases and looking for a pattern. If one person is on each side, 3 moves are necessary. If two people are on each side, 8 moves are necessary. With 3 people on each side, 15 moves are necessary. If n people are on both sides, $(n + 1)^2 - 1$ moves are required.
36. (a) 21, 24, 27 (b) 243, 2, 729
37. $22 + (n - 1)10$ or $10n + 12$
38. 21 terms
39. 903
40. (a) The digits in the product always sum to 9. The tens digit in the answer is always one less than the number that is multiplied by 9. This pattern works with the other exercises presented. (b) The pattern can be used to check if you remembered the product of a digit and 9 correctly.

Brain Teaser (p. 38) Thursday

ONGOING ASSESSMENT 1-3

1. (a) (i) 541×72 (ii) divide 754 by 12
   (b) (i) 257×14 (ii) divide 124 by 75
2. (b)
3. $3.99 + $5.87 + $6.47 = $16.33
4. Hint: $259 \times 429 = 111,111$
5. 17 terms
6. 275,000,000
7. Depends on the calculator. For example, with an eight-digit display there are 19.
8. (a) Answers vary, for example:
   (i) Add $500 + 200 + 56 + 100 + 60 + 20 + 3$
   (ii) Subtract 31 from 155 until there is a remainder less than 31. Count the number of times that 31 was subtracted.
   (b) Answers vary, for example, $90 - 16 - 1$
9. (a) $(6 \times 7) + 8 = 50$ (b) $(6 - 2) + (60 \div 3)$
10. 14
11. $5,256,000
12. Answers vary depending on calculator, for example,
(a) $+ 5 = = = = = ...$ (b) $\times 2$ Cons 1 Cons Cons Cons ...
13. 625
14. 3,628,800
15. (a) If the product were abcd, then $a + c = 9$ and $b + d = 9$ (b) If the product were abcde, then $c = 9$, $a + d = 9$, and $b + e = 9$.
16. Divide the display by 10.
17. (a) $2^6 - 1$ (b) $2^n - 1$ (c) Answers check

18. (i) 334,956
   (ii) 5202 No calculator needed because any number times 1 is itself.
   (iii) 335,166
   (iv) 334, 956 No calculator because of part (i)
   (v) 0 No calculator because any number times 0 is 0.
   (vi) 335,166 No calculator because of part (iii).
   (vii) 334,956 No calculator needed because $542 \times 600 + 542 \times 18 = 542(600 + 18) = 542 \times 618$ which is part (i).
19. Answers vary, for example,
   (i) 1000 because $499 + 501 = 500 + 500 = 1000$
   (ii) 249,999 because $499 \times 501 = (500 - 1)(500 + 1) = 500^2 - 1 = 249,999$.
   (iii) 2, because $501 - 499 = 2$.
   (iv) 249,999 because of part (ii).
   (v) 49,900 because multiplying any natural number by 100 can be done by just annexing two 0's to the number.
   (vi) 249,999 because $A \times 500 + A = A \times 501 = 499 \times 501$ which was done in part (ii).
   (vii) 0 because 0 divided by any nonzero number is 0.
   (viii) 0 because 0 times any number is 0.

Communication
20. (a) $37 \times 18 = 666$, $37 \times 21 = 777$, $37 \times 24 = 888$ (b) 999
(c) Answers vary, for example, we could notice that the numbers we multiply 37 by are all multiples of 3 and that $3 \times 37 = 111$. Therefore, $37 \times 27 = 37 \times (3 \times 9) = (37 \times 3) \times 9 = 111 \times 9 = 999$. Because this can be done with the multiples of three, the pattern of answers in parts (a) and (b) is possible.
21. (a) 53×103 (b) Answers vary, for example, start testing 5459 for divisibility by consecutive primes until one is found. The memory feature of the calculator can be useful here.

Open-ended
22. Answers vary, students could tear paper for one minute, find the average number of pieces that could be torn in one minute and then compute how long it would take to tear a piece for everyone in the United States.
23. Answers vary

Cooperative Learning
24. Answers vary, for example, if the average reach of people in your group was 1.8 m, then it would take 40,000,000 m/1.8m = 22,222,222 people.
25. (a) Play second and make sure that the sum showing when you hand the calculator to your opponent is a multiple of 3.
(b) Play first and press 4. After that, make sure that each time that you hand the calculator to your opponent it displays 1 less than a multiple of 5. (c) Play first and press 3. After that, make sure that each time you hand the calculator to your opponent that it displays 3 more than a multiple of 10.
(d) Play second. Make sure the calculator displays a multiple of 3 each time you hand it to your opponent. (e) Play second. Make sure the calculator displays a multiple of 4 each time you hand it to your opponent. (f) Play first and subtract 3. Then make sure the calculator displays a multiple of 10 each time.
26. (a) 35, 42, 49 (b) 1, 16, 1
27. $20n - 8$
28. 21 terms
29. 9 ways

Brain Teaser (p. 46)
Christmas (Notice that there is no L (NOEL) in the display.)

Chapter Review

1. (**a**) 15, 21, 28 (**b**) 32, 27, 22 (**c**) 400, 200, 100 (**d**) 21, 34, 55 (**e**) 17, 20, 23 (**f**) 256, 1024, 4096 (**g**) 16, 20, 24 (**h**) 125, 216, 343

2. (**a**) neither (**b**) arithmetic (**c**) geometric (**d**) neither (**e**) arithmetic (**f**) geometric (**g**) arithmetic (**h**) neither

3. (**a**) $3n + 2$ (**b**) n^3 (**c**) 3^n

4. (**a**) 5, 8, 11, 14, 17, ... (**b**) 2, 6, 12, 20, 30, ... (**c**) 3, 7, 11, 15, 19, ...

5. (**a**) 10,100 (**b**) 10,201

6. (**a**) 123456, 1234567, 12345678, ... (**b**) 1234567890. The last digit of the nth term in the sequence matches the last digit of the number n.

7.

16	3	2	13
5	10	11	8
9	6	7	12
4	15	14	1

8. 89 years

9. The worm will climb out on the 10th day.

10. 26

11. $2.00

12. 21 posts

13. 128 matches

14. $19,305 = 3 \cdot 5 \cdot 9 \cdot 11 \cdot 13$

15. 44,000,000 rotations

16. 20 students

17. 39 boxes

18. 48 triangles

19. 9 hours

20. width is 10 ft, length is 24 ft

21. There will be 96,000 ants on the seventh day and 192,000 ants on the eighth day so it will certainly be full.

22. 4 questions

23. Select the basket labeled APPLES AND ORANGES and reach in and select a piece of fruit. If the fruit is an orange, move the ORANGES label here, move the APPLES label to where the ORANGES label was, and put the APPLES AND ORANGES label in the remaining slot. If the fruit drawn is an apple, move the APPLES sign to this basket, move the ORANGES sign to where the APPLES sign was, and place the APPLES AND ORANGES label in the remaining slot.

CHAPTER 2

ONGOING ASSESSMENT 2-1

1. (**a**) {m, a, t, h, e, i, c, s} (**b**) {x | x is a state in the United States, but x is not Alaska or Hawaii} (**c**) {x | x is a natural number, and x > 20} or {21, 21, 23, ...} (**d**) {Oregon, California, Washington, Hawaii, Alaska}

2. (**a**) B = {x, y, z, w} (**b**) $\{1, 2\} \subset \{1, 2, 3, 4\}$ (**c**) $0 \notin \varnothing$ (**d**) $\{0\} \neq \varnothing$

3. (**a**) Yes (**b**) No (**c**) Yes (**d**) No (**e**) No

4. (**a**) 120 (**b**) 720 (**c**) n!

5. (**a**) 24 (**b**) 6 (**c**) 12

6. A, C, and D are equal sets. Also, E = H.

7. (**a**) 501 (**b**) 11 (**c**) 100 (**d**) 3 (**e**) 5

8. $\overline{A}$ is the set of all students with at least one grade that is not an A, i.e., those students who do not have a straight-A average.

9. (**a**) 7 (**b**) 1

10. (**a**) n(D) = 5 (**b**) C = D

11. (**a**) $\in$ (**b**) $\notin$ (**c**) $\notin$ (**d**) $\notin$ (**e**) $\notin$

12. (**a**) $\not\subset$ (**b**) $\not\subset$ (**c**) $\subseteq$ (**d**) $\subseteq$ (**e**) $\subseteq$

13. No. Consider the sets A = {1} and B = {2}.

14. (**a**) True. (**b**) False. A may equal B. (**c**) True. (**d**) False. Consider A = {1} and B = {1, 2}.

15. (**a**) Let A = {a, b} and B = {a, b, c, d}. Then n(A) = 2 and n(B) = 4. Since $A \subset B$, n(A) is less than n(B), i.e., 2 is less than 4. (**b**) Let A = {1, 2, 3} and B = {1, 2, 3, 4, ... ,100}. Since $A \subset B$, n(A) is less than n(B). So 3 < 100. (**c**) Let A = $\varnothing$ and B = {1, 2, 3}. Since $A \subset B$, n(A) = 0 is less than n(B) = 3.

16. (**a**) $2^6 - 1$ or 63 (**b**) $2^n - 1$

17. $7 \cdot 6 \cdot 5 = 210$

Communication

18. (**a**) This set is not well defined, since we do not know what is meant by "wealthy." (**b**) This set is not well defined, since we do not know what is meant by "great." (**c**) This set is well defined. Given a number, we can easily tell whether it is a natural number greater than 100. (**d**) This set is well defined. We could just list them all. (**e**) This set is not well defined, since we do not know what is meant by "$\neq$." (We cannot assume that x refers to a number.)

19. (**a**) Answers vary. For example: You are a member of the set of all humans, the set of all college (or university) students, and the set of all males or the set of all females (among many others that are probably more interesting). (**b**) Answers vary. For example: The set of all atheists who believe in God, the set of all people who have been to Mars, and the set of all elementary school teachers who are less than 8 yrs old.

20. Answers vary. For example: The set of tenured college professors, the set of mathematics professors, the set of female college professors, the set of college professors who wear suits to school, and the set of college professors without an advanced degree.

21. No, the empty set is not a proper subset of itself, since it equals itself.

22. If A and B are finite subsets, we say $n(A) \leq n(B)$ in case A is a subset (not necessarily proper) of B.

23. (**a**) Answers vary. For example:
    A = {1, 2, 3, 4, 5}, B = {1, 2, 3, 4, 5, 6, 7, 8, 9}, and
    U = {1, 2, 3,..., 20} $\overline{A}$ = {6, 7, 8, ..., 20}, and
    $\overline{B}$ = {10, 11, 12,... , 20}
(**b**) $\overline{B} \subset \overline{A}$
(**c**)

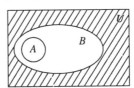

$\overline{B}$ contains only the shaded region. $\overline{A}$ contains all the area outside the circle labeled A.

Open-ended

24. (**a**) Let A be the set of all numbers not equal to 1. Then $\overline{A}$ = {1} is finite. (**b**) Let A be the set of even natural numbers. Its complement, $\overline{A}$, is the set of odd natural numbers and so is infinite. (Here U is the set of natural numbers.)

25. Let A = {1, 2, 3, 4, ... }, A_1 = {2, 3, 4, ... }, A_2 = {3, 4, 5, ... }, A_3 = {4, 5, 6, ... }, and so on. There are infinitely many subsets of the type A_n, where n is a natural number.

26. (**i**) Let A be the set of all human beings, and B the set of all female humans. (**ii**) Let A be the set of all nonvacant houses in the United States and B the set of all people in the United States.

Cooperative Learning

27. **(a)** There are $2^{64} \doteq 1.84 \times 10^{19}$ subsets of $\{1, 2, 3, \ldots, 64\}$. If a computer can list one every millionth of a second, then it would take $1.84 \times 10^{19} \times 0.000001 \sec \times \dfrac{1 \text{ yr}}{31{,}536{,}000 \sec}$

$\doteq 580{,}000$ yr to list all the subsets. **(b)** There are $64! = 64 \cdot 63 \cdot 62 \cdot \ \cdots \ \cdot 2 \cdot 1 \doteq 1.27 \times 10^{89}$ one-to-one correspondences between the 2 sets. So it would take

$1.27 \times 10^{89} \times 0.000001 \sec \times \dfrac{1 \text{ yr}}{31{,}536{,}000 \sec} \doteq 4 \times 10^{75}$ yr to list

all the subsets.

Brain Teaser (p. 62)

Because the town barber is a male, then he shaves himself. Because he shaves only those who do not shave themselves, he cannot shave himself. Consequently, the barber is not a male, but we know he is. Thus we have a paradox.

ONGOING ASSESSMENT 2-2

1. **(a)** Yes **(b)** Yes **(c)** Yes **(d)** Yes **(e)** Yes **(f)** No
2. **(a)** True. **(b)** False. Let A = {a, b, c} and B = {a, b}. Then A − B = {c}, but B − A = ∅. **(c)** True. **(d)** False. Let A = {a, b, c}, B = {a, b}, and U = {a, b, c, ... z}. Then $\overline{A \cap B}$ = (c, d, ... , z), but $\overline{A} \cap \overline{B}$ = {d, e, f, ... , z} **(e)** True. **(f)** False. Let A = {1, 2, 3}, B = {3, 4, 5}, and U = {1, 2, 3, ... , 10}. Then {A ∪ B} − A = {1, 2, 3, 4, 5} − {1, 2, 3} = {4, 5} ≠ B. **(g)** False. Let A, B, and U be as in the solution to **(f)**. Then (A − B) ∪ A = A = {1, 2, 3}, but (A − B) ∪ (B − A) = {1, 2} ∪ {4, 5} = {1, 2, 4, 5}.
3. **(a)** A ∩ B = B **(b)** A ∪ B = A
4. **(a)**   **(b)**

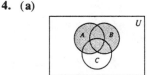

(c)   **(d)**

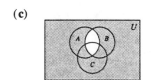

(e)   **(f)**

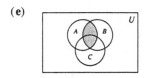

(g)   **(h)**

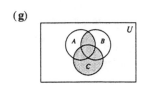

5. **(a)** $S \cup \overline{S}$ = U **(b)** S ∪ U = U **(c)** ∅ ∪ S = S
(d) $\overline{U}$ = ∅ **(e)** S ∩ U = S **(f)** $\overline{\varnothing}$ = U **(g)** $S \cap \overline{S}$ = ∅
(h) $S - \overline{S}$ = S **(i)** $U \cap \overline{S} = \overline{S}$ **(j)** $\overline{S}$ = U − S
(k) ∅ ∩ S = ∅ **(l)** $U - S = \overline{S}$
6. **(a)** A − B = A **(b)** A − B = ∅ **(c)** A − B = ∅
(d) A − B = ∅
7. **(a)** B − A or $B \cap \overline{A}$ **(b)** $A \cap \overline{B}$ or $\overline{A \cup B}$
(c) (A ∩ B) − C **(d)** A ∩ C **(e)** (A ∪ B) ∩ C, or
C − (A ∪ B) **(f)** $((B \cup C) \cap \overline{A}) \cup (A \cap B \cap C)$
8.

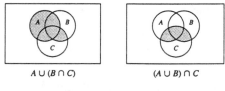

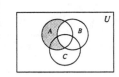

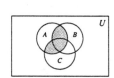

(a)   **(b)**

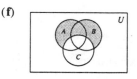

(c)   **(d)**

9. **(a)** False

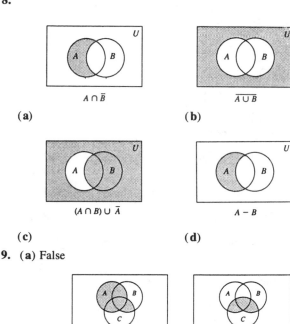

$A \cup (B \cap C)$ $(A \cup B) \cap C$

(b) False

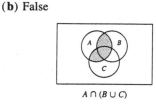

$A \cap (B \cup C)$ $(A \cap B) \cup C$

(c) False

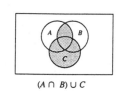

$A - (B - C)$ $(A - B) - C$

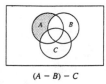

10. **(a)** A ∩ B ∩ C ⊆ A ∩ B **(b)** A ∪ B ⊆ A ∪ B ∪ C
(c) (A ∪ B) ∩ C ⊆ A ∪ B **(d)** Neither is, in general, a subset of the other. For example, if A and B are disjoint, then A − B = A and B − A = B and these are disjoint.
11. **(a)** (i) 5; (ii) 2; (iii) 2; (iv) 3 **(b)** (i) n + m;
(ii) The smaller of the two numbers m and n; (iii) m; (iv) n
12. **(a)** Greatest is 15, least is 6. **(b)** Greatest is 4, least is 0.

13. (a)

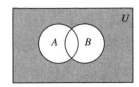

(b) The equation is $\overline{A \cap B} = \overline{A} \cup \overline{B}$.
(c) Let U = {a, b, c, d}, A = {a, b}, and B = {b, c}. Then
$\overline{A} \cap \overline{B}$ = {c, d} ∩ {a, d} = {d} = $\overline{A \cup B}$. Also,
$\overline{A} \cup \overline{B}$ = {c, d} ∪ {a, d} = {a, c, d} = $\overline{A \cap B}$.
14. A = B
15. (a) The set of college basketball players more than 200 cm
tall (b) The set of humans who are not college students or
who are college students less than or equal to 200 cm tall
(c) The set of humans who are college basketball players or
who are college students taller than 200 cm (d) The set of all
humans who are not college basketball players and who are not
college students taller than 200 cm (e) The set of all college
students taller than 200 cm who are not basketball players
(f) The set of all college basketball players less than or equal
to 200 cm tall
16. (a) The set of all Paxson fifth graders who are members of
the band but not the choir (b) The set of all Paxson fifth
graders who are members of both the band and the choir
(c) The set of all Paxson fifth graders who are members of the
choir but not the band (d) The set of all Paxson fifth graders
who are neither members of the band nor of the choir
17. 18
18. 4
19.

20. (a) 20 (b) 10 (c) 10
21. (a) False. Let A = {a, b, c} and B = {1, 2, 3} (b) False.
Let A = B (c) False. Let A = {1, 2, 3} and B = {1, 2, 3, 4}
(d) True. (e) True. (f) False. Let A = {1, 2, 3} and
B = {a, b, c, d}
22. Steelers versus Jets, Vikings versus Packers, Bills versus
Redskins, Cowboys versus Giants
23. (a) A × B = {(x, a), (x, b), (x, c), (y, a), (y, b), (y, c)}
(b) B × A = {(a, x), (a, y), (b, x), (b, y), (c, x), (c, y)}
(c) B × ∅ = ∅ (d) (A ∪ B) × C = {(x, 0), (y, 0), (a, 0),
(b, 0), (c, 0)} (e) A ∪ (B × C) = {(x, y), (a, 0), (b, 0),
(c, 0)}
24. (a) C = {a}, D = {b, c, d, e} (b) C = {1, 2},
D = {1, 2, 3} (c) C = D = {0, 1}
25. (a) 4 · 5 = 20 (b) m · n (c) m · n · p
26. (a) 0 (b) 0 (c) 0
27. n(A) = 5
28. Yes
29. (a) Always true. This is a special case of (b) below.
(b) Let (x, y) be a member of A × C. Then x ∈ A ⊆ B and
y ∈ C ⊆ D, so (x, y) is also a member of B × D.
30. 30
31. 60

Communication
32. (a) Yes. A ∩ B ⊆ A ⊆ A ∪ B (b) No. For example, let
A = {1, 2, 3}, and B = {4}. Then 2 ∈ A ∪ B, but 2 ∉ A ∩ B.
33. Answers vary.

34. The following Venn diagram indicates that only 490
cardholders are accounted for:

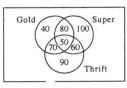

So either there is some other type of credit card the remaining
10 people could have, or else the editor was right.
35. (a) No. Let A = {1}, and B = {a}. Then A × B = {(1, a)},
but B × A = {(a, 1)}. These are not equal. (b) No. Let A and
B be as above, and C = {+}. Then the element ((1, a), +) is in
(A × B) × C but not in A × (B × C).
36. 3. Using the following Venn diagram and the fact that the
set of people who are O-negative is 100 − n (A ∪ B ∪ C), we
see that the answer is 3.

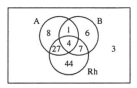

Open-ended
37.–38. Answers vary.

Cooperative Learning
39.–40. Answers vary.

Review Problems
41. (a) These are all the subsets of {2, 3, 4}. There are $2^3 = 8$
such subsets. (b) There are 8 subsets that contain the number
1. Every subset either contains 1 or it does not. So exactly half
of the $2^4 = 16$ subsets contain 1. (c) Twelve subsets contain 1
or 2 (or both). There are 4 subsets of {3, 4}. We can form
subsets that contain 1 or 2 or both by adding 1 to each, 2 to
each, or 1 and 2 to each. By the Fundamental Counting
Principle then, there are 3 · 4 = 12 possibilities. (It's also not
hard to list them.) (d) Four subsets contain neither 1 nor 2,
since 12 subsets do contain 1 or 2. (e) B has $2^5 = 32$ subsets.
Half contain 5 and half do not. (f) Every subset of A is a
subset of B. The others can be listed by adding the number 5 to
each subset of A. So there are twice as many subsets of B as
subsets of A($2^5 = 32$).
42. (a) A and B are equal. (b) C is a proper subset of A and a
proper subset of B, since C = (4, 8, 12, 16, …).
43. Answers vary.

ONGOING ASSESSMENT 2-3

1. (a) Double the input number. (b) Subtract 2 from the input
number. (c) Add 6 to the input number. (d) Square the input
number and add 1.
2. (a) This is not a function, since the input 1 is paired with 2
outputs (a and d). (b) This is not a function, since 2 is not
paired with any letter. (c) This is a function. (d) This is not a
function, since the input 1 is paired with several outputs.

3. (a)

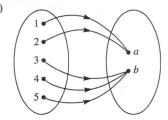

(b) 32

4. (a)

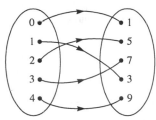

(b) {(0, 1), (1, 3), (2, 5), (3, 7), (4, 9)}
(c)

x	f (x)
0	1
1	3
2	5
3	7
4	9

(d)

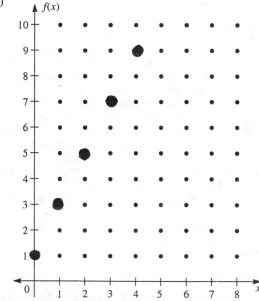

5. (a) This is a function. **(b)** This is a function. **(c)** This is a function. **(d)** This is not a function, since, for example, f(3) = 0 because 3 is in W and f(3) = 1 because 3 is in {3, 4, 5, 6 ...} **(e)** This is a function.
6. Assuming 32¢ for the first ounce and 23¢ for each additional ounce, **(a)** 0.32 + 0.23 (n − 1), where n = the number of ounces **(b)** 78¢

7.

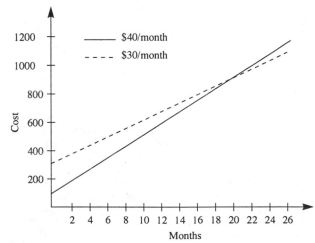

8. (a) 2 chirps per second **(b)** 50 degrees Fahrenheit
9. (a) 8 dollars **(b)** 3n + 2 dollars
10. (a) L(n) = 2n + (n − 1) or 3n − 1 **(b)** L(n) = n^2 + 1
(c) L(n) = n(n + 1)
11. (a) 7 **(b)** 55 **(c)** 2
12. (a) 5n − 2 **(b)** 3^n **(c)** 2n
13. (a) ⁻5 **(b)** 16 **(c)** 65
14. (a) 1, 385, 389 **(b)** 1, 4, 9, 900 **(c)** 2, 12, 2550
15. (a) 2 · 1 + 2 · 7 = 16; 2 · 2 + 2 · 6 = 16; 6 + 2 · 2 = 16; 2 · 5 + 2 · 5 = 20 **(b)** (1, 9), (2, 8), (3, 7), (4, 6), (5, 5), (6, 4), (7, 3), (8, 2), (9, 1) **(c)** The domain is N × N, and the range is the set of all even numbers greater than or equal to 4.
16. (a) 1 cm **(b)** The fourth and the fifth **(c)** Her height on her birthday
17. (a) 50 cars **(b)** Between 6 and 6:30 A.M. **(c)** 0
(d) Between 8:30 and 9 A.M.
18. (a) C(x) = 100 + 40 x
(b) and **(c)**:

19. (a) H(2) = 192. H(6) = 192. H(3) = 240. H(5) = 240. Some of the heights correspond to the ball going up, some to the ball coming down.

(**b**)

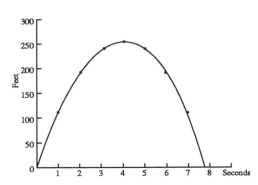

At t = 4 seconds the ball's height is H(4) = 256 feet above the ground.

(**c**) 8 seconds

(**d**) $0 \le t \le 8$

(**e**) $0 \le H(t) \le 256$

20. (**a**) $A(x) = x \cdot \frac{1}{2}(900 - x)$

(**b**)

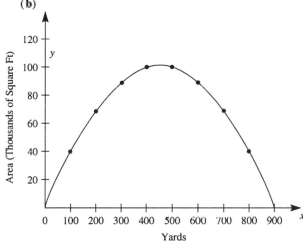

(**c**) Length = 450, width = 225

21. (**a**) (a) 4, 12, 24, 40

(b) 4, 10, 22, 38

(c) 4, 10, 16, 22

(**b**) (a) S(n) = 2n(n + 1)

(b) S(1) = 1, S(n) = 2n(n + 1) − 2 when n ≥ 2

(c) S(n) = 6n − 2

22. The converse is false. For example, the set of ordered pairs {(1, 2), (1, 3)} does not represent a function, since the element 1 is paired with two different second components.

23. (**a**) Boys: B, J; Girls: A, C, D, F, G, I (**b**) {(A, B), (A, C), (A, D), (C, A), (C, B), (C, D), (D, A), (D, B), (D, C), (F, G), (G, F), (I, J)} (**c**) No

24. (**a**) Function (**b**) Relation, but not a function (**c**) Relation, but not a function (assuming there is a mother in Birmingham who has more than one child) (**d**) Function (**e**) Relation, but not a function.

25. (**a**) Yes (**b**) No

26. (**a**) None (**b**) Reflexive, symmetric, and transitive (and so an equivalence relation) (**c**) Reflexive, symmetric, and transitive (and so an equivalence relation) (**d**) Reflexive,

symmetric, and transitive (and so an equivalence relation) (**e**) Symmetric (**f**) Reflexive and symmetric (**g**) Transitive

27. (**a**) Equivalence relation (**b**) Transitive (**c**) Symmetric (**d**) Equivalence relation

Communication

28. Yes, since each element of A is paired with exactly one element of B.

29. Yes. Answers vary.

30. (**a**) This is not a function, since a faculty member may teach more than one class. (**b**) This is a function (assuming only one teacher per class). (**c**) This is not a function, since not every senator is paired with a committee. (Not every senator is the chairperson of a committee.)

31. (**a**)

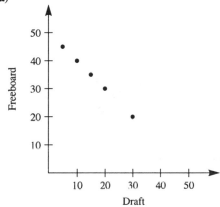

It is meaningful. Answers vary.

(**b**) f (d) = 50 − d

Open-ended

32.–36. Answers vary.

Cooperative Learning

37.–38. Answers vary.

Review Problems

39. (**a**) These are equivalent, since each has 500 elements. (**b**) Not equivalent. The function f(x) = 3x − 2 sets up a correspondence where the second set is the domain set. But then nothing corresponds to 3001 in the range. (In other words, the first set has 1001 elements and the second 1000.) (**c**) These are equivalent, since the function f(x) = x + 1 establishes a one-to-one correspondence between the two sets (with the first set as domain). (**d**) These are equivalent, since the function f(x) = 2n establishes a one-to-one correspondence between the two sets (with the first set as domain).

40. (**a**) True. $A - (B \cup C) = A \cap \overline{B \cup C} = A \cap (\overline{B} \cap \overline{C}) = A \cap \overline{B} \cap \overline{C} = (A \cap \overline{B}) \cap (A \cap \overline{C}) = (A - B) \cap (A - C)$ (**b**) True. $A \subseteq A \cup B = B$ (**c**) True. $\overline{A \cup B} = \overline{A} \cap \overline{B} = \varnothing = U$ (**d**) False. Let A = {1, 2, 3}, B = {2, 3, 4}, and C = A.

41. (**a**) 6 (**b**) 9

42. (**a**) False. Let A = {1, 2, 3}, B = {1, 2, 3, 4}, and C = {4}. (**b**) False. Let A = {1, 2, 3}, B = {3, 4}, and C = {3}. (**c**) False. Suppose A = C. (**d**) False. It is always true that $A \times \varnothing = B \times \varnothing = \varnothing$, regardless of whether A and B are equal. (**e**) True

43. 22

44. (**a**) 2200 (**b**) 500

45. (**a**) {2n | n is a natural number and n > 6} (**b**) {n | n is a natural number and n < 14}.

46. (a) $A \cup \overline{B} = \{a, b, c\} \cup \{a, d\} = \{a, b, c, d\} = U$
(b) $\overline{A \cap B} = \overline{\{b, c\}} = \{a, d\}$ (c) $A \cap \varnothing = \varnothing$ (d) $B \cap C = \{b, c\} \cap \{d\} = \varnothing$ (e) $B - A = B \cap \overline{A} = \{b, c\} \cap \{d\} = \varnothing$

Brain Teaser (p. 90)
The plan fails because we have not accounted for the eleventh man. The first and second men are in room 1, the third through tenth men are in rooms 2 through 9. Where is the eleventh man? He has not been mentioned. If the extra man in room 1 is put in room 10, then the eleventh man still has no room. Confusion results from the fact that by the time we read that the tenth man has been put into room 9, we think that the extra man in the first room is the eleventh man, when actually he is either the first or the second.

ONGOING ASSESSMENT 2-4

1. (a) False statement (b) Not a statement (c) False statement (d) Not a statement (e) Not a statement (f) Not a statement (g) True statement (h) Not a statement (i) Not a statement (j) Not a statement
2. (a) There exists a natural number x such that $x + 8 = 11$. (b) For all x, $x + 0 = x$. (c) There exists a natural number x such that $x^2 = 4$. (d) No natural number x exists such that $x + 1 = x + 2$. (e) For all natural numbers x, $x + 3 = 3 + x$. (f) There exists a natural number x such $3 \cdot (x + 2) = 12$. (g) For all natural numbers x, $5x + 4x = 9x$.
3. (a) For every natural number, x, $x + 8 = 11$. (b) No natural number x satisfies $x + 0 = x$. (c) Every natural number x satisfies $x^2 = 4$. (d) There exists a natural number x such that $x + 1 = x + 2$. (e) There is no natural number x such that $x + 3 = 3 + x$. (f) For every natural number x, $3 \cdot (x + 2) = 12$. (g) There is no natural number x such that $5x + 4x = 9x$.
4. (a) The book does not have 500 pages. (b) Six is greater than or equal to 8, or 6 is not less than 8. (c) $3 \cdot 5 \neq 15$. (d) No people have blond hair. (e) No dogs have four legs. (f) All cats have nine lives. (g) Not all squares are rectangles, or some squares are not rectangles. (h) All rectangles are squares.
5.

(a)
p	~p	~(~)p
T	F	T
F	T	F

(b)
p	~p	p∨~p	p∧~p
T	F	T	F
F	T	T	F

(c) Yes
(d) No
6. (a) $q \wedge r$ (b) $r \vee \sim q$ (c) $\sim (q \wedge r)$ (d) $\sim q$
7. (a) False (b) True (c) True (d) False (e) False (f) True (g) False (h) False (i) False (j) False
8. (a) False (b) False (c) True (d) True (e) False (f) True (g) False (h) True (i) True (j) True
9. (a) No (b) Yes (c) No (d) Yes
10.

p	q	~p	~q	~p∨q
T	T	F	F	T
T	F	F	T	F
F	T	T	F	T
F	F	T	T	T

11. (a) Either today is not Wednesday, or the month is not June. (b) Yesterday I either did not eat breakfast or did not watch television. (c) It is not true that it is both raining and the month is July.

12. (a) $p \rightarrow q$ (b) $\sim p \rightarrow q$ (c) $p \rightarrow \sim q$ (d) $p \rightarrow q$ (e) $\sim q \rightarrow \sim p$ (f) $q \leftrightarrow p$
13. (a) Converse: If you are good in sports, then you eat Meaties. Inverse: If you do not eat Meaties, then you are not good in sports. Contrapositive: If you are not good in sports, then you do not eat Meaties. (b) Converse: If you do not like mathematics, then you do not like this book. Inverse: If you like this book, then you like mathematics. Contrapositive: If you like mathematics, then you like this book. (c) Converse: If you have cavities, then you do not use Ultra Brush toothpaste. Inverse: If you use Ultra Brush toothpaste, then you do not have cavities. Contrapositive: If you do not have cavities, then you use Ultra Brush toothpaste. (d) Converse: If your grades are high, then you are good at logic. Inverse: If you are not good at logic, then your grades are not high. Contrapositive: If your grades are not high, then you are not good at logic.
14. No.
15. (a) No (b) Yes (c) No
16. If a number is not a multiple of 4, then it is not a multiple of 8. (Contrapositive)
17. (a) Valid (b) Valid (c) Valid (d) Invalid
18. (a) Helen is poor. (b) Some freshmen are intelligent. (c) If I study for the final, then I will look for a teaching job. (d) Since there may exist triangles that are not isoscles, there may exist triangles that are not equilateral.
19. (a) If a figure is a square, then it is a rectangle. (b) If a number is an integer, then it is a rational number. (c) If a figure has exactly three sides, then it may be a triangle. (d) If it rains, then it is cloudy.

Communication
20. (a) $\sim (p \vee q)$ is equivalent to $\sim p \wedge q$, and $\sim (p \wedge q)$ is equivalent to $\sim p \vee \sim q$. (b) Answers vary.
21. (a) p: "Mary's little lamb follows her to school."
q: "The lamb's appearance in school breaks the rules."
r: "Mary will be sent home."
Then $p \rightarrow (r \wedge q)$.
(b) p: "Jack is nimble."
q: "Jack is quick."
r: "Jack jumps over the candlestick."
Then $\sim (p \wedge q) \rightarrow \sim r$.
(c) p: "The apple hit Isaac Newton."
q: "The laws of gravity would have been discovered."
Then $\sim p \rightarrow \sim q$.
22. (a) Valid: p: "You study hard."
q: "You get at least a B in this course."
r: "You will graduate."
Then $p \rightarrow q$ and $q \rightarrow r$. By the Chain Rule, $p \rightarrow r$.
(b) Valid. The second statement is the contrapositive of the first; hence the two statements are logically equivalent.
(c) Invalid. Consider the following diagram:

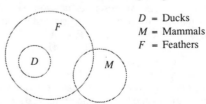

D = Ducks
M = Mammals
F = Feathers

23. (a) Therefore we go shopping. (Going shopping is equivalent to getting a bonus.) (b) Therefore the figure is not a rectangle. (Contrapositive) (c) Let p be the statement "It is sunny", q the statement "We go hiking", and r the statement "It is freezing". Symbolically, $p \rightarrow q$ and $r \rightarrow \sim q$. The second statement gives q → ~ r. So the Chain Rule tells us that p → ~ r, that is, if it is sunny then it is not freezing.

Open-ended

24. Answers vary.

Chapter 2 Review

1. {x | x is a letter of the Greek alphabet}

2. ∅, {m}, {a}, {t}, {h}, {m, a}, {m, t}, {m, h}, {a, t}, {a, h}, {t, h}, {m, a, t}, {m, a, h}, {m, t, h}, {a, t, h}, {m, a, t, h}

3. (**a**) A person living in Montana younger than 30 yr old (**b**) A person living in Montana 30 yr or older and who owns a truck (**c**) A person living in Montana (**d**) A person living in Montana who does not own a pickup truck (**e**) A person living in Montana less than 30 yr old or who does not own a pickup truck. (**f**) A person living in Montana 30 yr or older who does not own a pickup truck

4. (**a**) A ∪ B = A (**b**) C ∩ D = {l, e} (**c**) D̄ = {u, n, i, v, r} (**d**) A ∩ D = {r, v} (**e**) B∪C = {s, v, u} (**f**) (B ∪ C) ∩ D = {l, e, a} (**g**) {i, n} (**h**) {e} (**i**) 5 (**j**) 16

5.

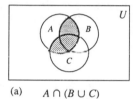

(a)   A ∩ (B ∪ C)

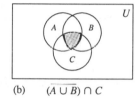

(b)   (A ∪ B) ∩ C

6. Assuming all seven letters are different, 5040.

7. (**a**) t → e   (**b**) 6
        h → n
        e → d

8. It is not true that A ∩ (B ∪ C) = (A ∩ B) ∪ C for all A, B, and C.

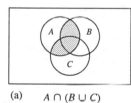

(a)   A ∩ (B ∪ C)

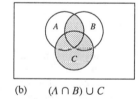

(b)   (A ∩ B) ∪ C

9. (**a**) B ∪ (C ∩ A) (**b**) B − C

10. (**a**) False. Consider the sets {a} and {2}. (**b**) False. It is not a proper subset of itself. (**c**) False. Consider the sets {t, h, e} and {e, n, d}. They have the same number of elements, but they are not equal. (**d**) False. This is in one-to-one correspondence with the set of natural numbers. (**e**) False. The set {5, 10, 15, 20, ... } is a proper subset of the natural numbers, and is equivalent to the natural numbers, since there is a one-to-one correspondence between the 2 sets. (**f**) False. Let B = {1, 2, 3} and A be the set of natural numbers. (**g**) True (**h**) False. Let A = {1, 2, 3} and B = {a, b, c}.

11. (**a**) 17 (**b**) 34 (**c**) 0 (**d**) 17

12. 7

13. The first question might be, "Is the state or province one of the 48 contiguous states in the United States?" If the answer is yes, the second question could be, "Does it begin with a vowel?" The third question can then be, "Is it _____?" If the answer to the first question is no, the second question could be, "Is it in Canada?", and the third question could be the same as above.

14.

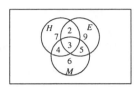

(**a**) 36 (**b**) 6 (**c**) 5

15. (**a**) Yes (**b**) No (**c**) Yes

16. (**a**) Pair each post office with the ZIP code in which it resides (**b**) Let A be the set of all addresses in the fifth set of states; B the set of all addresses in the ninety-eighth geographical region in A, and C the set of all addresses in the first local delivery area in B. Let x be my address. Then x ∈ A ∩ B ∩ C.

17. (**a**) range = {3, 4, 5 6} (**b**) range = {14, 29, 44, 59} (**c**) range = {0, 1, 4, 9, 16} (**d**) range = {5, 9, 15}

18. (**a**) This is not a function, since one student can have two majors. (**b**) This is a function. The range is the subset of the natural numbers that includes the number of pages in each book in the library. (**c**) This is a function. The range is {6, 8, 10, 12, ... }. (**d**) This is a function. The range is {0, 1}. (**e**) This is a function. The range is N.

19. (**a**) C(x) = 200 + 55(x − 1)
        (**b**)

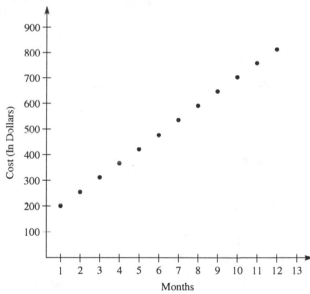

(**c**) After the ninth month, the cost exceeds $600.
(**d**) Solve the equation:
$$C(x) = 200 + 55(x - 1) = 6000$$
$$55x - 55 = 580$$
$$55x = 585$$
$$x = 106.5$$

Thus after the 107th month, the cost will exceed $6000.

20. (**a**) Yes (**b**) Yes (**c**) No (**d**) Yes

21. (**a**) No women smoke. (**b**) 3 + 5 ≠ 8. (**c**) Some heavy-metal rock is not loud, or not all heavy-metal rock is loud. (**d**) Beethoven wrote some music that is not classical.

22. Converse: If someone will faint, we are having a rock concert. Inverse: If we do not have a rock concert, then no one will faint. Contrapositive: If no one will faint, then we are not having a rock concert.

23. (**a**) Joe Czernyu loves Mom and apple pie. (**b**) The Statue of Liberty will eventually rust. (**c**) Albertina passed Math 100.

24. p: "You are fair-skinned."
q: "You will sunburn."
r: "You do not go to the dance."
s: "Your parents want to know why you didn't go to the dance."
Symbolically, p → q, q → r, r → s. The argument given is valid: ~ s → ~ r, ~ r → ~ q, ~ q → ~ p. By the Chain Rule, ~ s → ~ p, i.e., if your parents do not want to know why you didn't go to the dance, then you are not fair-skinned.

CHAPTER 3

ONGOING ASSESSMENT 3-1

1. (a) $\overline{\overline{\text{MCDXXIV}}}$; The double bar over M represents $1000 \cdot 1000 \cdot 1000$. (b) 46,032; The 4 in 46,032 represents 40,000 while the 4 in 4632 represents only 4000. (c) < ▼▼; The space in the latter number indicates < is multiplied by $10 \cdot 60$ rather than by 10. (d) The 𝓻 represents 1000 while 𝟫 represents only 100. (e) ☷ represents three groups of 20 plus zero 1's while ≡ represents three 5's and three 1's.

2. (a) MCML; MCMXLVIII (b) MII; M (c) M; CMXCVIII

(d) << <▼▼;<< < 𝓻991; 𝓻99 ∩∩∩∩∩ ||||| ∩∩∩∩ |||||

(f) ⁞⁞ ; ⁝⁝

3. 1922

4. (a) CXXI (b) XLII (c) LXXXIX, (d) $\overline{\text{VCCLXXXII}}$

5. (a) ∩∩∩∩∩|| (b) 𝟫||| (c) ⌒||| (d) ∩∩∩∩||||||||

6. (a) ▼<▼▼;∩∩∩∩∩∩∩|| ; LXXII; ⁝⁝

(b) 602; 𝟫𝟫𝟫/𝟫𝟫𝟫 ||, DCII; ⁞⁝·

(c) 1223; << <<▼▼; MCCXXIII; ⁝⁚

7. (a) Hundreds (b) Tens (c) Thousands (d) Hundred thousands

8. (a) 3,004,005 (b) 20,001 (c) 3,560 (d) 9,000,099

9. (a) 86 (b) 11

10. 811 or 910

11. (a) $(1, 10, 11, 100, 101, 110, 111, 1000, 1001, 1010, 1011, 1100, 1101, 1110, 1111)_{two}$ (b) $(1, 2, 10, 11, 12, 20, 21, 22, 100, 101, 102, 110, 111, 112, 120)_{three}$ (c) $(1, 2, 3, 10, 11, 12, 13, 20, 21, 22, 23, 30, 31, 32, 33)_{four}$ (d) $(1, 2, 3, 4, 5, 6, 7, 10, 11, 12, 13, 14, 15, 16, 17)_{eight}$

12. 20

13. $2032_{four} = (2 \cdot 10^3 + 0 \cdot 10^2 + 3 \cdot 10 + 2)_{four}$

14. a) 111_{two} (b) 555_{six} (c) 999_{ten} (d) EEE_{twelve}

15. (a) ETE_{twelve}; $EE1_{twelve}$ (b) 11111_{two}; 100001_{two} (c) 554_{six}; 1000_{six} (d) 66_{seven}; 101_{seven} (e) 444_{five}; 1001_{five} (f) 101_{two}; 111_{two}

16. (a) There is no numeral 4 in base four. (b) There are no numerals 6 or 7 in base 5. (c) There is no numeral T in base three.

17. (a) 3212_{five} (b) 1177_{twelve} (c) 12110_{four} (d) 100101_{two} (e) $1E3T4_{twelve}$

18. 100010_{two}

19. (a) 117 (b) 45 (c) 1331 (d) 1451 (e) 157 (f) 181

20. 72¢; 242_{five}

21. 1 prize of $625, 2 prizes of $125, and 1 of $25

22. 3 quarters, 4 nickels, and 2 pennies

23. (a) 8 weeks, 2 days (b) 4 years, 6 months (c) 1 day, 5 hours (d) 5 feet, 8 inches

24. $E66_{twelve}$; 1662

25. (a) 6 (b) 1 (c) nine

26. (a) 9, (4 quarters 3 nickels, 2 pennies) (b) 73 pennies

27. Above the bar are depicted 5's, 50's, 500's, and 5000's. Below the bar are 1's, 10's, 100's, and 1000's. Thus there are $1 \cdot 5000$, $1 \cdot 500$, $3 \cdot 100$, $1 \cdot 50$, $1 \cdot 5$, and $2 \cdot 1$ depicted for a total of 5857. The number 4869 could be depicted as follows:

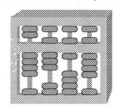

28. 4,782,969

29. Assume an eight-digit display without scientific notation. (a) 98,765,432 (b) 12,345,678 (c) 99,999,999 (d) 11,111,111

30. (a) Answers vary, e.g. subtract 2020. (b) Answers vary, e.g., subtract 50.

Communication

31. Answers will vary. Roman numerals may appear as chapter numbers, in outlines, as preface page numbers, as dates on buildings, among other things.

32. Answers will vary. Ben is incorrect. Zero is a place holder in the Hindu-Arabic system. It is used among other things to differentiate between 54 and 504. If zero were nothing, then we could eliminate it without changing our number system. Zero is the cardinal number of the empty set.

33. (a) The Egyptian system has no zero symbol and no place value. It is cumbersome to compute with this system and hard to work with large numbers. (b) The Babylonian system has too few symbols to be useful. Also the use of the spacing to indicate place value makes the system unusable unless the numbers can be read in context. (c) The Roman system is fairly complicated. It has no place value except for some subtractions. It has no zero symbol. Large numbers are difficult to write. Computation is not easy.

34. This is primarily for readability. It has been proposed with the metric system to drop the commas and simply use spaces instead. The comma in a number symbol has different meanings in some countries.

35. A primary disadvantage that students will learn about in Chapter 7 is that with only a few factors, there are fewer terminating decimals in the system. That will not be apparent at this stage. At this stage, students might answer that there will be fewer remainders of 0 with a base of fewer factors.

36. Around the world standardization of the use of commas and decimals would help the system. Students may make few suggestions here depending upon their knowledge.

Open-ended

37. The drawings of maize dollies, maize plants, flags, and blobs will certainly vary. With the depiction of 80, there should be four flags. With the depiction of 100, there should be five flags. With the depiction of 200, there should be 10 flags. With the depiction of 300, there should be 15 flags. With the depiction of 10,000, there should be one maize dolly and five maize plants.

38. The following is based upon using one hand only. If the thumb represented 5, then the numbers 1-5 could be depicted

on the right hand simply by raising the appropriate finger. The numbers 6-9 could be represented by raising two appropriate fingers on the right hand and using addition. For example, the thumb and 1 represent 6. To represent 10-14, the thumb on the right hand could be raised twice with an appropriate finger for each. To represent 15, the thumb on the right hand could be raised three times, and to represent numbers 16-19, the thumb could be raised three times with an appropriate finger.

Cooperative Learning
39. The answers to this problem are totally dependent on students and the properties that they select for the system. Most will probably emulate one of the systems studied in the section.
40. 4; 1, 2, 4, 8; 1, 2, 4, 8, 16

Brain Teaser (p. 119)
One box contains 2 nickels, one box contains 2 dimes, and one box contains a nickel and a dime. You would reach in the box labeled 15¢. If a nickel is drawn, the correct label for this box is 10¢. The 20¢ label would then be shifted to the box which was labeled 10¢, and then the 15¢ label would be placed on the remaining box. If a dime were drawn from the box labeled 15¢, then the 20¢ label would be placed on this box. Then the 10¢ label would be shifted to the box which was labeled 20¢, and the 15¢ label would be placed on the remaining box.

ONGOING ASSESSMENT 3-2
1. (a) k = 2 (b) k = 3
2. No. If k = 0, we would have k = 0 + k, implying k > k.
3. For example, let A = {1, 2}, B = {2, 3}, then A ∪ B = {1, 2, 3}. Thus n(A) = 2, n(B) = 2, n(A ∪ B) = 3, but n(A) + n(B) = 2 + 2 = 4 ≠ n(A ∪ B).
4. (a) Yes (b) Yes (c) Yes (d) No, 3 + 5 ∉ V (e) Yes
5. Answers may vary. For example,

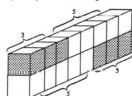

6. (a) x = 119 + 213 (b) 213 = x + 119 (c) 213 = 119 + x
7. (a) Commutative Property of Addition (b) Associative Property of Addition (c) Commutative Property of Addition
8. (a) 3820, 3802, 8023 (b) 2830, 3280, 3208, 3028, 3802, 3082
9. (a) 33, 38, 43 (b) 56, 49, 42
10. (a) 9 (b) 8 (c) 3 (d) 6 or 8 (e) 5 (f) 4 or 8 (g) 9
11. (a) 1 (b) No, because C = 1 (c) 8 or 9 (d) 2
12. 0

13.

8	1	6
3	5	7
4	9	2

(a)

17	10	15
12	14	16
13	18	11

(b)

14.

8	3
4	12

(a)

(b) Examples are not always possible. For example, in the following there are no solutions.

15. (a) Answers may vary. (b) Yes, for example,

1	2
3	5
4	6

,

1	3
2	5
4	6

, or

1	4
2	5
3	6

16. (a) 28 (b) If the domino is lying horizontally and one knows the sum of the dots in the right square plus the sum of the dots in the left square, that sum is the same if the domino were turned 180°.
17. 5 months
18. 45 points
19. (a) 70 (b) 9000 (c) 1100 (d) 560 (e) 3470
20. Depends on the calculator.
21. Depends on the calculator.
22. 26
23. 400
24. (a) Kent is the shortest and Vera is the tallest. (b) Kent 140 cm, Mischa 142 cm, Sally 143 cm, Vera 144 cm

Communication
25. An arrow starting at 0 and ending at 3 represents the same number as an arrow starting at 4 and ending at 7. One way to explain this to students is to make physical models of each and show that the lengths are the same by matching. Students will probabably not understand the difference in free and fixed vectors though teachers should.
26. In this situation, algebraic thinking might mean considering the missing addend as an unknown variable. The addition equation might be thought of as an equation in one unknown.
27. The authors believe that it is important for both students and teachers to know names of properties and their uses. One consideration for students is that if the properties are known, then barely more than one-half of the addition facts must be learned.
28. It is very useful to have students learn more than one method of addition and subtraction if the methods are to generalize to sets of numbers other than whole numbers. The missing addend approach is useful for all sets of numbers in solving subtraction problems. The method of adding-on to compute additions is not effective with sets of fractions or real numbers.
29. Answers may vary. For example, you can do estimations or mental math to tell if a calculator is correct.
30. Answers may vary. For example, students can think of 3 + 9 as 9 + 3 and use "counting on."

Open-ended
31. Colored rods may be used to teach addition to students using a principle of counting-on. Choose the rod representing the largest number and make a train of rods using unit rods until the second number is added. The total train represents the sum.
32. Answers will vary depending upon the calculator.
33. Answers may vary; for example, let A = {a, b}, B = {a, b, c, d}. Then 4 − 2 = n(B − A) = n ({c, d}) = 2.

Cooperative Learning
34. Answers may vary. In order for subtraction to be a function on the set of whole numbers, you must be able to find the difference of every two whole numbers. Otherwise, you will have a pair of numbers in the domain that can be paired with no difference. Hence, the definition of a function will not be met. For example, the difference 3 − 8 cannot be paired with any whole number. In other words, the set of whole numbers would have to be closed under subtraction.
35. The properties may be illustrated with groupings of people. For example, the commutative property may be illustrated by

showing that 2 people plus 3 people is the same as 3 people plus 2 people.

36. Students may use number line models to illustrate how the addition facts for base five may be found. The facts are shown in the table below.

+	0	1	2	3	4
0	0	1	2	3	4
1	1	?	3	4	10
2	2	3	4	10	11
3	3	4	10	11	12
4	4	10	11	12	13

Review Problems

37. (a) CMLIX (b) XXXVIII

38. There are fewer symbols to remember and place value is used.

39. $5 \cdot 10^3 + 2 \cdot 10^2 + 8 \cdot 10^1 + 6 \cdot 1$

Brain Teaser (p. 129)

Answers may vary, for example,

1	2	3
8	9	4
7	6	5

(a)

9	8	7
2	1	6
3	4	5

(b)

ONGOING ASSESSMENT 3-3

1. $35.00

2. (a) 5 (b) 4 (c) Any whole number

3. Each possible pairing of two of the sets is disjoint.

4. To model $2 \cdot 0$, you need to have a set with two elements such as {a, b} and the empty set and make all the ordered pairs in the Cartesian product. Because the empty set has no elements, the Cartesian product has no elements.

5. (a) Yes (b) Yes (c) Yes (d) Yes (e) Yes
(f) No, $2 \cdot 2 = 4$, which does not belong to the set.

6. (a) No, $2 + 3 = 5$ (b) Yes (c) Not closed for either, $2 + 4 = 6$ and $2 \cdot 3 = 6$.

7. (a) $ac + ad + bc + bd$ (b) $3x + 3y + 15$ (c) $\square\triangle + \square\bigcirc$
(d) $x^2 + 2xy + xz + y^2 + yz$

8. (a) $(4 + 3) \times 2 = 14$ (b) $(9 \div 3) + 1 = 4$ (c) $(5 + 4 + 9) \div 3 = 6$ (d) $3 + 6 - 2 \div 1 = 7$ or $(3 + 6 - 2) \div 1 = 7$

9. $a(b + c + d) = a[(b + c) + d] = a(b + c) + ad = ab + ac + ad$

10. (a) 6 (b) 0 (c) 4

11.

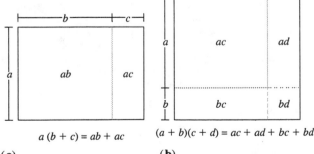

$a(b + c) = ab + ac$

(a)

$(a + b)(c + d) = ac + ad + bc + bd$

(b)

12. (a) $40 = 8 \cdot 5$ (b) $326 = 2 \cdot x$ (c) $48 = x \cdot 16$
(d) $x = 5 \cdot 17$

13. The number is always equal to the original number. It works all the time as seen in the following: Let n be the original number. $(2n + 2)/2 - 1 = 2(n + 1)/2 - 1 = n + 1 - 1 = n$

14. (a) $2 + 1 \neq 1 \div 2$ (b) $(8 \div 4) \div 2 \neq 8 \div (4 \div 2)$
(c) $8 \div (2 + 2) \neq (8 \div 2) + (8 \div 2)$ (d) $3 \div 4 \notin W$

15. $32

16. 2; 3 left

17. (a) (1,36), (2,18), (3,12), (4,9), (6,6), (9,4), (12,3), (18,2), (36,1)
(b)

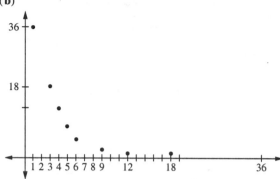

(c) The points in part (b) lie along a curve while the points from the addition lie along a line.

18. A possible answer is given.

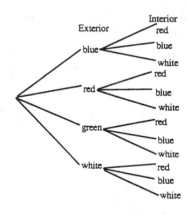

19. 30

20. 12

21. (a) 3 (b) 2 (c) 2 (d) 6 (e) 4

22. The answers depend upon the keys available on your calculator.
(a)

$3 = 1 + 9 - 7$	$12 = 19 - 7$
$4 = 1^7 + \sqrt{9}$	$13 = 91 \div 7$
$5 = 7 - \sqrt{9} + 1$	$14 = 7(\sqrt{9} - 1)$
$6 = 7 - 1^9$	$15 = 7 + 9 - 1$
$7 = 7 + 1^9$	$16 = (7 + 9) \div 1$
$8 = 7 + 1^9$	$17 = 7 + 9 + 1$
$9 = 1^7 \cdot 9$	$18 = \sqrt{9}(7 - 1)$
$10 = 1^7 + 9$	$19 = ?$
$11 = 7 + 1 + \sqrt{9}$	$20 = 7\sqrt{9} - 1$

(b) For example, $4 \cdot 4 - (4 + 4) - (4 + 4) - (4 + 4)$.
(c) For example, $22 + 2$. (d) For example, $111 - 11$.

23. (a) is the solution showing that each adult ticket costs $17 and a student ticket costs $15.

24. (a) Subtract 18 (b) Divide 54 by 9 (c) Add 11 and 48
(d) Add 8

25. This is not the case when $x = 0$.

26. This is the case when x is either 0 or 1.
27. x = 0 or x = 2
28. (a) A/π (b) f/3 (c) 60h (d) d/7

Communication

29. The argument is not true for several reasons. One reason follows: No number divided by 0 is 0. For example, does 1/0 = 0? If this is true, then by the definition of division 0 · 0 = 1, which is false.
30. The distributive property works with two operations. Only one operation is used in this example. Multiplication is not distributive over multiplication. Sue needs to look again at the associative property of multiplication.
31. 0 is not the identity for multiplication because if it were, then any number times 0 must be that number. The result in every case is 0, not the number multiplied by 0.
32. An array is virtually impossible to use to show the multiplication of large numbers. The counting of intersections becomes an impossible chore.
33. This can be done but many students may not believe it. Because the empty set has no elements, the Cartesian product of two empty sets has no elements and thus is empty.
34. Answers may vary here. Most students will consider numerical examples.

Open-ended

35. Mathematicians use the x symbol for a variable. Using it for both multiplication and as a variable causes much confusion.
36. Division is not a binary operation on the set of whole numbers because the set is not closed over division. For example, 3/5 has no solution.
37. A taxi driver charges $5 for entering a cab and $6 per minute for 8 minutes. (The prices here are unrealistic, but this is the type of problem students may suggest.)
38. (a) Yes (b) Yes (c) Yes, a (d) Yes

39. (i) ∩∩∩∩∩∩∩IIIII (ii) LXXV (iii) ▼ ◀▼▼▼▼▼

40. The points of the graph lie along a line.
41. An addition pattern is to find a term; then 5 is added to a previous term. A multiplication pattern is that the sequence is the set of multiples of 5.
42. $3 \cdot 10^4 + 5 \cdot 10^3 + 2 \cdot 10^2 + 0 \cdot 10^1 + 6$
43. For example, {0, 1}
44. No. For example, $5 - 2 \neq 2 - 5$.
45.

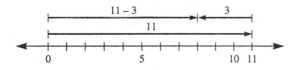

Brain Teaser (p. 139)

Rosalie made $20 on the transaction. The best way for students to understand this problem is to use play money and act the problem out.

Laboratory Activity (p. 139)

1. Yes **2.** 18 **3.** Even **4.** Student conjectures may vary.

Technology Corner (p. 145)

This problem is probably easier to do using trial and error. Students may want to use a spreadsheet to do the additions and multiplications. Writing program to do the work has in the past proven ineffective and very time-consuming. This is an open-ended problem and a definitive answer is not known.

Brain Teaser (p. 151)

The license plate number is 10968.

ONGOING ASSESSMENT 3-4

1. (a) 981 + 421 = 1402
(b) 2025 + 1196 + 3148 = 6369
(c) 1069 + 2094 + 9546 + 9003 + 7064 = 28776
(d) 291 + 451 + 584 = 1326

2. (a) 87693 − 46414 = 41279
(b) 8135 − 4682 = 3453
(c) 383 − 159 = 224
(d) 13296 − 8309 = 4987

3. (a) One possibility: 863 + 752 = 1615
(b) One possibility: 368 + 257 = 625

4. Only if positive numbers are used:
(a) 876 − 235 = 641
(b) 623 − 587 = 36

5. 15,782
6. (a) 34, 39, 44 (b) 82, 79, 76
7. 30¢
8. No, not all at dinner. He can have either the steak or the salad.
9. $124
10. 3428 + 5631 = 9059
11. (a) (i) No, not clustered (ii) Yes, clustered around 500 (b) Answers vary depending upon how each part is done.
12. Too high
13. (a) About 121 weeks (b) About 3 years (c) Answers vary (d) Answers vary
14.

Hawks	15	32	40	33	120
Elks	20	25	47	39	131

15. (a) (i) 1,236 (ii) 1,032 (b) The algorithm works because the placement of partial sums still accounts for place value. It is somewhat easier in the example because only two digits are added at a time. This process would become more confusing or have to be adapted if more than two numbers were added.
16. Answers may vary, for example, (a) No carry (b) Write down a carry, etc. (c) Lesser number is subtracted from the greater (d) Ignored 10's being subtracted.
17. 1 hour 34 minutes 15 seconds
18. (a) 121_{five} (b) 20_{five} (c) 1010_{five} (d) 14_{five} (e) 1001_{two} (f) 1010_{two}
19.

+	0	1	2	3	4	5	6	7
0	0	1	2	3	4	5	6	7
1	1	2	3	4	5	6	7	10
2	2	3	4	5	6	7	10	11
3	3	4	5	6	7	10	11	12
4	4	5	6	7	10	11	12	13
5	5	6	7	10	11	12	13	14
6	6	7	10	11	12	13	14	15
7	7	10	11	12	13	14	15	16

Base eight

•	0	1	2	3	4	5	6	7
0	0	0	0	0	0	0	0	0
1	0	1	2	3	4	5	6	7
2	0	2	4	6	10	12	14	16
3	0	3	6	11	14	17	22	25
4	0	4	10	14	20	24	30	34
5	0	5	12	17	24	31	36	43
6	0	6	14	22	30	36	44	52
7	0	7	16	25	34	43	52	61

Base eight

20. (a) 9 hours 33 minutes 25 seconds (b) 1 hour 39 minutes 40 seconds

21. (a) 2 quarts, 1 pint, 0 cups, or 1 half-gallon, 0 quarts, 1 pint, 0 cups (b) 1 pint, 0 cups (c) 2 quarts, 1 pint, 1 cup

22. $2\frac{1}{2}$, so buy 3 gallons

23. (a) Method produces a palindrome. (b) For example, 89.

24. Answers may vary, for example.

$$
\begin{array}{r}
000 \\
770 \\
000 \\
330 \\
+011 \\
\hline
1111
\end{array}
$$

25. $8 + 8 + 8 + 88 + 888$

26. (a)

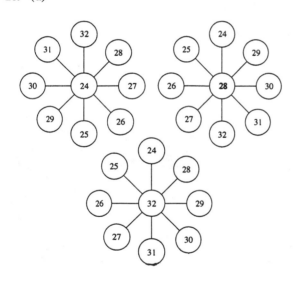

(b) 3

27. It is doubling the second number in the operation

28. (a) 34; 34; 34 (b) 34 (c) 34 (d) Yes (e) Yes

29. (a) $\begin{array}{r} {}^14{}^132 \text{ ten} \\ {}_1\mathcal{9}_4\mathcal{7}_16 \text{ ten} \\ + 141\mathcal{8}_6 \text{ ten} \\ \hline 2826 \end{array}$ (b) $\begin{array}{r} {}^3\mathcal{3}_1 2 \\ 1\mathcal{3}_0 \\ 22 \\ \mathcal{4}_3 3_0 \\ 2_0 3 \\ 1\,2_0 \\ \hline 3\,1\,0_{\text{fives}} \end{array}$

30. (a) 3 gross 10 dozen 9 ones (b) 6 gross 3 dozen 4 ones

31. (a) 22 students on Tuesday (b) 1 gal, 1 half-gal, 1 qt, 1 pint, and 1 cup

32. (a) 70 (b) 87

33. There is no numeral 5 in base five; $2_{\text{five}} + 3_{\text{five}} = 10_{\text{five}}$.

34. (a) $\begin{array}{r} 230_{\text{five}} \\ -22_{\text{five}} \\ \hline 203_{\text{five}} \end{array}$ (b) $\begin{array}{r} 20010_{\text{three}} \\ -2022_{\text{three}} \\ \hline 10211_{\text{three}} \end{array}$

Communication
35. Yes, the front-end estimate only considers the value of the leading digit to estimate the sum.

36. The "scratch marks" represent the normal "carries."

37. The columns separate place value and show that $7 + 8 = 15$ and $20 + 60 = 80$. Finally, $15 + 80 = 95$.

38. Answers may vary. For example, the diagram shows that an exact answer can be found by paper-and-pencil, calculator, or computer. In each case estimation is recommended.

39. The numbers in the quotation deal with the number of people slain in a battle. Of the 10,000 killed, there were 126 princes and nobles carrying banners, 8,400 knights, esquires, and gentlemen (including 500 recent knights), and 1600 mercenaries. The quotation is not mathematically meaningful if interpreted as here because the sum is 10,126.

Open-ended
40. Examples include the number of people in a state, the amount of the national debt, and the number of hairs on a head.

41. Answers will vary. A different version of this algorithm is seen below:

42. Students are encouraged to use the bibliographies at the end of the chapters to seek mathematics education research to answer this question.

Cooperative Learning
43. The US monetary system is not a true base ten system because of the coins and bills involved. A true base ten system would have only pennies, dimes, dollars, ten dollars, 100 dollars, etc. The system would not have nickels, quarters, half dollars, five-dollar bills, etc.

Review Problems
44. This will be studied in detail in later chapters. However with the meter as a basic unit of length, we have 10 meters = 1 decameter, 10 decameters = 1 hectometer, 10 hectometers = 1 kilometer.

45. $5280 = 5 \cdot 10^3 + 2 \cdot 10^2 + 8 \cdot 10 + 0 \cdot 1$

46. For example, $2 + (3 + 4) = (2 + 3) + 4$
$$2 + 7 = 5 + 4$$
$$9 = 9$$

47.

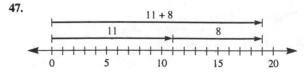

48. 1,000,410

49. (a) $a(x + 1)$ (b) $(3 + a)(x + y)$

50. 15

Laboratory Activity (p. 155)
Either abacus may be used. Both are comparable. Some may prefer the suan pan because there are two counters above the bar and five below the bar.

ONGOING ASSESSMENT 3-5

1.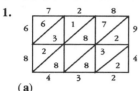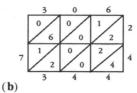

(a)   (b)

2. Diagonals separate place value as placement does in the traditional algorithm.

3. (a)
```
      426
   ×  783
     1278
     3408
     2982
   333558
```
(b)
```
      327
   ×  941
      327
     1308
     2943
   307707
```

4. Answers may vary. (c) 43,000,000,000 L/day
5. (a) 5^{19} (b) 6^{15} (c) 10^{313} (d) 10^{12}
6. (a) 2^{100} (b) 2^{102}

7.

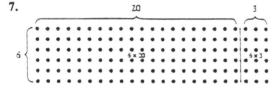

(a)
```
      23
   ×   6
      18  (6 × 3)
     120  (6 × 20)
     138
```

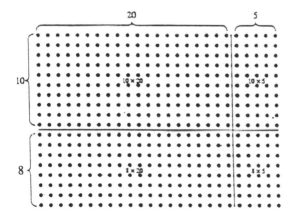

b)
```
      25
   ×  18
      40  (8 × 5)
     160  (8 × 20)
      50  (10 × 5)
     200  (10 × 20)
     450
```

8. (a) 293 · 476 = 139,468 (b) Placement still indicates place value. (c)
```
      363
   ×   84
     1452
     2904
    30492
```

9. →17 × 63   63
      8   126   + 1008
      2   504   1071
   →1 1008

10. (a) 21 (b) 355 (c) 304 (d) 164
11. (a) 22 (b) 190 (c) 7 (d) 39
12. (a) 15 · (10 + 2) = 150 + 30 = 180 (b) 14 · (100 + 2) = 1400 + 28 = 1428 (c) 30 · 99 = 30(100 −1) = 3000 − 30 = 2970

13.
a	b	a · b	a + b
67	56	3752	123
32	78	2496	110
15	18	270	33

14. (a) 1332 (b) Jane, 330 more calories (c) Maurice, 96 more calories
15. No, only 2352 calories, so he gained less than 1 lb.
16. $60
17. (a) 77 remainder 7 (b) 8 remainder 10 (c) 10 remainder 91
18. (a) $3\overline{)876}$ (b) $8\overline{)367}$
19. (a) Monthly payments are more expensive. (b) $3,700
20. 65,536 bits
21. 3
22. 8 cars (remember the match)
23.
2	11
4	15
0	7
6	19
12	31

24. (i) Yes, suppose the 3 numbers are a, b, and c. The 6 different numbers are

      ab
      ac
      bc
      ba
      cb
   +ca. The sum is 2(a + b + c) 10 + 2(a + b + c) = (a + b + c) · 22. Now if we divide by (a + b + c), we always obtain 22.

25. (a) Answers vary, for example, 12 42. (b) (10a + b) · (10c + d) = (10b + a) (10d + c) implies 100ac + 10bc + 10ad + bd = 100bd + 10ad + 10bc + ac or 99ac = 99bd, which implies that ac = bd.
26. 3 hrs
27. Her estimate is high, discussions vary.
28. Answers vary. For example, (a) Digits are not carried; place
34. (a) 233_{five} (b) 4_{five} R 1_{five} (c) 2144_{five} (d) 31_{five} (e) 67_{eight} (f) 15_{eight} R 3_{eight} (g) 110_{two} (h) 1101110_{two}
value is not observed. (b) 5 was multiplied by 6 to get 30; the 3 was carried, but then 3 was multiplied by 2 instead of by 6 again. (c) 4 was multiplied by 6 but then 6 and 3 were added instead of being multiplied. (d) When 1 was brought down, the quotient of 0 was not recorded.
29. 21 weeks
30. 58 buses needed, not all full
31. 11 km/L
32. Answers vary. For example, if the number is 10a + b, the product is 1000a + 100b + 10a + b.
33. (a) (i) $70 (ii) $10 (b) On the 12th trip
35. (a) Nine (b) Four (c) Six (d) Any base greater than or equal to 2.
36. (a) 30221_{five} (b) a = 3; b = 4
37. (a)
```
      763
   ×   8
     6104
```
(b)
```
      678
   ×   3
     2034
```

38. (a)
$$762 \times 83 = 63{,}246$$
(b)
$$378 \times 26 = 9828$$

39. 7,500,000 cows

40. (a)
$$37 \times 43$$
111
1480
1591

(b)
$$93 \times 36$$
558
2790
3348

(c) $9\overline{)123}$ = 13, $\dfrac{-9}{33}$ $\dfrac{-27}{6}$

41. (a) 1; 121; 12,321; 1,234,321 (b) 9801, 998001, 99980001 (c) The pattern continues only through 111,111,111,111,111,111

42. $60; $3600; $86,400; $604,800, $2,592,000 (30 days); $31,536,000 (365 days); $630,720,000 or $631,152,000 (with leap years)

43. 19

44. (a) (i) $27 \cdot 198 = 5346$ (ii) $48 \cdot 159 = 7632$ (iii) $39 \cdot 186 = 7254$ (b) (i) $1963 \cdot 4 = 7852$ (ii) $483 \cdot 12 = 5796$ (iii) $297 \cdot 18 = 5346$ (c) 1

Communication

45. The operations may be accomplished in the same manner. The facts are different.

46. Base sixteen, or the hexadecimal system has sixteen symbols, while the base ten system has only ten. The hexadecimal system has uses in computer science because of its relationship to base two.

47. The recommendation should be to try and complete a proof that the algorithm would work on a general set of numbers. If the student does not have the capacity to complete that task, one method of trial and error to use is to try a great number of cases. This is not a proof and that should be emphasized, but it might produce a counterexample.

48. The result is always 4. Let the original number be x. The operation appears as follows:
$$[(2x)3 + 24]/6 - x = 4$$

Open-ended

49. Answers will vary depending upon student choice. Many students may favor the lattice multiplication algorithm because only single digits are multiplied and addition is accomplished later.

50. A research design may be tested with two groups of comparable abilities tested with one group using the traditional algorithm and the other group using the lattice multiplication algorithm. The results of the tests may be compared using analysis of variance.

51. Answers will vary depending upon student opinion. You may want to suggest that students read the list of topics with decreased emphasis in the *Standards*.

Cooperative Learning

52. The sliding rulers work much in the same way that arrows are used with a number line to show addition.

Review Problems

53. 999999∩∩∩∩∩∩∩IIII

54. 300,260

55. For example, $3 + 0 = 3 = 0 + 3$.

56. (a) $x - (a + b + 2)$ (b) $(3 + x)(a + b)$

57. 6979 miles

58. 724

Brain Teaser (p. 168)

(a)
$$570{,}140 \times 6 = 3{,}420{,}840$$
(b)
$$38 \times 6 \quad \dfrac{38}{+38}{114}$$
or
$$39 \quad \dfrac{39}{+39}{117}$$

Laboratory Activity (p. 168)

1. (a) A computer

2. (a) When a person tells his or her age by listing cards, the person is giving the base two representation for his or her age. The number can then be determined by adding the numbers in the upper left-hand corners of the named cards.

Chapter Review

1. (a) 400,044 (b) 117 (c) 1704 (d) 11 (e) 1448

2. (a) CMXCIX (b) ꟿꟿꟿ|||||| (c) $\overset{\bullet}{\cdots}$ (d) 2341_{five} (e) 11011_{two}

3. (a) 3^{17} (b) 2^{21} (c) 3^5 (d) 2^{82}

4. (a) Distributive Property for Multiplication over Addition (b) Commutative Property of Addition (c) Identity Property for Multiplication (d) Distributive Property for Multiplication over Addition (e) Commutative Property for Multiplication (f) Associative Property of Multiplication

5. (a) $3 < 13$, because $3 + 10 = 13$ (b) $12 > 9$, because $12 = 9 + 3$

6.
$$\begin{aligned}1000 \cdot 483 &= 10^3 (4 \cdot 10^2 + 8 \cdot 10 + 3) \\ &= 4 \cdot 10^5 + 8 \cdot 10^4 + 3 \cdot 10^3 \\ &= 4 \cdot 10^5 + 8 \cdot 10^4 + 3 \cdot 10^3 + 0 \cdot 10^2 \\ &\quad + 0 \cdot 10^1 + 0 \cdot 1 \\ &= 483{,}000\end{aligned}$$

7. 1119

8. 60,074

9. (a) 5 remainder 243 (b) 91 remainder 10 (c) 120_{five} remainder 2_{five} (d) 11_{two} remainder 10_{two}

10. (a) $5 \cdot 912 + 243 = 4803$ (b) $91 \cdot 11 + 10 = 1011$ (c) $23_{\text{five}} \cdot 120_{\text{five}} + 2_{\text{five}} = 3312_{\text{five}}$ (d) $11_{\text{two}} \cdot 11_{\text{two}} + 10_{\text{two}} = 1011_{\text{two}}$

11. (a) tens (b) thousands (c) hundreds

12. (a) 10, 11, 12, 13, 14, 15 (b) 10 (c) All whole numbers (d) 0, 1, 2, ..., 26

13. (a) 15a (b) $5x^2$ (c) $xa + xb + xy$ (d) $(x + 5)(3 + y)$

14. (a) 1 (b) 6 (c) 9

15. $395

16. $4380

17. 2600

18. $3842

19. 40 cans

20. 12 outfits

21. 26

22. $2.16

23. $6000

24. There are 36 bikes and 18 trikes.

25. $214

26. $400

27. Answers will vary with student preferences.

28. Selling pencils by the units, dozens and gross is an example of the use of base 12.

29. Answers will vary.

30. If one computed on the calculator as follows, the units addition could be accomplished (7 + 5) INT 8 = ; the result should be 1 with a remainder of 4. By "carrying the 1" and computing as follows, the eights addition could be accomplished 189 (1 + 2 + 6) INT 8 = yielding 1 with a remainder of 1. Thus the sum is 114_{eight}.

CHAPTER 4

ONGOING ASSESSMENT 4-1

1. (a) ⁻2 (b) 5 (c) ⁻m (d) 0 (e) m (f) ⁻a + ⁻b or ⁻(a + b)
2. (a) 2 (b) m (c) 0
3. (a) 5 (b) 10 (c) ⁻5 (d) ⁻5
4. (a)

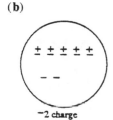

+5 charge   Add 3 negative charges; net result 2 positive charges

(b)

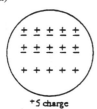

⁻2 charge   Add 3 positive charges; net result 1 positive charge

(c)

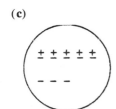

⁻3 charge on the field   Add 2 positive charges; net result 1 negative charge

(d)

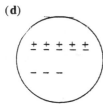

⁻3 charge on the field   Add 2 negative charges; net result 5 negative charges

5. Black chips represent positive numbers; blank chips represent negative numbers.
   (a)

Net result: 2 positive chips

   (b)

Net result: 1 positive chip

(c)

Net result: 1 negative chip

(d)

Net result: 5 negative chips

6. (a)

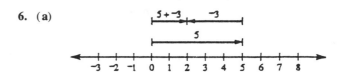

(b)

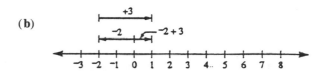

(c)

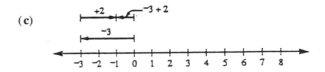

(d)

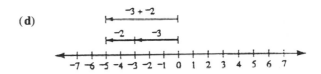

7. (a) ⁻7 (b) ⁻2°C (c) 4900 feet (d) ⁻$150 (e) ⁻3
8. (a) (⁻45) + (⁻55) + (⁻165) + (⁻35) + (⁻100) + 75 + 25 + 400
   (b) $400
9. (a)

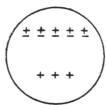 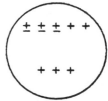

3 charge on field   Take away 2 negative charges; net result 5 positive charges on the field

(b)

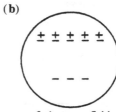 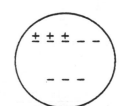

⁻3 charge on field   Take away 2 positive charges; net result 5 negative charges on the field

(c)

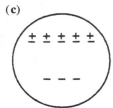
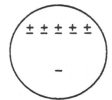

⁻3 charge on field

Take away 2 negative charges; net
result 1 negative charge on the field

10. (a)

(b)

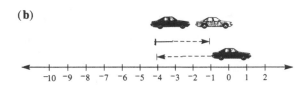

11. **(a)** ⁻4 − 2 = ⁻6; ⁻4 − 1 = ⁻5; ⁻4 − 0 = ⁻4; ⁻4 − ⁻1 = ⁻3
(b) 3 − 1 = 2; 2 − 1 = 1; 1 − 1 = 0; 0 − 1 = ⁻1; ⁻1 − 1 = ⁻2;
⁻2 − 1 = ⁻3
12. **(a)** ⁻1 **(b)** 1 **(c)** 3
13. **(a)** ⁻9 **(b)** 3 **(c)** 1 **(d)** ⁻19 **(e)** ⁻13 **(f)** ⁻6
14. **(a)** (i) 55 − 60 (ii) 55 + (⁻60) (iii) ⁻5 **(b)** (i) 200 − 220
(ii) 200 + (⁻220) (iii) ⁻20
15. 33 points
16. **(a)** 59 **(b)** ⁻269°C **(c)** 192°F
17. 2
18. 4 pounds
19. **(a)** 10W − 40 or 10W − 30 **(b)** 5W − 30 **(c)** 10W − 40,
5W − 30 or 10W − 30 **(d)** none **(e)** 10W − 30 or 10W − 40
20. **(a)** 1 + 4x **(b)** 2x + y **(c)** x − 2
21. **(a)** All negative integers **(b)** All positive integers **(c)** All
integers less than ⁻1 **(d)** 2 or ⁻2 **(e)** There are none. **(f)** All
integers except 0 **(g)** There are none.
22. 784 BC (there is no year 0)
23. **(a)** I **(b)** W **(c)** I − {0} **(d)** ∅ **(e)** ∅ **(f)** ⁻I **(g)** {0}
(h) W **(i)** I

24.

2	⁻13	8
5	⁻1	⁻7
⁻10	11	⁻4

Other answers are possible.

25.

	3	5	
7	1	8	2
	4	6	

Other answers are possible.

26. **(a)** 0 **(b)** ⁻101 **(c)** 1 **(d)** ⁻4
27. **(a)** 9 **(b)** 2 **(c)** 0 or 2 **(d)** The set of all integers greater
than or equal to 0
28. **(a)** All nonnegative integers **(b)** (i) 5 (ii) 5 (iii) 0 (iv) ⁻7
29. **(a)** 89 **(b)** 19 **(c)** 19 **(d)** y − x − 1 or y − (x + 1)
30. Greatest possible value: a − (b − c) − d, or 8. Least possible
value: a − b − (c − d), or ⁻6
31. **(a)** ⁻3; ...; ⁻12, ⁻15, ... **(b)** ⁻4; ...; ⁻9, ⁻13, ... **(c)** ⁻y; ...,
x − 2y, x − 3y ... **(d)** 2x; ..., 1 + 3x, 1 + 5x, ...
32. **(a)** 0 **(b)** 3775 **(c)** 2538
33. b − a = b + (⁻a) = ⁻a + b = ⁻a − (⁻b) = ⁻(a − b)

34. **(a)** True **(b)** True **(c)** True **(d)** True **(e)** False;
let x = ⁻1 **(f)** True
35. The smaller gear rotates 28 times in the opposite direction
of the larger gear.
36. **(a)** ⁻14 **(b)** ⁻24 **(c)** 2 **(d)** 5
37. **(a)** ⁻18 **(b)** ⁻106 **(c)** ⁻6 **(d)** 22 **(e)** ⁻11 **(f)** 2
(g) ⁻18 **(h)** 23
38. **(a)** ⁻101 **(b)** 516 **(c)** 10,894 **(d)** 5,995

Communication
39. Answers vary, for example, suppose Alice was figuring how
much money she spent yesterday. She had one bill for $50,
another bill for $85 arrived in the mail, and then she returned
some books for a $30 credit.
40. Answers vary, for example, some students might mention a
new vehicle that can go under water as well as fly. They could
use integers to describe the height or depth of the vehicle.
Integers could be modeled on a vertical number line. Students
might be interested in this type of model because they see
these types of things in movies and video games.
41. He could have driven 12 mi in either direction from
milepost 68. Therefore his location could either be at the
68 − 12 = 56 milepost or at the 68 + 12 = 80 milepost.
42. **(a)** (a + b) + (⁻a + ⁻b) = a + b + ⁻a + ⁻b = a + ⁻a
+ b + ⁻b = (a + ⁻a) + (b + ⁻b) = 0 + 0 = 0 **(b)** From part (a),
⁻a + ⁻b is a solution of the equation (a + b) + x = 0. Because
⁻(a + b) is the unique solution of this equation, we must have
⁻a + ⁻b = ⁻(a + b).
43. One way is to find the difference of the greater absolute
value and the lesser absolute value. The sum has the same sign
as the integer with the greater absolute value.

Open-ended
44. Answers vary, for example, the floors above ground could
be numbered as usual 1, 2, 3, 4, ..., n, the zero or ground floor
could be called G, and the floors below ground could be called
1B, 2B, 3B, 4B, ..., nB. The system could be modeled on a
vertical number line with G replacing 0, and 1B, 2B, 3B, ... ,
nB replacing the negative integers. We could have
computations like 3 + G = 3, or 5B + 3B = 8B.
45. Answers vary, for example, some people like the number line
model because each number is represented and there is
a carry-over to vectors. Others might like the colored chip
model because they can see that every number plus its additive
inverse is 0.
46. Answers will vary depending on the grade level and the
publisher chosen.

Cooperative Learning
47. Answers vary, for example, each student could carry either
a black or red disk to indicate that he/she is positive or
negative. When two students of different colors meet, they
become a neutral pair and have value 0. The answer is
determined by those who cannot find a partner.

Technology Corner (p. 179)
The entries in column A stay 4 while the entries in column B
start with 3 and decrease by 1. The sum of columns A and B is
entered in column C starting with 7. The entries in column C
are the integers in decreasing order starting with 7. The
patterns show that the sum of two positive numbers is positive.
The sum of a positive and a negative number is positive if the
absolute value of the positive number is greater than the
absolute value of the negative number. The sum is 0 if both
numbers have the same absolute value. The sum is negative
otherwise. Similar results can be obtained if column A is
changed to ⁻4.

Technology Corner (p. 186)

(a) The graph should appear as shown below.

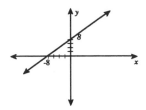

(b) When x is less than ⁻4, the y-values are negative; when x = ⁻4, y = 0; when x is greater than ⁻4, the y-values are positive.

Technology Corner (p. 189)

If the Logo program is run, the following outputs are obtained.
(a) 7 (b) 0 (c) 140 (d) 21

Brain Teaser (p. 189)

$123 - 45 - 67 + 89 = 100$

ONGOING ASSESSMENT 4-2

1. $3(^-1) = ^-3; 2(^-1) = ^-2; 1(^-1) = ^-1; 0(^-1) = 0; (^-1)(^-1) = 1$, by continuing the pattern.

2.

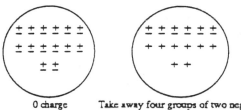

0 charge   Take away four groups of two negative
               charges; net result is eight positive charges.

3. If you are now at 0 moving west at 4 km/h, you will be at 8 km west of 0 two hours from now.

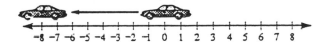

4. (a) ⁻20 · 4 (b) 20 · 4 (c) ⁻20n (d) 20n
5. (a) 5 (b) ⁻13 (c) ⁻11 (d) 0 (e) Impossible; division by 0 is not defined. (f) Impossible; division by 0 is not defined.
6. (a) ⁻10 (b) ⁻40 (c) a; if a/b is defined (d) ⁻10
(e) a; If b ≠ 0 (f) ⁻32 (g) ⁻5 (h) 0 (i) Impossible (j) ⁻4
(k) Impossible (l) 13 (m) ⁻1 (n) ⁻2
7. (a) 32°C − 30 · (3°C) (b) 0°C + 25·(4°C) (c) ⁻ 20 °C + 30 · (4°C) (d) 25°C − 20 ·(3°C) (e) 0°C + m · (d°C)
(f) 20°C − m · (d°C)
8. (a) 4(⁻11) = ⁻44 (b) ⁻66 divided by 11 = ⁻6; He lost 6 yards per play.
9. 7(⁻12,000), i.e., a loss of 84,000 acres
10. (a) ⁻1(⁻5 + ⁻2) = ⁻1(⁻7) = 7; (⁻1)(⁻5) + (⁻1)(⁻2) = 5 + 2 = 7
(b) ⁻3(⁻3 + 2) = ⁻3(⁻1) = 3; (⁻3)(⁻3) + (⁻3)(2) = 9 + ⁻6 = 3
(c) ⁻5(2 + ⁻6) = ⁻5(⁻4) = 20; (⁻5)(2) + (⁻5)(⁻6) = ⁻10 + 30 = 20
11. (a) ⁻8 (b) 16 (c) ⁻1000 (d) 81 (e) 1 (f) ⁻1 (g) 1 (h) ⁻1
12. (a) 12 (b) 0 (c) ⁻5 (d) 19 (e) 9 (f) ⁻9 (g) ⁻13 (h) ⁻8
(i) ⁻32 (j) ⁻16
13. (b), (c), (g), (h) are always positive; (a), (f) are always negative

14. (b) = (c); (d) = (e); (g) = (h)
15. (a) Commutative Property of Multiplication (b) Closure Property of Addition (c) Associative Property of Multiplication (d) Distributive Property of Multiplication over Addition
16. (a) xy (b) 2xy (c) 0 (d) ⁻x (e) x + 2y (f) b (g) x (h) y
17. (a) ⁻2 (b) 2 (c) 0 (d) ⁻6 (e) ⁻36 (f) 6 (g) All integers except 0 (h) All integers except 0 (i) No solution is possible (j) 3 or ⁻3 (k) No solution is possible (l) All integers except 0 (m) All integers except 0 (n) All integers (o) All integers
18. (a) ⁻2x + 2 (b) ⁻2x + 2y (c) $x^2 - xy$ (d) ⁻$x^2 + xy$
(e) ⁻2x − 2y + 2z (f) ⁻$x^2 + xy + 3x$ (g) ⁻25 − 10x − x^2
(h) $x^2 - y^2 - 1 - 2y$ (i) ⁻$x^4 + 3x^2 - 2$
19. (a) $(50 + 2)(50 - 2) = 50^2 - 2^2 = 2500 - 4 = 2496$
(b) 25 − 10,000 = ⁻9975 (c) $x^2 - y^2$ (d) $4 - 9x^2$
(e) $x^2 - 1$ (f) $(213 + 13)(213 - 13) = 226 · 200 = 45,200$
20. (a) 8x (b) (a + 2)x (c) x(y + 1) (d) (a − 2)x
(e) x(x + y) (f) 6x (g) x(3y + 2 − z) (h) x(3x + y − 1)
(i) a(b(c + 1) − 1) (j) (a + b)c (k) (4 + a)(4 − a)
(l) (x + 3y)(x − 3y) (m) (2x + 5y)(2x − 5y)
(n) (x + y)(x − y) + x + y = (x + y)(x − y + 1)
21. (a) $(a - b)^2 = a^2 + 2ab + b^2$ (b) (i) $98^2 = (100 - 2)^2 = 100^2 - 2(200) + 2^2 = 10,000 - 400 + 4 = 9604$ (ii) $99^2 = (100 - 1)^2 = 100^2 - 2(100) + 1^2 = 10,000 - 200 + 1 = 9801$
(iii) $997^2 = (100 - 3)^2 = 1000^2 - 2(3000) + 3^2 = 1,000,000 - 6000 + 9 = 994,009$
22. (a) False (b) True (c) True (d) True
23. (a) The sums are 9 times the middle number. (b) Let a be the middle number. Then we have the following 9 numbers:

a − 8	a − 7	a − 6
a − 1	a	a + 1
a + 6	a + 7	a + 8

The sum of these numbers is 9a, which is 9 times the middle number.
24. (a) 8, 11, d = 3, nth term is 3n − 13 (b) ⁻8, ⁻11, d = ⁻3, nth term is ⁻3n + 13 (c) ⁻128, ⁻256, r = 2, nth term ⁻(2)ⁿ
(d) ⁻128, 256, r = ⁻2, nth term is (⁻2)ⁿ (e) $2^7, ⁻2^8$, r = ⁻2, nth term is 2 · (⁻2)ⁿ⁻¹ or ⁻(⁻2)ⁿ
25. (a) 13,850 (b) ⁻13,850
26. (a) ⁻9, ⁻6, ⁻1, 6, 15 (b) ⁻2, ⁻7, ⁻12, ⁻17, ⁻22 (c) ⁻3, 3, ⁻9, 15, ⁻33 (d) 0, 8, 0, 32, 0 (e) ⁻1, 4, ⁻9, 16, ⁻25 (f) 2, ⁻8, 24, ⁻64, 160 (g) 9, 8, 7, 6, 5 (h) 0, 8, 0, 32, 0
27. 7, 2
28. (a) (⁻a)b + ab = (⁻a + a)b = 0b = 0, so (⁻a)b = ⁻(ab)
(b) (⁻a)(⁻b) + ⁻(ab) = (⁻a)(⁻b) + (⁻a)b = (⁻a)(⁻b + b) = (⁻a)0 = 0, so (⁻a)(⁻b) = ⁻(⁻(ab)) = ab
29. (a) ⁻81 (b) 184 (c) ⁻2 (d) 2

Communication

30. No; it is not of the form (a − b)(a + b)
31. $a^2 + 2a(^-b) + (^-b)^2$
$= a^2 + (^-2ab) + (^-b)^2$ since 2a(⁻b) = ⁻2ab
$= a^2 - 2ab + (^-b)^2$
$= a^2 - 2ab + b^2$ since (⁻b)² = b²
32. (⁻1)a + a = (⁻1)a + (1)a = (⁻1 + 1)a = 0a = 0, so (⁻1)a = ⁻a
Now: (⁻a)b = [(⁻1)a]b
       = ⁻1(ab)   by the Associative Property of Multiplication
       = ⁻(ab)   by first part
33. ⁻(a + b) = (⁻1)(a + b)   by first part of problem 32
       = (⁻1)a + (⁻1)b   by Distributive Property
       = ⁻a + ⁻b   by first part of problem 33
34. Answers vary, for example, a student might reason that the 0 represents the border between the BC dates and the AD dates. The numbers that are negative represent years that are BC, for example, ⁻1000 represents 1000 BC while 2000 represents AD 2000.

Open-ended

35. Answers vary. For example, if someone has $100 and owes someone $200, there is no way to record $100 - 200$. Also, if someone has 13 cookies to divide among six children, then there is no way to indicate that each child would receive $2\frac{1}{6}$ cookies.

36. Answers vary, for example, if the student only answered one problem and missed it, he/she would score $^-1$. If the student answered five correct and missed more than 20, he/she would receive a negative score. Any coordinate falling above the line $4x - y = 0$ would result in a negative score where x is the number correct and y is the number incorrect.

37. Answers vary.

38. Answers vary depending on grade level and publisher selected.

Cooperative Learning

39. (a) Answers vary. For example, use negative quality points for an F. We could use 3 for A, 2 for B, 1 for C, 0 for D, and $^-1$ for F.

Review Problems

40.

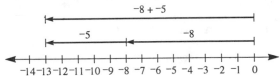

41. (a) 5 (b) $^-7$ (c) 0

42. (a) 14 (b) 21 (c) $^-4$ (d) 22

43. 400 lbs

Brain Teaser (p. 196)

Answers may vary. $1 = 4^4/4^4$; $2 = (4 \cdot 4)/(4 + 4)$; $3 = 4 - (4/4)^4$; $4 = [(4 - 4)/4] + 4$; $5 = 4 + 4^{(4 - 4)}$; $6 = 4 + [(4 + 4)/4]$; $7 = (44/4) - 4$; $8 (4 \cdot 4)/(4+)$; $9 = 4 + 4 + 4/4$; $10 = (44 - 4)/4$

Brain Teaser (p. 199)

0 because $(x - x) = 0$

Technology Corner (p. 196)

The entries in columns A and B are the same and are the integers less than or equal to 5 in decreasing order. The entries in column C form the sequence of square numbers 25, 16, 9, 4, 1, 0, 1, 4, 9, ...

ONGOING ASSESSMENT 4-3

1. (a) True (b) True (c) True (d) True (e) True (f) False, 6 is a factor of 30 not a multiple of 30.

2. (a) Yes (b) No (c) Yes (d) No (e) Yes

3. (a) 2, 3, 4, 6, 11 (b) 2, 3, 6, 9 (c) 2, 3, 5, 6, 10 (d) 2, 4 (e) 11 (f) none of them

4. (a) No, $17 \mid 34000$ and $17 \nmid 15$, so $17 \nmid 34,015$. (b) Yes, $17 \mid 34000$ and $17 \mid 51$, so $17 \mid 34,051$. (c) No, $19 \mid 19000$ and $19 \nmid 31$, so $19 \nmid 19,031$. (d) Yes, 5 is factor of $2 \cdot 3 \cdot 5 \cdot 7$. (e) No, $5 \mid 2 \cdot 3 \cdot 5 \cdot 7$ and $5 \nmid 1$, so $5 \nmid (2 \cdot 3 \cdot 5 \cdot 7) + 1$.

5. (a) True by Theorem 4–1 (b) True by Theorem 4–2(b) (c) None (d) True by Theorem 4–2(b) (e) True by Theorem 4–1

6. (a) True (b) False (c) False (d) True (e) True (f) False (g) True

7. (a) Always (b) Sometimes (c) Never (d) Always (e) Always (f) Sometimes (g) Always

8. (a) A number is divisible by 16 if and only if the last four digits form a number divisible by 16. (b) A number is divisible by 25 if and only if the number formed by the last two digits is divisible by 25.

9. 85,041

10. (a) 7 (b) 7 (c) 6

11. (a) Any digit $0 - 9$ (b) 1, 4, 7 (c) 1, 3, 5, 7, 9 (d) 7 (e) 7

12. 17

13. Each bar costs 19¢.

14. (a) Yes (b) No (c) Yes (d) Yes

15. (a) 1, 2, 4, 5, 8, 11 (b) 4 TD's with extra points and 4 field goals or 1 TD and 11 field goals (c) 5 field goals

16.

(a)	4	4	4
(b)	8	8	8
(c)	3	12	3
(d)	8	26	8
(e)	2	20	2

(f) The remainder when n is divided by 9 is equal to the remainder when the sum of the digits of n is divided by nine.

17. (a) $12,343 + 4546 + 56; = 16,945; 4 + 1 + 2 = 7$

(b) $987 + 456 + 8765 = 10,208; 6 + 6 + 8 = 20$ has a remainder of 2 when divided by 9, as does $1 + 0 + 2 + 0 + 8 = 11$.

(c) $10,034 + 3004 + 400 + 20 = 13,458; 8 + 7 + 4 + 2 = 21$ has a remainder 3 when divided by 9, as does $1 + 3 + 4 + 5 + 8$.

(d) Answers vary.

(e) $1003 - 46 = 957; 4 - 1 = 3$ has a remainder of 3 when divided by 9, as does $9 + 5 + 7 = 21$.

(f) $345 \cdot 56 = 19,320.$ 345 has a remainder of 3 when divided by 9; 56 has a remainder of 2 when divided by 9; $3 \cdot 2 = 6$ as does $345 \cdot 56 = 19,320$ when divided by 9.

(g) Answers vary.

18. (a) False; $2 \mid 4$, but $2 \nmid 1$ and $2 \nmid 3$ (b) False (same example as in 18 (a)) (c) False; $12 \mid 72$ but $12 \nmid 8$ and $12 \nmid 9$ (d) True (e) True (f) True (g) False; If $a = 5$ and $b = ^-5$, then $a \mid b$ and $b \mid a$, but $a \neq b$. (h) True (i) False; $2 \nmid 3$ and $2 \nmid 9$ but $2 \mid (3 + 9)$ (j) False; $50 \mid 10^2$, but $50 \nmid 10$ (k) False; $50 \nmid 10$, but $50 \mid 100$ (l) True

19. Prove the following theorem. For any integers a, b, and c, with $a \neq 0$ and $b \neq 0$. If $a \mid b$ and $b \mid c$, then $a \mid c$.

If $a \mid b$, there exists an integer m such that $ma = b$.

If $b \mid c$, there exists an integer n such that $nb = c$.

Using substitution, $n(ma) = c$.

Using the associative property of multiplication,

$(nm)a = c$. Because m and n are integers, nm is an integer and $a \mid c$.

20. Suppose that $d \mid a$, $d \nmid b$, and $d \mid (a + b) \cdot d \mid a$ implies that there exists an integer c such that $cd = a$. $d \mid (a + b)$ implies that there exists an integer e such that $ed = a + b$

Using substitution: $ed = cd + b$

$ed - cd = b$

$(e - c)d = b$ which implies $d \mid b$. This contradicts the assumption that $d \nmid b$.

Therefore $d \nmid (a + b)$.

21. Let $n = a \cdot 10^4 + b \cdot 10^3 + c \cdot 10^2 + d \cdot 10 + e$

$a \cdot 10^4 = a \cdot (10,000) = a \cdot (9999 + 1) = a \cdot 9999 + a$

$b \cdot 10^3 = b \cdot (1000) = b \cdot (999 + 1) = b \cdot 999 + b$

$c \cdot 10^2 = c \cdot (100) = c \cdot (99 + 1) = c \cdot 99 + c$

$d \cdot 10 = d \cdot (10) = d \cdot (9 + 1) = d \cdot 9 + d$

Thus, $n = (a \cdot 9999 + b \cdot 999 + c \cdot 99 + d \cdot 9) + (a + b + c + d + e)$. Because $9 \mid 9, 9 \mid 99, 9 \mid 999, 9 \mid 9999$, it follows that $9 \mid [(a \cdot 9999 + b \cdot 999 + c \cdot 99 + d \cdot 9) + (a + b + c + d + e)]$; that is, $9 \mid n$. If, on the other hand, $9 \nmid (a + b + c + d + e)$, it follows that $9 \nmid n$.

22. (**a**) The result is always 9. (**b**) The result is always 18. (**c**) Let the number be $a \cdot 10 + b$. The number with the digits reversed is $b \cdot 10 + a$.

Now, $a \cdot 10 + b - (b \cdot 10 + a) = a \cdot 10 + b - b \cdot 10 - a$

$= a \cdot 10 - a + b - b \cdot 10$

$= 9a - 9b$

$= 9(a - b)$

Thus, the difference is a multiple of 9.
(**d**) The result is a multiple of 9.

23. 6,868,395 is divisible by 15 because it is divisible by both 3 and 5. The last digit is 5 and the sum of the digits is 45 which is divisible by 3.

Communication

24. No, in order for the 6¢ and 15¢ stamps to be used for the exact postage, 286 must be divisible by 6 or by 15 or both. Both 6 and 15 are multiples of 3 and 286 is not divisible by 3, so 286 is not divisible by either 6 or 15.

25. (**a**) Yes, $d \mid n$ because a display of 32 implies that $n = 32 \cdot d$ and this implies that $d \mid n$. (**b**) No, $d \nmid n$ because the display implies that n is not a multiple of d. If the display was 16, then $d \mid n$.

26. Answers vary, for example, some people might choose 2, 5, or 10 because all they have to do is look at the last digit.

27. (**a**) Yes, if $5 \mid x$ and $5 \mid y$, then $5 \mid (x + y)$.

(**b**) Yes, if $5 \mid y$, then $5 \mid (^-y)$. If $5 \mid x$ and $5 \mid (^-y)$, then $5 \mid (x + (^-y))$ or $5 \mid x - y$.

(**c**) Yes, if $5 \mid x$, then 5 divides all the multiples of x and in particular $5 \mid xy$.

(**d**) No, $5 \mid 5$ and $5 \mid 10$, but $5 \nmid (5/10)$.

28. Answers vary, for example, the number might have too many digits for the calculator to handle.

29. (**a**) Yes, $4 \mid 52,832$, so 4 divides anything times 52,832. Therefore 4 divides $52,832 \cdot 324,518$ which is the area.
(**b**) Yes, 2 is a factor of 52,834 and 2 is a factor of 324,514, so $2 \cdot 2$ or 4 is a factor of $52,834 \cdot 324,514$ which is the area.

30. (**a**) 1, 3, and 7 divide n. 1 divides every number. Also, because $n = 21 \cdot d, d \in I$, then $n = (3 \cdot 7)d = 3(7d) = 7(3d)$ which implies that n is divisible by 3 and by 7. (**b**) 1, 2, 4, and 8 divide n. 1 divides every number. Also, because $16 \mid n$, then $n = 16 \cdot d, d \in I$. Therefore, $n = (2 \cdot 8)d = 2(8d) = 8(2d) = 4(4d)$. Hence n is divisible by 2, 4, and 8.

31. No, the multiples of 3 occur every third number in the natural numbers, that is, 1, 2, **3**, 4, 5, **6**, 7, 8, **9**, 10, 11, **12**, ... Therefore if a natural number is chosen at random it will either be a multiple of 3 or one less or one more than a multiple of 3. In no case can you find three consecutive natural numbers none of which is a multiple of 3.

32. (**a**) No. If $5 \nmid d$ for any integer d, then there is no integer m such that $5m = d$. If we assume $10 \mid d$, this means there exists n

such that $10n = d$ or $5(2n) = d$. This contradicts the original assumption that d is not divisible by 5. (**b**) Yes. All odd multiples of 5 are not divisible by 10 but are divisible by 5.

33. Suppose a number n has the digits $a, b, c, ... n, n \in I$, repeated exactly 3 times. Then the sum of the digits is $3a + 3b + 3c + ... 3n$ or $3(a + b + c + ... + n)$. By the divisibility test for 3, this implies that $3 \mid n$.

34. (**a**) All of the numbers are divisible by 11. (**b**) Yes, by definition all four-digit palindromes are in the form abba for integers a and b. (a might equal b.) The divisibility test for 11 states that the number is divisible by 11 if $11 \mid (a + b) - (b + a)$ or $11 \mid 0$. Because $11 \mid 0$, then 11 divides the four-digit palindrome. (**c**) No, for example, consider 12321 which is a five-digit palindrome and it is not divisible by 11. (**d**) Yes, a six-digit palindrome is in the form abccba for integers a, b, and c where a, b, and c do not have to be distinct. Therefore 11 divides the palindrome if $11 \mid (a + c + b) - (b + c + a)$ or $11 \mid 0$. Because $11 \mid 0$, then 11 divides the six-digit palindrome.

35. In a palindromic pair, the sum of the digits in one number is the same as the sum of the digits in the other number. Therefore if 3 divides one number, then 3 must divide the other number.

36. 243; Yes; Consider any number n of the form abcabc. Then we have the following:

$n = (a \cdot 10^5) + (b \cdot 10^4) + (c \cdot 10^3) + (a \cdot 10^2) + (b \cdot 10^1) + c$

$= a(10^5 + 10^2) + b(10^4 + 10^1) + c(10^3 + 1)$

$= a(100,000 + 100) + b(10,000 + 10) + c(1001)$

$= a(1001 \cdot 100) + b(1001 \cdot 10) + c(1001)$

$= (1001)[(a \cdot 100) + b(10) + c(1)]$

$= (7 \cdot 11 \cdot 13)[(a \cdot 100) + b(10) + c(1)]$

Therefore, $7 \mid n$, $11 \mid n$, and $13 \mid n$.

Open-ended

37. (**a**) Answers vary, for example, upon inspection of the given numbers we notice that all the numbers are multiples of 3. Since 3 divides each number, then 3 divides the sum of any of the numbers. Because 100 is not divisible by 3, there is no winning combination of the given numbers that will sum to 100. (**b**) Answers vary, for example, since many of these multiples of 3 sum to 99 (33 + 66, 45 + 51 + 3, etc) the company could place at most 1000 cards with the number 1 on the card. This would ensure that there are at most 1000 winners. Other numbers could also be used.

38. 34 stamps

Technology Corner (p. 211)

(**a**) This program will print "OKAY" if :N is divisible by :X, and print "NOT DIVISIBLE" otherwise. (**b**) The integer division button gives more information. If the first number is not divisible by the second number, it will show a remainder of 0.

Brain Teaser (p. 208)

The part of the explanation that is incorrect is the division by $(e - a - d)$ which is equal to 0. Division by 0 is impossible.

Brain Teaser (p. 211)

The number is 381–65–4729.

ONGOING ASSESSMENT 4-4

1. (**a**) Prime (**b**) Not prime (**c**) Prime (**d**) Prime (**e**) Prime (**f**) Not prime

2. 73

3. (a)

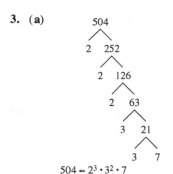

$$504 = 2^3 \cdot 3^2 \cdot 7$$

(b)

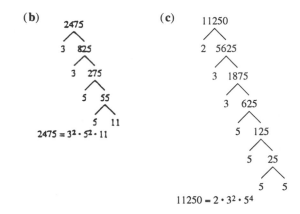

$$2475 = 3^2 \cdot 5^2 \cdot 11$$

(c)

$$11250 = 2 \cdot 3^2 \cdot 5^4$$

4. (a)

(b) You could multiply the $2 \cdot 3 \cdot 7 \cdot 5$.

5. 30

6. (a) 1×48, 2×24, 3×16, 4×12 **(b)** Only one, 1×47.

7. Yes; 177 flotillas of one ship each, one flotilla of 177 ships; 59 flotillas of three ships each; three flotillas of 59 ships.

8. (a) 3, 5, 15, 29, people **(b)** 145 committees of 3; 87 committees of 5; 29 committees of 15; 15 committees of 29.

9. (a) 1, 2, 3, 4, 6, 9, 12, 18, or 36 **(b)** 1, 2, 4, 7, 14, or 28 **(c)** 1 or 17 **(d)** 1, 2, 3, 4, 6, 8, 9, 12, 16, 18, 24, 36, 48, 72, or 144

10. 27,720

11. 90

12. (a) The Fundamental Theorem of Arithmetic says that n can be written as a product of primes in one and only one way. Since $2 \mid n$ and $3 \mid n$ and 2 and 3 are both prime, they must be included in the unique factorization.

That is, $2 \cdot 3 \cdot p_1 \cdot p_2 \cdot \ldots \cdot p_m = n$

Therefore, $(2 \cdot 3)(p_1 \cdot p_2 \cdot \ldots \cdot p_m) = n$

Thus, $6 \mid n$.

(b) Yes. If $a \mid n$, there exists an integer c such that $ca = n$. If $b \mid n$, there exists an integer d such that $db = n$.

Therefore, $(ca)(db) = n^2$

$(cd)(ab) = n^2$

Hence, $ab \mid n^2$

13. $97^2 = 9409$

14. 101, 103, 107, 109, 113, 127, 131, 137, 139, 149, 151, 157, 163, 167, 173, 179, 181, 191, 193, 197, 199

15. 3, 5; 5, 7; 11, 13; 17, 19; 29, 31; 41, 43; 59, 61; 71, 73; 101, 103; 107, 109; 137, 139; 149, 151; 179, 181; 191, 193; 197, 199

16. (a) Answers may vary. For example, $82^2 - 82 + 41 = 6683 = 41(163)$. **(b)** Let $n = 41a$ where $a \in N$. Then, $n^2 - n + 41 = (41a)^2 - 41a + 41 = 41(41a^2 - a + 1)$.

17. Every number would have its "usual" factorization $1(p_1 \cdot p_2 \cdot p_3 \cdot \ldots \cdot p_n)$, along with infinitely many other such factorizations because $1^n = 1$; n may be any natural number.

18. 1, 2, 3, 6, 7, 14, 21

19. No, because 5^z has no factors of either 2 or 3.

20. (a) 4, 6, 8, 0 or 10 **(b)** 1 and 9 **(c)** 23, 29, 31, 37, 53, 59, 71, 73, 79 **(d)** Answers vary. For example, 233 or 373.

21. There are infinitely many composites of the form 1, 11, 111, 1111, 11111, 111111... since every third member of this sequence will be divisible by 3.

22. $3n + 1$, where $n \in \{1, 2, 3, \ldots\}$ When n is odd, $3n + 1$ is even. Thus, $3n + 1$ is divisible by 2 and is not prime. Since there are infinitely many even integers, there are infinitely many composites in the sequence, $3n + 1$, when n is odd.

23. None of the primes 2, 3, 5, ... p divides N because if any one of the primes divided N, then it must also divide 1, which is impossible.

24. If $2N = 2^6 \cdot 3^5 \cdot 5^4 \cdot 7^3 \cdot 11^7$, then $N = 2^5 \cdot 3^5 \cdot 5^4 \cdot 7^3 \cdot 11^7 = (2 \cdot 3 \cdot 5 \cdot 7 \cdot 11)(2^4 \cdot 3^4 \cdot 5^3 \cdot 7^2 \cdot 11^6)$, which implies that $(2 \cdot 3 \cdot 5 \cdot 7 \cdot 11)$ is a factor of N.

25. Yes, because $(3^2 \cdot 2^4) \cdot (3^2 \cdot 2^3) = 3^4 \cdot 2^7$.

26. (a) $3 \times 5 \times 7 \times 11 \times 13$ is composite because it is divisible by 3, 5, 7, 11, and 13. **(b)** $(3 \times 4 \times 5 \times 6 \times 7 \times 8) + 2 = 2((3 \times 2 \times 5 \times 6 \times 7 \times 8) + 1)$ and so it is composite. **(c)** $(3 \times 5 \times 7 \times 11 \times 13) + 5 = 5((3 \times 7 \times 11 \times 13) + 1)$ and so it is composite. **(d)** $10! + 7 = 7((10 \times 9 \times 8 \times 6 \times 5 \times 4 \times 3 \times 2 \times 1) + 1)$ and so it is composite. **(e)** $10! + k$ can be factored as in part **(d)** depending on the value of k and so it is composite.

27. $2^3 \cdot 3^2 \cdot 25^3$ is not a prime factorization because 25 is not prime. The prime factorization is $2^3 \cdot 3^2 \cdot 5^6$.

Communication

28. To check if 173 is prime, we must only check for divisibility by primes whose squares are less than 173. In this case we must check for divisibility by 2, 3, 5, 7, 11, and 13.

29. The product of two consecutive natural numbers greater than 1 must be the product of an even and an odd number. Because the product of an even and an odd number is always even, the product must always have a factor of 2 and it must be composite.

30. A prime number is a number that is divisible only by itself and 1. Because 1 is not considered prime, this implies that a prime has only one prime factor and 1 is odd.

31. In any set of three consecutive numbers, there is one number that is divisible by 3 and at least one of the other two numbers is divisible by 2. Therefore the product will be divisible by 2 and by 3 and so it is divisible by 6.

32. In any set of four consecutive numbers, there are one or two numbers divisible by 3, a number divisible by 4, and a number divisible by 2 but not 4. Therefore the product of the four consecutive numbers will have 2, 4, and 3 as distinct factors and so the product is divisible by $2 \cdot 3 \cdot 4 = 24$.

33. No, they are not both correct. Using 3 and 4 is correct because they have no common divisors. Using 2 and 6 there is a common divisor of 2. Using this test will only ensure that the number is divisible by 6.

34. The multiples of 4, 8, and 10 were crossed out with the multiples of 2. The multiples of 6 were crossed out when the multiples of 2 and 3 were crossed out. The multiples of 9 were crossed out when the multiples of 3 were crossed out. All composite numbers less than 100 must have a factor less than or equal to 10 and these are all accounted for. Therefore the remaining numbers that have not been crossed out are prime.

Open-ended

35. Answers vary, for example, with a calculator with a $\boxed{\text{SIMP}}$ button, you could find the prime factorization of 124 by entering 124/124 and pressing the $\boxed{\text{SIMP}}$ and then the $\boxed{=}$ buttons. The display now reads 62/62. If the $\boxed{xy}$ button is pushed we see a factor of 2 has been removed.

We now record the factor of 2 and press $\boxed{xy}$ again and go through the same process. This time the display reads 31/31 and a factor of 2 is again removed. When the process is repeated again for 31/31 the display reads 1/1 and a factor of 31 is removed. Keeping track of the factors we have $124 = 2 \cdot 2 \cdot 31$ and we have the prime factorization. Other calculators may need a different sequence of keys pressed.

36. (a) Answers vary (i) 25 (ii) 21 (iii) 16 (b) 13, in the interval 100–199 (c) (i) 8 (ii) 7 (iii) 4 (d) Answers vary

37. Answers vary depending on the size of the print. If the number was typed, then there are about 10 numbers per inch. Therefore, there are 65050/10 in. or 542.08 ft of numbers. Using standard 8 1/2 in. paper, it would take about 765.3 sheets of paper to print the number in a single line or 12.75 sheets if printed 60 lines per page.

38. (a) (i) $1 + 2 + 3 + 4 + 6 = 16$, so 12 is abundant. (ii) $1 + 4 + 7 + 14 = 28$, so 28 is perfect. (iii) $1 + 5 + 7 = 13$, so 35 is deficient. (b) Answers vary, for example 10 and 14 are deficient, 18 is abundant, and 496 and 8128 are perfect.

Cooperative Learning

39. The students must have had the first 23 prime numbers for the number of tiles; that is, 2, 3, 5, 7, 11, 13, 17, 19, 23, 29, 31, 37, 41, 43, 47, 53, 59, 61, 67, 71, 73, 79, 83 tiles. Therefore the number of tiles is the sum of the first 23 prime numbers, which is 874 tiles.

40. Answers vary.

Review Problems

41. (a) False (b) True (c) True (d) True

42. (a) 2, 3, 6 (b) 2, 3, 5, 6, 9, 10

43. If $12 \mid n$, there exists an integer a such that $12a = n$.
$(3 \cdot 4) a = n$
$3(4a) = n$
Thus, $3 \mid n$.

44. Yes, among 8 people. Each would get $422.

ONGOING ASSESSMENT 4-5

1. (a) $D_{18} = \{1, 2, 3, 6, 9, 18\}$
$D_{10} = \{1, 2, 5, 10\}$
GCD(18, 10) = 2
$M_{18} = \{18, 36, 54, 72, 90...\}$
$M_{10} = \{10, 20, 30, 40, 50, 60, 70, 80, 90, ...\}$
LCM(18, 10) = 90
(b) $D_{24} = \{1, 2, 3, 4, 6, 8, 12, 24\}$
$D_{36} = \{1, 2, 3, 4, 6, 9, 12, 18, 36\}$
GCD(24, 36) = 12

$M_{24} = \{24, 48, 72, 96, 120, 144, 168...\}$
$M_{36} = \{36, 72, 108, 144, 180...\}$
LCM(24, 36) = 72
(c) $D_8 = \{1, 2, 4, 8\}$
$D_{24} = \{1, 2, 3, 4, 6, 8, 12, 24\}$
$D_{52} = \{1, 2, 4, 13, 26, 52\}$
GCD(8, 24, 52) = 4
$M_8 = \{8, 16, 24, 32, 40, 48, 56, 64, 72, 80, 88, 96...\}$
$M_{24} = \{24, 48, 72, 96, 120, 144, 168, 192, 216, 240, 264, 288, 312...\}$
$M_{52} = \{52, 104, 156, 208, 160, 312...\}$
LCM(8, 24, 52) = 312

2. (a) $132 = 2^2 \cdot 3 \cdot 11$
$504 = 2^3 \cdot 3^2 \cdot 7$
GCD(132, 504) $= 2^2 \cdot 3 = 12$
LCM(132, 504) $= 2^3 \cdot 3^2 \cdot 7 \cdot 11 = 5544$
(b) $65 = 5 \cdot 13$
$1690 = 2 \cdot 5 \cdot 13^2$
GCD(65, 1690) $= 5 \cdot 13 = 65$
LCM(65, 1690) $= 2 \cdot 5 \cdot 13^2 = 1690$
(c) $96 = 2^5 \cdot 3$
$900 = 2^2 \cdot 3^2 \cdot 5^2$
$630 = 2 \cdot 3^2 \cdot 5 \cdot 7$
GCD(96, 900, 630) $= 2 \cdot 3 = 6$
LCM(96, 900, 630) $= 2^5 \cdot 3^2 \cdot 5^2 \cdot 7 = 50,400$
(d) $108 = 2^2 \cdot 3^3$
$360 = 2^3 \cdot 3^2 \cdot 5$
GCD(108, 360) $= 2^2 \cdot 3^2 = 36$
LCM(108, 360) $= 2^3 \cdot 3^3 \cdot 5 = 1080$
(e) $63 = 3^2 \cdot 7$
$147 = 3 \cdot 7^2$
GCD(63, 147) $= 3 \cdot 7 = 21$
LCM(63, 147) $= 3^2 \cdot 7^2 = 441$
(f) $625 = 5^4$
$750 = 2 \cdot 3 \cdot 5^3$
$1000 = 2^3 \cdot 5^3$
GCD(625, 750) $= 5^3 = 125$
LCM(625, 750) $= 2^3 \cdot 3 \cdot 5^4 = 15,000$

3. (a) GCD(2924, 220) = GCD(220, 64) = GCD(64, 28) = GCD(28, 8) = GCD(8, 4) = GCD(4, 0) = 4 (b) GCD(14,595, 10,856) = GCD(10,856, 3739) = GCD(3739, 3378) = GCD(3378, 361) = GCD(361, 129) = GCD(129, 103) = GCD(103, 26) = GCD(26, 25) = GCD(25, 1) = 1 (c) GCD(123, 152, 122, 368) = GCD(122, 368, 784) = GCD(784, 64) = GCD(64, 16) = GCD(16, 0) = 16

4. (a) 72 (b) 1440 (c) 630

5. (a) $220 \cdot 2924/4$ or 160,820 (b) $14,595 \cdot 10,856/1$ or 158,443,320 (c) $123,152 \cdot 122,368/16$ or 941,866,496

6. GCD(6, 10) = 2, LCM(6, 10) = 30

7. (a) LCM(15, 40, 60) = 120 minutes = 2 hours
So the clocks alarm again together at 8:00 A.M. (b) No

8. 5

9. (a) $60 (b) $12 each (c) 30

10. 24

11. 24 nights

12. 15 cookies

13. After 7 1/2 hours, or 2:30 A.M.

14. 36 minutes (a, a)

15. (a) ab (b) GCD(a, a) = a; LCM(a, a) = a (c) GCD(a^2, a) = a; LCM(a^2, a) = a^2 (d) GCD(a, b) = a; LCM(a, b) = b (e) GCD(a, b) = 1; LCM(a, b) = ab (f) a $\mid$ b (g) b $\mid$ a

16. (a) True. If a and b are even, then GCD(a, b) > 2. (b) True. GCD(a, b) = 2 implies that a and b are even. (c) False. The GCD could be a multiple of 2; for example, GCD(8, 12) = 4. (d) False. For a ≠ b, LCM > GCD. (e) True, by Theorem 4–9. (f) True. If the GCD(a, b) > a, then the GCD could not divide a. (g) True. If LCM(a, b) < a, then the LCM could not be a multiple.

17. GCD(120, 75) = 15; GCD(15, 105) = 15; GCD(120, 75, 105) = 15.

18. (**a**) $4 = 2^2$. Since 97,219,988,751 is odd, it has no prime factors of two. Consequently, 1 is their only common divisor and they are relatively prime. (**b**) 11 only has prime factor 11. 181,345,913 is not divisible by 11: Therefore 1 is the only common divisor and they're relatively prime.

19. 20th caller

20. $48

21. 120 days

22. Two packages of plates, four packages of cups, and three packages of napkins

23. 12 revolutions

24. 3 for Gear 1, 5 for Gear 2, and 2 for Gear 3

25.

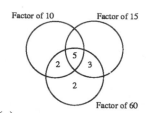

Factor of 10   Factor of 15

Factor of 60

(**a**)

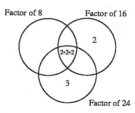

Factor of 8   Factor of 16

Factor of 24

(**b**)

26. 1, p, and p^2

27. {1, 2, 3, 4, 6, 7, 8, 9, 11, 12, 13, 14, 16, 17, 18, 19, 21, 22, 23, 24}

28. 70

Communication

29. No, the set of common multiples is infinite and therefore there could be no greatest common multiple.

30. Answers vary, most teachers will use an example such as 6. The divisors are {1, 2, 3, 6} whereas the multiples of 6 are {6, 12, 18, 24, 36, ...}.

31. No, for example, consider GCD(2, 4, 10) = 2, LCM(2, 4, 10) = 20, and the GCD · LCM = (2 · 20) = 40 while abc = 2 · 4 · 10 = 80.

32. (**a**) Answers vary, but for smaller numbers the intersection of sets method helps students to see exactly what a common divisor is and how to pick the greatest common divisor. (**b**) Answers vary, but for smaller numbers the intersection of sets method helps students to understand the concept better.

33. No, while this is true in many places it is not true all the time. For example, consider the primes 73, 79, 83, 89, 97.

Open-ended

34. Answers vary, for example, the GCD(a, b) must be less than or equal to the smaller of the two numbers while the LCM(a, b) must be greater than or equal to the greater of the two numbers. Because the two numbers are different, the GCD must be less than the LCM.

Review Problems

35. x = 15,625; y = 64

36. (**a**) 83,151; 83,451; 83,751 (**b**) 86,691 (**c**) 10,396

37. 17 · 183 = 3111; thus 3111 is not prime.

38. Answers may vary. $30,030 = 2 \cdot 3 \cdot 5 \cdot 7 \cdot 11 \cdot 13$

39. 27,720

40. 43

Technology Corner (p. 237)

1. The intersection is the first twelve multiples of 12.

2. You only need to fill down to 47.

3. (**a**) 180 (**b**) You need to use one of the techniques in the section to find LCM(6, 9, 12, 15).

Technology Corner (p. 238)

1. (**a**) GCD(676, 221) = 13 (**b**) GCD(10,764, 2300) = 92

2. TO LCM :A :B
OUTPUT (:A * :B)/GCD :A :B
END

Brain Teaser (p. 238)

If n is the width of the rectangle and m is the length of the rectangle, then the number of squares the diagonal crosses is (n + m) − GCD(n, m) or (n + m) − 1.

ONGOING ASSESSMENT 4-6

1. 2:00 PM

2. 2:00 PM

3. (**a**) 3 (**b**) 2 (**c**) 6 (**d**) 8 (**e**) 3 (**f**) 4 (**g**) Does not exist (**h**) 10

4. (**a**) 2 (**b**) 1 (**c**) 2 (**d**) 4 (**e**) 2 (**f**) 1 (**g**) 2 (**h**) 4

5. (**a**)

$\oplus$	1	2	3	4	5	6	7
1	2	3	4	5	6	7	1
2	3	4	5	6	7	1	2
3	4	5	6	7	1	2	3
4	5	6	7	1	2	3	4
5	6	7	1	2	3	4	5
6	7	1	2	3	4	5	6
7	1	2	3	4	5	6	7

(**b**) $6 = 5 \ominus 1; 4 = 2 \ominus 5$ (**c**) Every subtraction problem can be written as an addition problem, which can always be performed.

6. (**a**)

$\oplus$	1	2	3	4	5	6	7
1	1	2	3	4	5	6	7
2	2	4	6	1	3	5	7
3	3	6	2	5	1	4	7
4	4	1	5	2	6	3	7
5	5	3	1	6	4	2	7
6	6	5	4	3	2	1	7
7	7	7	7	7	7	7	7

(**b**) $3 \div 5 = 2; 4 \div 6 = 3$ (**c**) Yes. Division by numbers different than 7 is possible since each row and column in the table contains every element 1 through 6.

7. (**a**) 10 (**b**) 9 (**c**) 7 (**d**) 7 (**e**) 1 (**f**) 6

8. (**a**) 2, 9, 16, 30 (**b**) 3, 10, 17, 24, 31 (**c**) $366 \equiv 2(\bmod 7)$; Wednesday

9. (**a**) 4 (**b**) 0 (**c**) 0 (**d**) 7

10. (**a**) $8 \mid (81 - 1)$ (**b**) $10 \mid (81 - 1)$ (**c**) $13 \mid (1000 - (\bar{\ }1))$ (**d**) $10^1 \equiv 1(\bmod 9)$ implies $10^{84} \equiv 1^{84} (\bmod 9)$ (**e**) $10^2 \equiv 1(\bmod 11)$ implies $(10^2)^{50} \equiv 1^{50} (\bmod 11)$ (**f**) $100 \mid (937 - 37)$

11. (**a**) $a \equiv 0(\bmod m)$ if and only if $m \mid a$. By definition, $a \equiv b(\bmod m)$ if and only if $a - b$ is a multiple of m; where m is a positive integer greater than 1. Suppose $a \equiv 0(\bmod m)$. $(a - 0) = nm$ where n is a positive integer. Therefore, $a = nm$ so that $m \mid a$. Suppose $m \mid a$. $mn = a$ where n is an integer $mn = a - 0$ which implies $a \equiv 0(\bmod m)$.

12. (**a**) $24 \equiv 0(\bmod 8)$ (**b**) $\bar{\ }90 \equiv 0 (\bmod 3)$ (**c**) $n \equiv 0(\bmod n)$

13. (**a**) x = 2k, k is an integer (**b**) x – 1 = 2k implies x = 2k + 1 where k is an integer. (**c**) x – 3 = 5k implies x = 3 + 5k where k is an integer.

14. (**a**) 1 (**b**) 5 (**c**) 10 (**d**) 1

15. Tuesday

16. Wednesday

17. $N = a_k \cdot 10^k + a_{k-1} \cdot 10^{k-1} + \dots + a_2 \cdot 10^2 + a_1 \cdot 10^1 + a_0$
4 | N if and only if 4 | $(a_1 \cdot 10 + a_0)$.
Proof. $100 \equiv 0 \pmod 4$. Hence,
$N = 100(a_k \cdot 10^{k-2} + a_{k-1} \cdot 10^{k-3} + \dots + a_2) + a_1 \cdot 10 + a_0 \equiv a_1 \cdot 10 + a_0 \pmod 4$
Consequently, 4 | n if and only if 4 | $(a_1 \cdot 10 + a_0)$.

18. For example, $2 \cdot 11 \equiv 1 \cdot 11 \pmod{11}$ but $2 \equiv 1 \pmod{11}$ is false.

Communication

19. Each wheel (or place) uses mod 10; that is, on the first wheel 25 tenths of a mile is congruent to 5 tenths of a mile. Most cars have six wheels, and so the odometer when considered as a whole is a mod 100,000 system.

Open-ended

20. This discussion will depend on the resource consulted.

Cooperative Learning

21. (**a**)

⊗	1	2	3
1	1	2	3
2	2	1	3
3	3	3	3

⊗	1	2	3	4
1	1	2	3	4
2	2	4	2	4
3	3	2	1	4
4	4	4	4	4

⊗	1	2	3	4	5	6
1	1	2	3	4	5	6
2	2	4	6	2	4	6
3	3	6	3	6	3	6
4	4	2	6	4	2	6
5	5	4	3	2	1	6
6	6	6	6	6	6	6

⊗	1	2	3	4	5	6	7	8	9	10	11
1	1	2	3	4	5	6	7	8	9	10	11
2	2	4	6	8	10	1	3	5	7	9	11
3	3	6	9	1	4	7	10	2	5	8	11
4	4	8	1	5	9	2	6	10	3	7	11
5	5	10	4	9	3	8	2	7	1	6	11
6	6	1	7	2	8	3	9	4	10	5	11
7	7	3	10	6	2	9	5	1	8	4	11
8	8	5	2	10	7	4	1	9	6	3	11
9	9	7	5	3	1	10	8	6	4	2	11
10	10	9	8	7	6	5	4	3	2	1	11
11	11	11	11	11	11	11	11	11	11	11	11

(**b**) Divisions by numbers other than the additive identity can be performed on the 3 and 11 tables, since all the numbers appear in each row. This is true of all prime number clocks. (**c**) The rows and columns in each contain all the elements except for the identity.

Brain Teaser (p. 245)
There are no primes in this list.

Chapter Review

1. (**a**) ⁻3 (**b**) a (**c**) 0 (**d**) ⁻x – y (**e**) x – y (**f**) 32 (**g**) 32

2. (**a**) ⁻7 (**b**) 8 (**c**) 8 (**d**) 0 (**e**) 8 (**f**) 15

3. (**a**) 3 (**b**) ⁻5 (**c**) Any integer except 0 (**d**) No integer will work (**e**) ⁻41 (**f**) Any integer

4. $2(^-3) = {}^-6; 1(^-3) = {}^-3; 0(^-3) = 0$; if the pattern continued then: $^-1(^-3) = 3; \; ^-2(^-3) = 6$

5. (**a**) 10 – 5 = 5 (**b**) 1 – (⁻2) = 3

6. (**a**) $(x - y)(x + y) = (x - y) x + (x - y)y$
$$= x^2 - yx + xy - y^2$$
$$= x^2 - xy + xy - y^2$$
$$= x^2 - y^2$$
(**b**) $4 - x^2$

7. (**a**) ⁻x (**b**) y – x (**c**) 3x – 1 (**d**) 2x² (**e**) 0 (**f**) ⁻x² – 6x – 9

8. (**a**) ⁻2x (**b**) x(x + 1) (**c**) (x – 6)(x + 6) (**d**) $(9y^3 + 4x^2)(9y^3 - 4x^2)$ (**e**) 5(1 + x) (**f**) (x – y)x

9. (**a**) False, it is not positive for x = 0. (**b**) False, if one value is positive and one is negative. (**c**) False, if b < 0. (**d**) True (**e**) False, it is equal to ab.

10. (**a**) 2/1 ≠ 1/2 (**b**) 3 – (4 – 5) ≠ (3 – 4) – 5 (**c**) 1/2 is not an integer (**d**) 8/(4 – 2) ≠ 8/4 – 8/2

11. ⁻7°C

12. 115 2-kg packages, 35 1-kg packages

13. (**a**) False (**b**) False (**c**) True (**d**) False; 12, for example (**e**) False; 9, for example

14. (**a**) False; 7 | 7 and 7 ∤ 3 yet 7 | 3 · 7 (**b**) False; 3 ∤ (3 + 4) but 3 | 3 and 3 ∤ 4 (**c**) True (**d**) True (**e**) True (**f**) False; 4 ∤ 2 and 4 ∤ 22 but 4 | 44

15. (**a**) Divisible by 2, 3, 4, 5, 6, 8, 9, 11 (**b**) Divisible by 3, 11

16. If 10,007 is prime, 17 ∤ 10,007. We know 17 | 17, so 17 ∤ (10,007 + 17) by Theorem 4–2(b).

17. (**a**) 87<u>2</u>4; 86<u>5</u>4; 87<u>8</u>4 (**b**) 4<u>1</u>,856; 44,856; 47,856 (**c**) 87,<u>1</u>74; 87,<u>4</u>64; 87,<u>7</u>54

18. (**a**) Composite (**b**) Prime

19. Check for divisibility by 3 and 8, 24 | 4152.

20. (**a**) 4 (**b**) 73

21. (**a**) $2^4 \cdot 5^3 \cdot 7^4 \cdot 13 \cdot 29$ (**b**) 77,562

22. Answers vary, for example 16. To obtain 5 divisors, we raise a prime (2) to the (5 – 1) power.

23. 1, 2, 3, 4, 6, 8, 9, 12, 16, 18, 24, 36, 48, 72, 144

24. (**a**) $2^2 \cdot 43$ (**b**) $2^5 \cdot 3^2$ (**c**) $2^2 \cdot 5 \cdot 13$ (**d**) 3 · 37

25. 15 minutes

26. $31

27. 9:30 AM

28. We know that the GCD(a, b) · LCM(a, b) = ab. Because GCD(a, b) = 1, then LCM(a, b) = ab.

29. One month of 365 days; five months of 73 days; 365 months of 1 day; 73 months of 5 days

30. 5 packages

31. $n = a \cdot 10^2 + b \cdot 10 + c$
$n = a(99 + 1) + b(9 + 1) + c$
$n = 99a + 9b + c + b + a$
Since 9 | 99a and 9 | 9b, 9 | [99a + 9b + (a + b + c)] if and only if 9 | (a + b + c)

32. (**a**) 1 (**b**) 4 (**c**) 3

33. Friday

34. mod 360. It would cover all the area encircling the lighthouse.

CHAPTER 5

ONGOING ASSESSMENT 5-1

1. (**a**) The solution to 8x = 7 is 7/8. (**b**) Jane ate seven of Jane's eight pieces of candy. (**c**) The ratio of boys to girls is seven to eight.

2. (**a**) 1/6 (**b**) 1/4 (**c**) 2/6 or 1/3 (**d**) 7/12 (**e**) 5/16 (**f**) 2/16 = 1/8

3. (**a**) 2/3 (**b**) 4/6 or 2/3 (**c**) 6/9 or 2/3 (**d**) 8/12 or 2/3. The diagram illustrates the Fundamental Law of Fractions.

4. (a)

(b)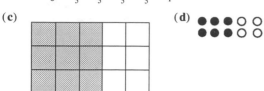

(c)

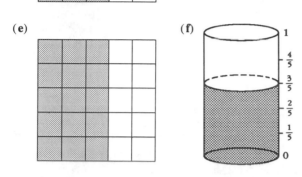

(d)

(e)

(f)

5. (a) 9/24 or 3/8 **(b)** 12/24 or 1/2 **(c)** 4/24 or 1/6 **(d)** 8/24 or 1/3

6. (a) 4/18, 6/27, 8/36 **(b)** ⁻4/10, 2/⁻5, ⁻10/25 **(c)** 0/1, 0/2, 0/4 **(d)** 2a/4, 3a/6, 4a/8

7. (a) 52/31 **(b)** 3/5 **(c)** ⁻5/7 **(d)** 0/1 **(e)** 144/169 **(f)** Reduced

8. Impossible to determine. Because 20/25 = 24/30 = 4/5, the same fraction of students passed in each class, but the actual scores in one class could have been higher than in the other.

9. (a) undefined **(b)** undefined **(c)** 0 **(d)** cannot be simplified **(e)** cannot be simplified **(f)** 2/3 **(g)** 5/3

10. (a) 1 **(b)** 2x/9y **(c)** a/1 **(d)** $(a^3 + 1)/a^3 b$ **(e)** 1/(3 + b) **(f)** cannot be simplified

11. (a) equal **(b)** equal **(c)** equal **(d)** not equal

12. (a) not equal **(b)** not equal **(c)** equal **(d)** not equal

13. Yes, 1/32 in.

14.

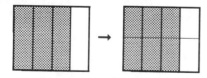

15. 36/48

16. A. 3 minutes

17.

18. (a) $2\frac{7}{8}$ in. **(b)** $2\frac{3}{8}$ in. **(c)** $1\frac{3}{8}$ in. **(d)** $\frac{7}{8}$ in.

19. 12/21, 24/42, 48/84

20. (a) 32/3 **(b)** ⁻36 **(c)** x is any rational number except 0

21. (a) a = b, c ≠ 0 **(b)** b = c ≠ 0 or a = 0, but b ≠ 0 and c ≠ 0.

22. (a) not equal **(b)** not equal **(c)** equal

23. (a) T **(b)** T **(c)** F **(d)** F **(e)** T

24. Bren's class

25. (a) > **(b)** > **(c)** < **(d)** < **(e)** = **(f)** =

26. (a) $\frac{11}{13}, \frac{11}{16}, \frac{11}{22}$ **(b)** $\frac{⁻1}{5}, \frac{⁻19}{36}, \frac{⁻17}{30}$

27. (a) A positive proper fraction is greater than its square.

(b) Let $\frac{a}{b}$ be a positive proper fraction; that is $0 < \frac{a}{b} < 1$.

Therefore, $\frac{a}{b} > 0, \frac{a}{b} < 1$ implies $\frac{a}{b} \cdot \frac{a}{b} < 1 \cdot \frac{a}{b}$ or $\left(\frac{a}{b}\right)^2 < \frac{a}{b}$.

(c) If a fraction is greater than 1, it is less than its square.

(d) Let $\frac{a}{b}$ be a fraction greater than 1. Then $\frac{a}{b} \cdot \frac{a}{b} < 1 \cdot \frac{a}{b}$

or $\left(\frac{a}{b}\right)^2 > \frac{a}{b}$.

28. $\frac{a}{b} < 1$ and $\frac{c}{b} > 0$ imply $\frac{a}{b} \cdot \frac{c}{d} < 1 \cdot \frac{c}{d}$ or $\frac{a}{b} \cdot \frac{c}{d} < \frac{c}{d}$.

29. xy > y because x > 1 and y > 0 implies $x \cdot y > 1 \cdot y$ or xy > y.

30. We need to show that $\frac{n}{n+1} < \frac{n+1}{n+2}$. This inequality is equivalent to $n^2 + 2n < n^2 + 2n + 1$, or 0 < 1.

31. (a) There is no whole number between 3 and 4 for example. **(b)** The example in Part (a) suffices for the set of integers as well.

32. Answers may vary. The following are possible answers.

(a) $\frac{10}{21}, \frac{11}{21}$ **(b)** $\frac{⁻22}{27}, \frac{⁻23}{27}$ **(c)** $\frac{997}{1200}, \frac{998}{1200}$ **(d)** $0, \frac{1}{2}$

33. (a) 1 **(b)** 1 **(c)** The ratios are the same. To show this, let x equal the top circled number. Then the sum of the circled numbers is x + (x + 12) + (x + 19) + (x + 31) = 4x + 62. The sum of the four interior numbers is (x + 10) + (x + 11) + (x + 20) + (x + 21) = 4x + 62. Here the ratio is always 1.

34. 456 mi

35. 6/16, or 3/8 of a pound; 6/32,000, or 3/16,000 of a ton

36. 100 yd = 300 ft. The estimate should be between 13 and 14 sec, but closer to 13 sec.

Communication

37. It is less than either factor. If $\frac{a}{b} < 1$ and $\frac{c}{d} < 1$, then by multiplying the first inequality by $\frac{c}{d}$, we have $\frac{ac}{bd} < \frac{c}{d}$.

Similarly, multiplying the second inequality by $\frac{a}{b}$ yields $\frac{ca}{db} < \frac{a}{b}$.

38. 0 has no reciprocal because 1/0 is undefined.

39. No; depends on the context of problem.

40. Answers vary.

(a) Suppose the rational numbers are $\frac{2}{16}$ and $\frac{1}{4}$. $\frac{1}{4} > \frac{2}{16}$.

Iris is incorrect.

(b) Suppose the rational numbers are $\frac{5}{1}$ and $\frac{1}{2}$. $\frac{5}{1} > \frac{1}{2}$.

Shirley is incorrect.

41. The points determined by the coordinates lie along a line. Students will not realize this yet, but essentially they are graphing points along the line with slope 1/3.

42. Because 36 in. = 1 yd, then to convert x in. to yards, we could consider how to write equivalent fractions 36/1 and x/1 unknown yards. By seeing how many 36's are in x, we could determine the unknown number of yards. Because 1 in. = 1/36 yd, the process to convert yards to inches could be accomplished using similar methods.

Open-ended

43. Frequently in recipes, measurements are found in fractional parts of cups, teaspoons, tablespoons. For example, a recipe might call for 1/2 teaspoon of salt and 2/3 cup of flour.

44. Answers will certainly vary. Some mathematics educators argue that positive and negative integers are easier for students to comprehend than are rational numbers. Such educators also argue that the operations on integers are easier than are operations on rational numbers.

Cooperative Learning

45. In this assessment, students must work together to determine the heights and to order the people according to height. Once that is done, the students may decide how many are in the class, for example 24, and then number the people in the class from 1/24 to 24/24, or 1. Many other rational numbers may be used.

ONGOING ASSESSMENT 5-2

1. (a)

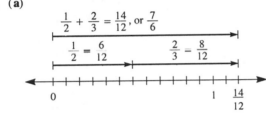

(b) $\dfrac{^-11}{16}$ (c) $\dfrac{^-4}{12}$ or $\dfrac{^-1}{3}$ (d) $\dfrac{5y-3x}{xy}$ (e) $\dfrac{^-9y+5x+42y^2}{6x^2y^2}$

(f) $\dfrac{^-6y+6x-1}{4xy}$ (g) $\dfrac{71}{24}$ or $2\dfrac{23}{24}$ (h) $\dfrac{43}{2^4\cdot3^4}$

(i) $\dfrac{^-23}{3}$ or $^-7\dfrac{2}{3}$

2. (a) $18\dfrac{2}{3}$ (b) $2\dfrac{4}{5}$ (c) $2\dfrac{93}{100}$ (d) $^-5\dfrac{7}{8}$

3. (a) $\dfrac{27}{4}$ (b) $\dfrac{15}{2}$ (c) $\dfrac{^-29}{8}$ (d) $\dfrac{^-14}{3}$

4. $\dfrac{2}{6}+\dfrac{5}{8}$

5. (a) 1/3, high (b) 1/6, low (c) 3/4, low (d) 1/2, low

6. (a) Beavers (b) Ducks (c) Bears (d) Tigers (e) Lions (f) Wildcats, Badgers

7.

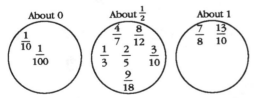

8. (a) 1/2, high (b) 0, low (c) 3/4, high (d) 1, high (e) 1, low (f) 0, high (g) 3/4, low (h) 1/2, high

9. (a) 2 (b) 3/4 (c) 0 (d) 0

10. (a) No (b) No

11. (a) 1/4 (b) $5\dfrac{1}{8}$ (c) 0 (d) 10

12. (a) A (b) H (c) T (d) H

13. (a) $\dfrac{3+3}{3}\neq\dfrac{3}{3}+3$ (b) $\dfrac{4}{2+2}\neq\dfrac{4}{2}+\dfrac{4}{2}$ (c) $\dfrac{ab+c}{a}\neq\dfrac{\cancel{a}b+c}{\cancel{a}}$

(d) $\dfrac{a\cdot a-b\cdot b}{a-b}\neq\dfrac{\cancel{a}\cdot a-b\cdot\cancel{b}}{\cancel{a}-\cancel{b}}$ (e) $\dfrac{a+c}{b+c}\neq\dfrac{a+\cancel{c}}{b+\cancel{c}}$

14. $\dfrac{1}{4}$

15. (a) $\dfrac{1}{30}$ (b) $\dfrac{2}{20}$ or $\dfrac{1}{10}$ (c) $\dfrac{1}{60}$ (d) No, the total number of dollars might have been greater in 1980 than in 1990, but the fraction of the total dollars might still be greater in 1990.

16. $6\dfrac{7}{12}$ yards

17. $1\dfrac{3}{4}$ cups

18. $2\dfrac{5}{6}$ yards

19. $22\dfrac{1}{8}$ inches

20. (a) Team 4, $76\dfrac{11}{16}$ pounds (b) $3\dfrac{11}{16}$ pounds

21. (a) $\dfrac{1}{2}+\dfrac{3}{4}\in Q$ (b) $\dfrac{1}{2}+\dfrac{3}{4}=\dfrac{3}{4}+\dfrac{1}{2}$

(c) $\left(\dfrac{1}{2}+\dfrac{1}{3}\right)+\dfrac{1}{4}=\dfrac{1}{2}+\left(\dfrac{1}{3}+\dfrac{1}{4}\right)$

22. (a) $\dfrac{6}{4},\dfrac{7}{2},2$; arithmetic, $\dfrac{1}{2}-\dfrac{1}{4}=\dfrac{3}{4}-\dfrac{1}{2}=1-\dfrac{3}{4}=\dfrac{5}{4}-1$

(b) $\dfrac{6}{7},\dfrac{7}{8},\dfrac{8}{9}$; not arithmetic; $\dfrac{2}{3}-\dfrac{1}{2}\neq\dfrac{3}{4}-\dfrac{2}{3}$

(c) $\dfrac{17}{3},\dfrac{20}{3},\dfrac{23}{3}$; arithmetic; $\dfrac{5}{3}-\dfrac{2}{3}=\dfrac{8}{3}-\dfrac{5}{3}=$ $\dfrac{11}{3}-\dfrac{8}{3}=\dfrac{14}{3}-\dfrac{11}{3}$

(d) $\dfrac{^-5}{4},\dfrac{^-7}{4},\dfrac{^-9}{4}$; arithmetic; $\dfrac{3}{4}-\dfrac{5}{4}=\dfrac{1}{4}-\dfrac{3}{4}=$ $\dfrac{^-1}{4}-\dfrac{1}{4}=\dfrac{^-3}{4}-\left(\dfrac{^-1}{4}\right)$

23. (a) $\dfrac{1}{4}n$ (b) $\dfrac{n}{n+1}$ (c) $\dfrac{3n-1}{3}$ or $n-\dfrac{1}{3}$

(d) $\dfrac{^-2n+7}{4}$ or $\dfrac{7}{4}-\dfrac{1}{2}n$

24. (a) 622/985 (b) 592/716 (c) $\dfrac{24}{985}$

25. (a) Afghanistan (b) 4540/13,523

26. $1,\dfrac{7}{6},\dfrac{8}{6},\dfrac{9}{6},\dfrac{10}{6},\dfrac{11}{6},2$

27. (a) (i) $\dfrac{3}{4}$ (ii) $\dfrac{25}{12}$ or $2\dfrac{1}{12}$ (iii) 0 (b) (i) $\dfrac{1}{4}$ (ii) $\dfrac{^-7}{4}$ (iii) $\dfrac{^-1}{4}$

28. (a) f(0) = $^-2$ (b) f($^-2$) = 0 (c) f($^-5$) = $\dfrac{1}{2}$ (d) f(5) = $\dfrac{7}{4}$

29. (b) $\dfrac{1}{n}=\dfrac{1}{n+1}+\dfrac{1}{n(n+1)}$

(c) $\dfrac{1}{n+1}+\dfrac{1}{n(n+1)}=\dfrac{n\cdot1}{n(n+1)}+\dfrac{1}{n(n+1)}=\dfrac{n+1}{n(n+1)}=\dfrac{1}{n}$

Communication

30. Although they are not whole quantities, they still may add to whole quantities. A single fractional part may be far from negligible if the mixed number is small. For example consider 1 7/8.

31. It might be easier but she would not have a correct solution. Think of the numerator as the number of pieces of pie cut into the denominator's value of slices. Then to add the pieces of pie, we would add the numerators and have that number of pieces.

32. No. Because 4/5 is a proper fraction, there is no equivalent that can be improper.

33. (**a**) Yes. If a, b, c, and d are integers, then $\dfrac{a}{b} - \dfrac{c}{d} = \dfrac{ad - bc}{bd}$ is a rational number. (**b**) No. For example, $\dfrac{1}{2} - \dfrac{1}{4} \neq \dfrac{1}{4} - \dfrac{1}{2}$.
(**c**) No. For example, $\dfrac{1}{2} - \left(\dfrac{1}{4} - \dfrac{1}{8}\right) \neq \left(\dfrac{1}{2} - \dfrac{1}{4}\right) - \dfrac{1}{8}$. (**d**) No. If there is an identity for subtraction it must be 0, since only for 0 does $\dfrac{a}{b} - 0 = \dfrac{a}{b}$. However, in general $0 - \dfrac{a}{b} \neq \dfrac{a}{b} - 0$, and hence there is no identity. (**e**) No. Since there is no identity, an inverse cannot be defined.

34. (**a**) Like digits are being canceled. (**b**) Numerators and denominators are both being added. (**c**) Numerators and denominators of fractional portions are both being subtracted. (**d**) Multiplication is by a/a rather than by a/1.

Open-ended

35. (**a**) It is feasible to add the numbers in the table for Montana and Russia to determine the population density of the combined country and state because the population density is the number of people per square mile in each case. In terms of rational numbers, the denominator in each case is 1 mi². (**b**) It is not reasonable to decide that the population of Bangladesh is approximately 355 times that of Montana based on the information given. It is possible to decide that the population of Bangladesh is approximately 355 times that of Montana per square mile; the number of square miles in the two countries is so disparate that it is impossible to conclude the given information accurately. (**c**) Answers will vary. For example, one question might be "If the population of Montana is removed from the United States' population, is the population density of the remaining portion of the United States 62?"

Cooperative Learning

36. This question is more likely to be given in a school setting than in a college class, but the question requires students to decide on a menu, check the recipes, and determine the total amount of ingredients necessary to prepare the meal.

37. Depending on the people interviewed, students may hear an answer like the following from a teacher: I use fractions in determining total grades for my classes. For example, if a paper is 1/2 of the grade and a test is another 1/3 of the grade, I need to know what fractional part of the grade is yet to be determined.

Review Problems

38. (**a**) The triangles created will vary. (**b**) The ratio of the directed segments is always 1/1. (**c**) The conjecture should be that all triangles created in this manner will have sides in the ratio of 1/1. This ratio of change in y-coordinates to change in x-coordinates is the slope of the line created.

39. (**a**) $\dfrac{2}{3}$ (**b**) $\dfrac{13}{17}$ (**c**) $\dfrac{25}{49}$ (**d**) $\dfrac{a}{1}$ or a (**e**) reduced

40. (**a**) equal (**b**) not equal (**c**) equal (**d**) not equal

41. (**a**) February (**b**) The answer depends upon whether or not the year is a leap year. If it is a leap year, the answer is 185/366; if not, the answer is 184/365. (**c**) Most people consider there to be 365 1/4 days in a year. As an improper fraction, this number is 1461/4.

42. $0 < \dfrac{a}{b} < \dfrac{c}{d}$ so that $0 < \dfrac{1}{2} \cdot \dfrac{a}{b} < \dfrac{1}{2} \cdot \dfrac{c}{d}$. Also.
$0 < \dfrac{a}{b} = \dfrac{1}{2} \cdot \dfrac{a}{b} + \dfrac{1}{2} \cdot \dfrac{a}{b} < \dfrac{1}{2} \cdot \dfrac{a}{b} + \dfrac{1}{2} \cdot \dfrac{c}{d} = \dfrac{1}{2}\left(\dfrac{a}{b} + \dfrac{c}{d}\right)$. Similarly,
$\dfrac{1}{2}\left(\dfrac{a}{b} + \dfrac{c}{d}\right) < \dfrac{c}{d}$, and therefore $0 < \dfrac{a}{b} < \dfrac{1}{2}\left(\dfrac{a}{b} + \dfrac{c}{d}\right) < \dfrac{c}{d}$.

43. We are considering $\dfrac{a}{b}$ and $\dfrac{a+x}{b+x}$ when a < b. $\dfrac{a}{b} < \dfrac{a+x}{b+x}$ because ab + ax < ab + bx.

Brain Teaser (p. 277)

Let x = number of students, $\dfrac{1}{2}x + \dfrac{1}{7}x + 20 = x$

$$20 = \dfrac{5}{14}x$$

$$56 = x$$

Brain Teaser (p. 285)

Observe that after crossing each bridge, the prince was left with half the bags he had previously minus one additional bag of gold. To determine the number he had prior to crossing the bridge, we can use the inverse operations; that is, add 1 and multiply by 2. The prince had one bag left after crossing the fourth bridge. He must have had two before he gave the guard the extra bag. Finally he must have had four bags before he gave the guard at the fourth bridge any bags. The entire procedure is summarized in the following table.

Bridge	Bags After Crossing	Bags Before Guard Given Extra	Bags Prior to Crossing
Fourth	1	2	4
Third	4	5	10
Second	10	11	22
First	22	23	46

ONGOING ASSESSMENT 5-3

1. (**a**) $\dfrac{1}{4} \cdot \dfrac{1}{3} = \dfrac{1}{12}$ (**b**) $\dfrac{2}{4} \cdot \dfrac{3}{5} = \dfrac{6}{20}$

2.

(**a**)

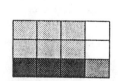

(**b**)

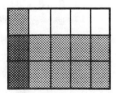

(**c**)

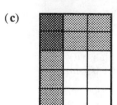

3. (a) $\dfrac{1}{5}$ (b) $\dfrac{b}{a}$ (c) $\dfrac{za}{x^2y}$ (d) $\dfrac{35}{4}$ or $8\dfrac{3}{4}$ (e) $\dfrac{44}{3}$ or $14\dfrac{2}{3}$

(f) $\dfrac{^-25}{4}$ or $^-6\dfrac{1}{4}$

4. (a) $10\dfrac{1}{2}$ (b) $8\dfrac{1}{3}$ (c) $24,871\dfrac{1}{20}$

5. (a) $^-3$ (b) $\dfrac{3}{10}$ (c) $\dfrac{y}{x}$ (d) $\dfrac{^-1}{7}$

6. (a) 26 (b) 29 (c) 92 (d) 18 (e) 6 (f) 7 (g) 9 (h) $2\dfrac{1}{4}$

7. (a) 20 (b) 16 (c) 2 (d) 1
8. (a) 18 (b) 25 (c) 7 (d) 6
9. (a) Less than 1 (b) Less than 1 (c) Greater than 2 (d) Less than 4 (e) Greater than 4
10. (C)
11. $\dfrac{29}{36}$
12. 9600
13. 400
14. $\dfrac{1}{6}$
15. (a) 39 uniforms (b) $\dfrac{1}{4}$ yards left
16. $240
17. (a) $121,000 (b) $90,000 (c) $300,000
18. 1/4
19. 246
20. $225
21. (a) Peter, 30 min.; Paul, 25 min.; Mary, 20 min. (b) Peter, 10; Paul, 12; Mary, 15
22. (a) $89\dfrac{3}{5}$°F (b) $^-40$°C
23. $2253\dfrac{1}{8}$
24. 32 marbles
25. The arithmetic is not true. There are 3600 seconds in an hour. $2264/3600 \neq 1\,1/2$
26. 70,848 in.
27. 120 1/4 lb.

28. (a) $2S = 2\left(\dfrac{1}{2}+\dfrac{1}{2^2}+...+\dfrac{1}{2^{64}}\right)=1+\dfrac{1}{2}+\dfrac{1}{2^2}+...+\dfrac{1}{2^{63}}$

(b) Note that $2S = 1+S-\dfrac{1}{2^{64}}$. Hence, $2S-S = 1+S-\dfrac{1}{2^{64}}-S$

$=1-\dfrac{1}{2^{64}}$ (c) $1-\dfrac{1}{2^n}$

29. (a) $1\dfrac{49}{99}$ (b) $25\cdot\left(2\dfrac{49}{99}\right)=62\dfrac{37}{99}$

30. (i) $\dfrac{1}{32},\dfrac{1}{64}$; geometric ratio $=\dfrac{1}{2}$ (ii) $\dfrac{^-1}{32},\dfrac{1}{64}$;

geometric ratio $=\dfrac{^-1}{2}$ (iii) $\dfrac{81}{256},\dfrac{243}{1024}$; geometric ratio $=\dfrac{3}{4}$

(iv) $\dfrac{5}{3^5},\dfrac{6}{3^6}$; not geometric, $\dfrac{2}{3^2}\div\dfrac{1}{3}\neq\dfrac{3}{3^3}\div\dfrac{2}{3^2}$

31. (a) $n(n+1)+\left(\dfrac{1}{2}\right)^2$ (b) $\left(n+\dfrac{1}{2}\right)^2=n^2+2n\cdot\dfrac{1}{2}+\left(\dfrac{1}{2}\right)^2$

$=n^2+n+\left(\dfrac{1}{2}\right)^2=n(n+1)+\left(\dfrac{1}{2}\right)^2$

32. (a) (i) $\dfrac{^-4}{5}$ (ii) $\dfrac{^-26}{17}$ (iii) $\dfrac{^-14}{33}$ (b) (i) $\dfrac{^-4}{3}$ (ii) $\dfrac{^-30}{7}$

(iii) $\dfrac{^-3}{10}$ (c) $\dfrac{5}{4}$

33. (a) First 3, second 4, third 5. Guess 6. The guess is correct since

$$\left(1+\dfrac{1}{1}\right)\left(1+\dfrac{1}{2}\right)\left(1+\dfrac{1}{3}\right)\left(1+\dfrac{1}{4}\right)\left(1+\dfrac{1}{5}\right)=5\left(1+\dfrac{1}{5}\right)=6 \quad \textbf{(b)} \ 102$$

(c) $n+2$

Communication

34. Never less than n. $0<\dfrac{a}{b}<\mid$ implies $0<\mid<\dfrac{b}{a}$. The last

inequality implies $<n<\left(\dfrac{a}{b}\right)$. Also $n\div\left(\dfrac{a}{b}\right)=n\cdot\dfrac{b}{a}>n$.

35. B is the closest. Because both C and D are less than 1, then their product should be less than either.
36. One estimate might be 5 1/2 because 1/7 of 35 is 5 and 1/7 of 42 is 6; and 39 is approximately half way between 35 and 42. Another reasonable estimate might be found by finding 1/13 of 39 to be 3 and then use two of these as 6. 2/13 is reasonably close to 2/14 or 1/7.
37. The second number must be the reciprocal of the first and must be less than 1.
38. The plumber needs 10 5/8 ft of pipe. It can be cut from the 12-ft section. With no waste in cutting, 1 3/8 ft of pipe is left.
39. The first factor in each product is inverted before multiplying.
40. Mentally might be better if commutativity of multiplication is used.
41. (a) $2+1\neq 1+2$ (b) $(1+2)+3\neq 1+(2+3)$
(c) There is no rational number a such that $2+a=a+2=2$.
(d) Because there is no identity, there can be no inverse.
42. Answers will vary about class use. 7 ounces
43. Answers will vary tremendously here depending on what research students are able to find. Many believe that calculations with decimals are far easier than calculations with fractions. However, to understand decimals may require an understanding of fractions. There was a movement at one point when it appeared the metric system was to be introduced to downplay the teaching of fractions.

Cooperative Learning
44. The answers here may vary depending upon the size of the bricks and the size of the joints. In all likelihood, the measurements will be made in fractions of inches for the size of the joints. The size of the bricks may be done in inches. An alternative is to measure in centimeters. Thus, all measurement is approximate and some rounding or estimation may occur.

Review Problems
45. (a) 17 minutes after the experiment started (b) –108°C
46. (a) $\dfrac{25}{16}$ or $1\dfrac{9}{16}$ (b) $\dfrac{25}{18}$ or $1\dfrac{7}{18}$ (c) $\dfrac{5}{216}$ (d) $\dfrac{259}{30}$ or

$8\dfrac{19}{30}$ (e) $\dfrac{37}{24}$ or $1\dfrac{13}{24}$ (f) $\dfrac{^-39}{4}$ or $^-9\dfrac{3}{4}$

47. 120 students

Brain Teaser (p. 288)
No. The legacy is impossible because the fractions of cats to be shared do not add up to the whole units of cats.

$\dfrac{1}{2}x+\dfrac{1}{3}x+\dfrac{1}{9}x=\dfrac{17}{18}x$, but the sum should be 1x, or $\dfrac{18}{18}x$.

Chapter Review

1.

(a)

(b) ▨▨▨ (shaded figure)

(c)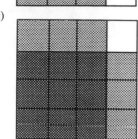

2. Answers may vary. For example, $\frac{10}{12}, \frac{15}{18}, \frac{20}{24}$

3. **(a)** $\frac{6}{7}$ **(b)** $\frac{ax}{b}$ **(c)** $\frac{0}{1}$ **(d)** $\frac{5}{9}$ **(e)** $\frac{b}{1}$ **(f)** $\frac{2}{27}$

4. **(a)** = **(b)** > **(c)** > **(d)** <

5. **(a)** $^-3, \frac{1}{3}$ **(b)** $^-3\frac{1}{7}, \frac{7}{22}$ **(c)** $\frac{^-5}{6}, \frac{6}{5}$ **(d)** $\frac{3}{4}, \frac{^-4}{3}$

6. $^-2\frac{1}{3}, ^-1\frac{7}{8}, 0, (71/140)^{300}, 69/140, 1/2, 71/140, (74/73)^{300}$

7. 17 pieces, $\frac{11}{6}$ yards left

8. **(a)** 15 **(b)** 15 **(c)** 4

9. $\frac{a}{b} \div \frac{c}{d} = x$ if and only if $\frac{a}{b} = \frac{c}{d} \cdot x$ $x = \frac{d}{c} \cdot \frac{a}{b}$ is the solution of

the equation because $\frac{c}{d} \cdot \left(\frac{d}{c} \cdot \frac{a}{b} \right) = \frac{a}{b}$.

10. 9

11. 76/100, 78/100, but answers may vary.

12. ⊡ 5 ⊡ 0 ⊡ 4 ⊡ 7 ⊡ 9 ⊡ 2 ⊡ x ⊡ 2 ⊡ 3 ⊡ $\frac{1}{x}$ ⊡ = ⊡

13. $333\frac{1}{3}$ calories

14. 752 times

15. $240/1000 = 6/25$

16. It is not reasonable to say that the University won 3/4 + 5/8 of its basketball games. One way for this to be reasonable is to make sure that the men and women play the same number of games. That is not known.

17. The numerators of the rational numbers are integers and follow the properties of integers; the same is true of the denominators. Thus both the numerator and denominator of the answer are integers, and we can apply another property of integers to determine the sign of the answer.

18. You should show him that the given fraction could be written as an integer over an integer. In this case, the result is 8/9.

19. 4/15

20. The minute hand points directly at a numeral only one minute out of the entire hour or 1/60 of an hour.

21. $^-12/10$ is greater than $^-11/9$ because $^-12/10 - (^-11/9)$ is a positive number.

CHAPTER 6

ONGOING ASSESSMENT 6-1

1. **(a)** $1/3^{13}$ **(b)** 3^{13} **(c)** 5^{11} **(d)** 5^{19} **(e)** $1/(^-5)^2$ or $1/5^2$ **(f)** a^5
(g) a^2 **(h)** $1/a$

2. **(a)** $(1/2)^{10}$ **(b)** $(1/2)^3$ **(c)** $(2/3)^9$ **(d)** 1 **(e)** $(5/3)^3$ **(f)** $(5/6)^{21}$

3. **(a)** False. $2^3 \cdot 2^4 \neq (2 \cdot 2)^{3+4}$ **(b)** False. $2^3 \cdot 2^2 \neq (2 \cdot 2)^{3 \cdot 4}$
(c) False. $2^3 \cdot 2^3 \neq (2 \cdot 2)^{2 \cdot 3}$ **(d)** False. $a^0 = 1$ if $a \neq 0$
(e) False. $(2 + 3)^2 \neq 2^2 + 3^2$ **(f)** False. $(2 + 3)^{-2} \neq$
$\frac{1}{2^3} + \frac{1}{3^2}$ **(g)** False. $2^{2 \cdot 3} \neq 2^2 \cdot 2^3$ **(h)** True. $\left(\frac{a}{b} \right)^{-1} = \frac{1}{a/b} = \frac{b}{a}$

4. **(a)** 5 **(b)** 6 or $^-6$ **(c)** $^-2$ **(d)** $^-4$ **(e)** 0 **(f)** 15

5. **(a)** $2 \cdot 10^{11}$ **(b)** $2 \cdot 10^5$

6. **(a)** $x \leq 4$ **(b)** $x \leq 1$ **(c)** $x \geq 2$ **(d)** $x \geq 1$

7. **(a)** $\left(\frac{1}{2} \right)^3$ **(b)** $\left(\frac{3}{4} \right)^8$ **(c)** $\left(\frac{4}{3} \right)^{10}$ **(d)** $\left(\frac{4}{5} \right)^{10}$ **(e)** $\left(\frac{4}{3} \right)^{10}$

(f) $\left(\frac{3}{4} \right)^{100}$

8. **(a)** 10^{10} **(b)** $10^{10} \cdot \left(\frac{6}{5} \right)^2 = 1.44 \cdot 10^{10} = 14.4$ billion

9. **(a)** $\frac{3}{4}$ **(b)** 24 **(c)** $\frac{3}{128}$ **(d)** $^-7$

10. **(a)** $\frac{3}{2}, \frac{3}{4}, \frac{3}{8}, \frac{3}{16}, \frac{3}{32}$ **(b)** Each of the four ratios is $\frac{1}{2}$.

(c) $\frac{3}{1024}$

11. **(a)** 32^{50}, since $32^{50} = (2^5)^{50} = 2^{250}$ and $4^{100} = (2^2)^{100} = 2^{200}$

(b) $(^-3)^{-75}$, since $(^-27)^{-15} = (^-3)^{-45} = \frac{^-1}{3^{45}} < \frac{^-1}{3^{75}}$

12. **(a)** $0 \cdot 10^0 + 0 \cdot 10^{-1} + 2 \cdot 10^{-2} + 3 \cdot 10^{-3}$ **(b)** $2 \cdot 10^2 + 0 \cdot 10 + 6 \cdot 10^0 + 0 \cdot 10^{-1} + 6 \cdot 10^{-2}$ **(c)** $3 \cdot 10^2 + 1 \cdot 10 + 2 \cdot 10^0 + 0 \cdot 10^{-1} + 1 \cdot 10^{-2} + 0 \cdot 10^{-3} + 3 \cdot 10^{-4}$ **(d)** $0 \cdot 10^0 + 0 \cdot 10^{-1} + 0 \cdot 10^{-2} + 0 \cdot 10^{-3} + 1 \cdot 10^{-4} + 3 \cdot 10^{-5} + 2 \cdot 10^{-6}$

13. **(a)** 4356.78 **(b)** 4000.608 **(c)** 40,000.03 **(d)** 0.2004007

14. **(a)** 536.0076 **(b)** 3.008 **(c)** 0.000436 **(d)** 5,000,000.2

15. **(a)** $\frac{436}{1000} = \frac{109}{250}$ **(b)** $\frac{2516}{100} = \frac{629}{25}$ **(c)** $\frac{^-316,027}{1000}$

(d) $\frac{281902}{10000} = \frac{140951}{5000}$ **(e)** $\frac{^-43}{20}$ **(f)** $\frac{^-6201}{100}$

16. **(a)**, **(b)**, **(c)**, **(d)**, **(e)**, **(f)**, and **(h)** can be represented as terminating decimals.

17. **(a)** 0.8 **(b)** 3.05 **(c)** 0.5 **(d)** 0.03125 **(e)** 0.01152 **(f)** 0.2128 **(h)** 0.08

18. **(a)** 13.492, 13.49199, 13,4919, 13,49183 **(b)** $^-1.4053, ^-1.45, ^-1.453, ^-1.493$

19. **(a)** 0.0000000032 **(b)** 3,200,000,000 **(c)** 0.42 **(d)** 620,000

20. **(a)** $1.27 \cdot 10^7$ **(b)** $5.797 \cdot 10^6$ **(c)** $5 \cdot 10^7$

21. **(a)** 0.0000044 **(b)** 19,900 **(c)** 3,000,000,000

22. **(a)** $4.8 \cdot 10^{28}$ **(b)** $4 \cdot 10^7$ **(c)** $2 \cdot 10^2$

23. The number of digits in the terminating decimal is the greater of m or n.

Communication

24. $100,000^3 = 1000^5$ and these are the greatest. To see this, write the numbers in scientific notation. Then it is easy to compare them.

$$100,000^3 = (1 \times 10^5)^3 = 1 \times 10^{15}$$
$$1000^5 = (1 \times 10^3)^5 = 1 \times 10^{15}$$
$$100,000^2 = (1 \times 10^5)^2 = 1 \times 10^{10}$$

25. Let $m = n$. Then $1 = \frac{a^n}{a^m} = a^{m-n} = a^0$.

26. Division by zero is not defined.

27. If the exponent is an odd number, the result is negative. If the exponent is even, the result is positive. Explanations will vary.

28. **(a)** 3^{400} **(b)** $4^{300} = (4^3)^{100} = 64^{100}$, $3^{400} = (3^4)^{100} = 81^{100}$, and $81^{100} > 64^{100}$. **(c)** You get an error in the display.

Open-ended
29. Answers vary.
30. Answers vary.
31. Answers vary.

Cooperative Learning
32. (a) 2^{22}; this number has seven digits. (b) $2^{2^{22}}$; this number has over 4,000,000 digits (compare it to $10^{2^{22}}$, which has 2^{22} digits).
33. Answers vary.

ONGOING ASSESSMENT 6-2

1. $231.24
2. 62.298 lb
3.

8.2	1.9	6.4
3.7	5.5	7.3
4.6	9.1	2.8

4. $8.00
5. (a) It costs $3.21 to heat the house for one day. (b) The light bulb would have to stay on 358.9 hr.
6. (a) 6390.955 cubic cm (b) 183.07123 cubic in.
7. 21.324 mi/hr
8. (a) 5.4, 6.3, 7.2, 8.1, 9.0, 9.9, 10.8, ... (b) 1.3, 1.5, 1.7, 1.9, 2.1, 2.3, ... (c) 0.0625, 0.03125, 0.015625, 0.0078125, ... (d) 6.7, 8.0, 9.3, 10.6, 11.9, 13.2, 14.5, 15.8, 17.1, ...
9. (a) $0.\overline{4}$ (b) $0.\overline{285714}$ (c) $0.2\overline{7}$ (d) $0.0\overline{6}$ (e) $0.02\overline{6}$ (f) $0.0\overline{1}$ (g) $0.8\overline{3}$ (h) $0.0\overline{76923}$
10. Divide 93,000,000/1565. It would take 59,424.92 hr. (If a calculator doesn't have enough digits in its display, one could divide 93,000/1565 and multiply the result by 1000.)
11. No, the bank is over $7.74.
12. (a) $0.\overline{076923}$ (b) $0.\overline{047619}$ (c) $0.\overline{157894736842105263}$
13. (a) 200 (b) 200 (c) 204 (d) 203.7 (e) 203.65
14. 19
15. (a) 4/9 (b) 2/3 (c) 7/5 (d) 5/9 (e) $^-$211/90 (f) $^-$2/99
16. $^-1.\overline{454} < {}^-1.4\overline{54} = {}^-1.\overline{45} < {}^-1.45\overline{4} < {}^-1.454$
    $^-1.454 > {}^-1.45\overline{4} > {}^-1.\overline{45} = {}^-1.4\overline{54} > {}^-1.\overline{454}$
17. Answers vary. For example:
(a) 3.21, 3.213, 3.214 (b) 462.241, 462.2415, 462.242
18. (a) 0.45 (b) 1.0
19. $55 + 5 + 18 = 78$ dollars
20. Estimates may vary. Exact answers are the following:
(a) 122.06 (b) 57.31 (c) 25.40 (d) 136.15
21. $2.35 \cdot 10^{13}$
22. (a) $1.\overline{6}, 2, 2.\overline{3}, 2.\overline{6}, 3, 3.\overline{3}, 3.\overline{6}, 4, \ldots$ (b) $6/7 = 0.\overline{857142}$, $7/8 = 0.875, 8/9 = 0.\overline{8}, 9/10 = 0.9, \ldots$
23. (a) $0.4\overline{46355}; 6$ (b) $1.3\overline{5775}$; yes, 4
24. (a) $2.66 \cdot 10^{-5}$ (b) $4.32 \cdot 10^{-5}$ (c) $1.64 \cdot 10^{43}$
(d) $(1.001)^{10^6} = \left((1.001)^{100,000}\right)^{10} \doteq \left(2.557 \cdot 10^{43}\right)^{10} \doteq 1.2 \cdot 10^{434}$
25. Profit of $2098
26. (a) $279.65 (b) $620 (c) 5 hundreds and 4 twenties

Communication
27. (a) Interest = $26.47 (b) $53.20 (c) $97,365.75
28. Lining up the decimal points acts as using place value.
29. 0.0770
30. 406
31. Because $1/99 = 0.0101010101\ldots$, then $51/99 = 51(1/99) = 51(0.0101010101\ldots) = 0.5151515151\ldots$. However, $x/99$ behaves differently if $x > 99$.
32. Second option; it is $4,368,709.12 more profitable.

33. Yes. Replace the rightmost nonzero decimal digit d with $d - 1$ and tack on the repetend $\overline{9}$. If all decimal digits are zero, subtract 1 from the number and tack on $\overline{9}$.
Examples: $0.265 = 0.264\overline{9}$ and $34 = 33.\overline{9}$.

Open-ended
34. (a) They each have six-digit repetends using each of 1, 2, 4, 5, 7, 8 exactly once. (b) Notice that the patterns of digits are cyclic permutations of each other. (c) n/14 (d) If k/14 cannot be reduced, then knowing $\frac{1}{14} = 0.0\overline{714285}$ we can start dividing k by 14 until two consecutive digits from the repetend appear. We then continue the cyclic pattern. For example because $\frac{9}{14} = 0.642\ldots$ we know that the digits following 42 are 8571.

Cooperative Learning
35. (a) $3^9 = 19683$ (b) 3^{2-1} (c) (i) $3^{99}/10^{12} = 1.7 \cdot 10^{35}$ sec $= 5.4 \cdot 10^{27}$ yr (ii) $3^{99}/10^{12} = 3^{1000}/(3 \cdot 10^{12}) = (3^{100})^{10}/(3 \cdot 10^{12}) = (5.2 \cdot 10^{47})^{10}/(3 \cdot 10^{12}) = 1.4 \cdot 10^{477}/(3 \cdot 10^{12}) = 4.7 \cdot 10^{464}$ sec $\doteq 1.49 \cdot 10^{457}$ yr (d) $(0.75)^3 = 0.421875$ is the black area; $1 - \left(\frac{3}{4}\right)^3$ or 37/64 is the white area. The area of the white region approaches 1. (e) Area of the black region approaches zero.

Review Problems
37. (a) True (b) False (c) False (d) False (e) False (f) False
38. (a) $x = 9$ is the greatest. (b) $x = {}^-10$ is the greatest. (c) $x = 3$ is the smallest. (d) $x = {}^-5$ is the greatest.
39. (a) $(a^4)^5 = a^4 \cdot a^4 \cdot a^4 \cdot a^4 \cdot a^4 = a^{4+4+4+4+4} = a^{4 \cdot 5}$
(b) $(a^{-4})^{-5} = 1/(a^{-4})^5 = 1/(a^{-4} \cdot a^{-4} \cdot a^{-4} \cdot a^{-4} \cdot a^{-4}) = 1/a^{-4 \cdot 5} = a^{(-4)(-5)}$
40. (a) 49,736.5281 (b) 41,235.6789
1. $22,761.95

ONGOING ASSESSMENT 6-3

1. Answers vary. One answer is 0.232233222333 . . . .
2. $0.77, 0.\overline{7}, 0.78, 0.787787778\ldots, 0.7\overline{8}, 0.788, 0.78 = 0.78\overline{8}$
3. $0.9, 0.98, 0.988, 0.9, 0.8\overline{98}$
4. (a), (d), (e), and (f) represent irrational numbers.
5. (a) 15 (b) 15.8 (c) 13 (d) 22.6 (e) Impossible (f) 25
6. (a) 4.12 (b) 2.65 (c) 4.58 (d) 0.11 (e) 4.51 (f) 1.28
7. (a) False; $\sqrt{2} + 0$ (b) False; $^-\sqrt{2} + \sqrt{2}$ (c) False; $\sqrt{2} \cdot \sqrt{2}$ (d) False; $\sqrt{2} - \sqrt{2}$
8. Answers vary. For example, $\sqrt{2}, \sqrt{3}$, and $\sqrt{5}$.
9. Answers vary. For example, assume the following pattern continues: 0.54544544454444 ...
10. (a) R (b) 0 (c) Q (d) 0 (e) R (f) R
11. (a) N, I, Q, R (b) Q, R (c) R, S (d) N, I, Q, R (e) 0 (f) Q, R
12. (a) 64 (b) None (c) $^-$64 (d) None (e) All real numbers greater than zero. (f) None
13. 6.4 ft
14. (a) 8.98 sec (b) 2.007 sec
15. 13/99 because each term is less than $0.\overline{13}$.
16. (a) $\sqrt{180} = 6\sqrt{5}$ (b) $\sqrt{363} = 11\sqrt{3}$ (c) $\sqrt{252} = 6\sqrt{7}$
17. (a) $^-3\sqrt[3]{2}$ (b) $2\sqrt[5]{3}$ (c) $5\sqrt[3]{2}$ (d) $^-3$

18. (a) $5, 5\sqrt[3]{2}, 5\sqrt[3]{4}, 10$ (b) $2, 2\sqrt[4]{1/2}, 2\sqrt[4]{1/4}, 2\sqrt[4]{1/8}, 1$
(c) $\sqrt{2} \cdot \sqrt[6]{2/5}, \sqrt{2}, \sqrt{2} \cdot \sqrt[6]{5/2}, \sqrt{2} \cdot \sqrt[6]{25/4}, \sqrt{5}$
19. (a) 2^{10} (b) 2^{11} (c) 2^{12}
20. (a) $\sqrt{3}$ (b) $\sqrt[3]{3}$ (c) $\sqrt{12} + \sqrt{14}$ because
$\sqrt{12} + \sqrt{14} > \sqrt{11} + \sqrt{15}$ if and only if,

$$\frac{\left(\sqrt{12} - \sqrt{11}\right)\left(\sqrt{12} + \sqrt{11}\right)}{\sqrt{15} + \sqrt{11}} > \frac{\left(\sqrt{15} - \sqrt{14}\right)\left(\sqrt{15} + \sqrt{14}\right)}{\sqrt{15} + \sqrt{14}}$$

if and only if $\dfrac{1}{\sqrt{12} + \sqrt{11}} > \dfrac{1}{\sqrt{15} + \sqrt{14}}$ if and only if
$\sqrt{15} + \sqrt{14} > \sqrt{12} + \sqrt{11}$ which is true.
21. $\sqrt[8]{2^7}$
22. (a) 4 (b) 3/2 (c) ‾4/7 (d) 5/6
23. $\sqrt[3]{1/16}$
24. (a) n is odd. (b) When m is even, the n can be any number except 0. When m is odd, then n must also be odd.
25. (a) Rational (b) Rational (c) Irrational (d) Rational
26. (a)

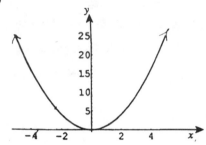

(b)

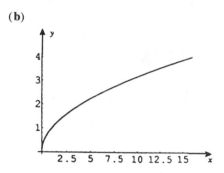

(c)

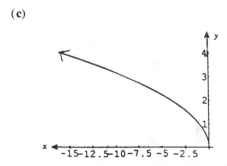

27. Suppose $\sqrt{3}$ is rational. Then $\sqrt{3} = a/b$, where a and b are integers and $b \neq 0$. Thus $3 = a^2/b^2$ or $3b^2 = a^2$. Now a^2 has an

even number of threes in its prime factorization, but $3b^2$ has an odd number of threes in its prime factorization and this is impossible. Thus $\sqrt{3}$ is irrational.
28. Suppose $\sqrt{p}$ is rational, where p is prime. Then $\sqrt{p} = a/b$, where a and b are integers and $b \neq 0$. Thus $p = a^2/b^2$ or $pb^2 = a^2$. Since b^2 has an even number of p's in its prime factorization, pb^2 has an odd number of p's in its prime factorization. Also, a^2 can have only an even number of p's in its prime factorization. But this is impossible. Thus $\sqrt{p}$ is irrational.
29. (a) m is a perfect square. (b) Use the result of Problem 28.
30. (a) $0.5 + 1/0.5 = 0.5 + 2 = 2.5 \geq 2$ (b) Suppose $x + 1/x < 2$. Since $x > 0$, $x^2 + 1 < 2x$, so $x^2 - 2x + 1 < 0$, or $(x - 1)^2 < 0$, which is false. Therefore $x + 1/x \geq 2$.

Communication
31. False: $\sqrt{64 + 36} \neq \sqrt{64} + \sqrt{36}$.
32. No; 22/7 is a rational number that can be represented by the repeating decimal $3.\overline{142857}$.
33. No; $\sqrt{13}$ is an irrational number. So when it is expressed as a decimal it is nonterminating and nonrepeating.
34. No; $\sqrt{9 + 16} = 5$ but $3 + 4 = 7$.
35. (a) Sometimes (if $a \geq 0$) (b) Sometimes (if $x \leq 0$)
(c) Always (d) Sometimes (if $a + b \geq 0$) (e) Sometimes (if $a \geq 0$)
36. Notice that $(4/25)^{-1/3} = (25/4)^{1/3}$ and $(4/25)^{-1/4} = (25/4)^{1/4}$. Because $(25/4)^{1/4} < (25/4)^{1/3}$, we have $(4/25)^{-1/4} < (4/25)^{-1/3} = (25/4)^{1/3}$.
37. A calculator can only give an approximation.
38. (a) Yes; $z = \left(\sqrt{x} + \sqrt{y}\right)^2$. (b) No. If $y > z$, then it will be impossible.

Open-ended
39. Answers vary. For example:
(a) $1, 2, 3, 4, 5,...$ (b) $\sqrt{2}, \sqrt{3}, \sqrt{5}, \sqrt{7},...$ or $\pi, \pi^2, \pi^3, \pi^4,...$
40. Answers vary. For example:
(a) $\sqrt{1/2}, \pi/6, \sqrt[3]{2/5}, 0.505005000500005 ..., \sqrt{3/10}$
(b) $0.51500500050005 ..., 0.5051050050005 ...,$
   $0.50501500500005 ..., 0.505005100500005 ....$
41. (a) When a number between 0 and 1 is raised to larger and larger exponents, the results approach 0. (b) Answers vary. (c) Answers vary.
42. $3.7^{2\cdot4} = 3.7^{\frac{24}{100}} = 3.7^{\frac{6}{25}} = \sqrt[25]{3.7^6}$

Review
43. (a) 21.6 lbs (b) 48 lbs.
44. $22,761.95
45. (a) 418/25 (b) 3/1000 (c) ‾507/100 (d) 123/1000
46. (a) $4.\overline{9}$ (b) $5.0\overline{9}$ (c) $.\overline{49}$
47. 3/12,500
48. $4.09, 4.09\overline{1}, 4.099, .4\overline{9}$
49. 8/33
50. (a) 208,000 (b) 0.00038
51. (a) $2^n + 2^{n+1} = 2^n + 2 \cdot 2^n = (1 + 2)2^n = 3 \cdot 2^n$
(b) $3^n + 3^{n+1} = 1 \cdot 3^n + 3 \cdot 3^n = (1 + 3) \cdot 3^n = 4 \cdot 3^n$
52. (a) False; $2^1 + 2^2 \neq 2^3$ (b) False; $1^2 \cdot 3^4 \neq 3^6$ (c) False; 0^{-13} is undefined. (d) True; $(a^{-m})^{-n} = a^{(-m)(-n)} = a^{mn}$.
   Also $1/a^{-mn} = \dfrac{1}{1/a^{mn}} = 1 \cdot a^{mn}/1 = a^{mn}$.
53. (a) 800 parts per million (b) $c(n) = 25 \cdot 2^{n/5}$ parts per million (c) Use guess and check strategy. The least n for which $2^n > 400^5 = 1.024 \cdot 10^{13}$ is n = 44.

Chapter Review

1. (a) $1/2^{11}$ (b) $1/5^{20}$ (c) $(3/2)^{28}$ (d) 3^{18}
2. (a) $3 \cdot 10 + 2 \cdot 10^0 + 0 \cdot 10^{-1} + 1 \cdot 10^{-2} + 2 \cdot 10^{-3}$
(b) $0 \cdot 10^0 + 0 \cdot 10^{-1} + 0 \cdot 10^{-2} + 1 \cdot 10^{-3} + 0 \cdot 10^{-4} + 3 \cdot 10^{-5}$
3. A fraction in simplest form, a/b, can be written as a terminating decimal if, and only if, the prime factorization of the denominator contains no primes other than 2 or 5.
4. 8
5. (a) $0.\overline{571428}$ (b) 0.125 (c) $0.\overline{6}$ (d) 0.625
6. (a) $7/25$ (b) $^{-}507/100$ (c) $1/3$ (d) $94/45$
7. (a) 307.63 (b) 307.6 (c) 308 (d) 300
8. (a) No; $\sqrt{2} + \left(^{-}\sqrt{2}\right)$ is rational. (b) No; see (a).
(c) No; $\sqrt{2} \cdot \sqrt{2}$ is rational. (d) No; $\sqrt{2}/\sqrt{2}$ is rational.
9. 4.796
10. (a) $4.26 \cdot 10^5$ (b) $3.24 \cdot 10^{-4}$ (c) $2.37 \cdot 10^{-6}$ (d) $3.25 \cdot 10^{-1}$
11. (a) 3 (b) 3 (c) 3 (d) 3
12. (a) Irrational (b) Irrational (c) Rational (d) Rational
(e) Irrational
13. (a) $11\sqrt{2}$ (b) $12\sqrt{2}$ (c) $6\sqrt{10}$ (d) $3\sqrt[3]{6}$
14. (a) 10^{14} (b) Approximately $1.62 \cdot 10^{13}$ (c) 177 seconds since $Q(176) \doteq 1.159$ and $Q(177) \doteq 0.966$
15. (a) The greatest integer is 6. (b) The least integer is $^{-}6$.
(c) The least integer is 10. (d) The greatest integer is 9.
16. $1.45\overline{19}, 1.45\overline{19}, 1.45\overline{19}, 1.4519, 0.13\overline{401}, 0.13401, 0.134$
17. (a) $5\sqrt{2}$ (b) $1/\sqrt[4]{4}, 1/\sqrt[4]{16}, 1/\sqrt[4]{64}$ (c) $0.4, ^{-}0.4$
(d) $10/\sqrt[3]{10}, 10\sqrt[3]{100}, 10\sqrt[3]{1000}, 10\sqrt[3]{10,000}$
18. (a) $1.78341156 \cdot 10^6$ (b) $3.47 \cdot 10^{-6}$ (c) $4.93 \cdot 10^9$
(d) $2.94 \cdot 10^{17}$ (e) $4.7 \cdot 10^{35}$ (f) $1.5 \cdot 10^{-6}$
19. Answers vary. For example:
(a) 0.105, 0.104, 0.103, 0.102, 0.101 (b) 0.004, 0.002, 0.001, 0.005 (c) 0.15, 0.175, 0.1875, 0.19375
20. (a) A = 0.02, B = 0.05, C = 0.11
(b)

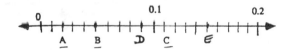

CHAPTER 7

ONGOING ASSESSMENT 7-1

1. (a) $60t$ (b) $20 + 25x$ (c) $175d$ (d) $3x + 3$ (e) $q \cdot 2^n$
(f) $40 - 3t$ (g) $4s + 15,000$ (h) $3x + 6$ (i) $3m$ (j) $m^3 - m$
2. (a) $P = 0.04E$ (b) $E = 25P$ (c) 6 lbs (d) 2500 lbs
3. (a) $g = 0.607165d$ (b) $d = 1.647g$
4. (a) 220 (b) $n(2n + 2)$ or $2n(n + 1)$
5. (a) 89.6 (b) $^{-}40$
6. $C = \dfrac{5}{9}(F - 32)$
7. (a) $K = 273.15 + C$ (b) $C = K - 273.15$
(c) $F = \dfrac{9}{5}(K - 273.15) + 32$ and $K = 273.15 + \dfrac{5}{9}(F - 32)$
8. (a) $P = 8t$ (b) $P = 15 + 10(t - 1)$ (c) $P = 20 + 10t$
(d) $C = 300 + 4n$ (e) $C = 30 + 0.35m$
9. (a) $x = 18$ (b) $x < 18$ (c) $x = ^{-}18$ (d) $x \le ^{-}18$ (e) $x = ^{-}2$
(f) $x \ge ^{-}2$ (g) $x < ^{-}3$ (h) $x = ^{-}2$ (i) $x \doteq 5.51$ (j) $x = ^{-}0.0096$
(k) $x \ge 1$ (l) $x \le 1$

10. (a) $x \ge \left(\sqrt{5} - 4\right)/10$ (b) $x = \dfrac{1 \pm \sqrt{2}}{2}$ (c) $x \ge \sqrt{7}$ or $x \le ^{-}\sqrt{7}$
(d) $^{-}\sqrt{2} \le x \le \sqrt{2}$ (e) $x = \dfrac{8}{3}$ (f) $x = 1.8$
11. (a) $x = 6/7$ (b) $x = 3/35$ (c) $x = ^{-}28$ (d) $x = ^{-}56/5$
(e) $x = 13$ (f) $x = 15/32$ (g) $x = 13$ (h) $x = ^{-}7/15$
12. The new value is $\dfrac{w}{12}$.
13. If x is any number, then the teacher's instructions were $\left(\dfrac{3x + 49}{7} - 7\right) \div 3$. This expression is equivalent to
$\left(\dfrac{3x + 49}{7} - 7\right) \div 3 = \dfrac{3x}{7} \cdot \dfrac{1}{3} = \dfrac{x}{7}$. Thus to tell the value of x, the
teacher multiplies the answer $\dfrac{x}{7}$ by 7.
14. Show that if the number is x, then the answer is
$\left(\dfrac{x \cdot 0.3 - 0.6}{3 \cdot 100} - 0.55\right) \cdot 100$. This can be simplified to $x - 2 - 550$
or $x - 5$. Hence adding 552 to the answer results in the original number x.
15. a, c, d, e, and g

Communication
16. Both are correct. For the first student, x is the first of the three consecutive integers. The second chose x to be the second of the three consecutive integers.
17. $\ell/2^n$. Explanation: In the first step, when ℓ is halved then
each piece has length $\dfrac{\ell}{2}$. In the second step, when one of the
previous pieces is halved, the result is a piece of length
$\dfrac{1}{2} \cdot \dfrac{\ell}{2} = \dfrac{\ell}{2^2}$. Because each time we halve a piece we multiply
by $\dfrac{1}{2}$ to get the length of the new piece, after n cuts we get a
piece of length $\dfrac{\ell}{2^n}$.

Open-ended
18. Answers vary. For example:
(a) Take any number, subtract 3, multiply by 4, add 8, and divide by 4. (b) Take any number, subtract 20, divide by 6, add 3, multiply by 3, and add 1. (c) Take any positive number and divide it by its square root. (d) Take any positive number, add 1, multiply the result by the original number, and subtract the original number.
19. Answers vary. For example, $x^2 \ge 0$.
20. Answers vary. For example:
(a) $x + 2 = 2 + x$ (b) $x = x + 1$ (c) $x/x = 1$ (d) $x + y = y + x$

Cooperative Learning
21. Answers vary. For example: The student justification is not valid. One can substitute only equal for equal. If $c = d + e$, one could substitute $d + e$ for c. However, the conclusion is valid because if we add b to both sides of $c > d + e$, we get $b + c > b + d + e$. By the transitive property of "greater than", $a > b + c$ and $b + c > b + d + e$, implies $a > b + d + e$.
22. Answers vary.

Brain Teaser (p. 357)
The part of the explanation that is incorrect is the division by $(e - a - d)$ which is equal to 0. Division by zero is impossible.

ONGOING ASSESSMENT 7-2

1. ⁻5
2. Rick has $100 and David has $300.
3. Factory A produces 2800 cars per day, Factory B 1400 cars per day, and Factory C 3100 cars per day.
4. 524 student tickets
5. 78, 79, 80
6. 78, 80, 82
7. 14 and 7
8. Eldest, $30,000; middle, $24,000; youngest, $10,000
9. 10, 12, 14
10. 400
11. 29/36
12. 9600
13. $240
14. (a) $121,000 (b) $90,000 (c) $300,000
15. 1/4
16. 246
17. $225
18. Work backwards: 600 students got a C. This is three fourths of the number of students who received a B or a C. We solve 600 = (3/4)x to see that x = 800 students received either a B or a C. This is four fifths of the overall total. So we solve 800 = (4/5)y to see that there are y = 1000 students in the school.
19. In the first experiment, the total temperature change in 5 min was 28 − (⁻12) = 40 degrees. Thus the rate of change is 8 degrees per minute. The temperature of the reaction is given by $T_1 = 28 − 8t$ where t is the number of minutes since the reaction began. In the second experiment, the temperature is given by $T_2 = ⁻57 − 3t$. Solve 28 − 8t = ⁻57 − 3t. Thus t = 17 min. The common temperature is ⁻108°.

Communication

20. The equation is equivalent to 2x − 1 = 2x − 12. This says that by using the number 2x, you will get the same result whether you subtract 1 or 12, which cannot happen.
21. No. A solution is x = 0. (One can divide by x only under the stipulation that x ≠ 0.)

Open-ended

22. Answers vary.
23. Answers vary.

Cooperative Learning

24. Answers vary.
25. Answers vary. Assuming n months of employment, the problem can be analyzed in general as follows. Using a formula for the sum of an arithmetic sequence, the second salary option will be better if and only if:

$$\left(\frac{2b+(n-1)c}{2}\right)n > \left(\frac{2a+(n-1)d}{2}\right)n,$$

$$2b + (n − 1)c > 2a + (n − 1)d$$

$$(n − 1)(c − d) > 2(a − b).$$

Because c > d, this inequality is equivalent to:

$$n − 1 > \frac{2(a-b)}{c-d},$$

$$n > \frac{2(a-b)}{c-d} + 1.$$

For example, if a = 2000, b = 1000, d = 100, and c = 150, then $\frac{2(a-b)}{c-d} + 1 = 41$. Thus if n > 41, the second salary option is better in this case.

ONGOING ASSESSMENT 7-3

1.

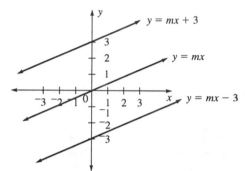

2. For every x, the point on y = mx + 3 is 3 units higher than the point on y = x. Consequently the graph of y = mx + 3 contains the point (0, 3) and is parallel to the line y = mx. Similarly the graph of y = mx − 3 contains the point (0, ⁻3) and is parallel to y = mx.

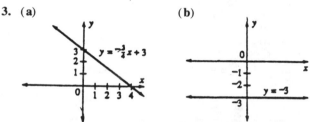

3. (a)   (b)

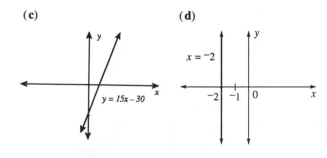

(c)   (d)

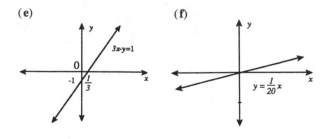

(e)   (f)

4.

	x–intercept	y–intercept
(a)	4	3
(b)	None	¯3
(c)	2	¯30
(d)	¯2	None
(e)	1/3	¯1
(f)	0	0

5. (a) Using (0, 32) and (100, 212), the slope is
$(212 - 32)/(100 - 0) = 9/5$. So F = (9/5)C + b. Plug in the
point (0, 32). Thus b = 32, and the equation is F = (9/5)C + 32.
(b) C = 5/9(F − 32)
6. (a) y = (1/3)x (b) y = ¯x + 3 (c) y = ¯4x/3 + 4
(d) y = (3/4)x + 7/4 (e) y = (1/3)x (f) y = x
7. (a) y = ¯x − 1 (b) y = (1/2)x (c) y = 1 (d) x = 2
(e) y = x − 1/2 (f) y = 0
8. Answers vary.
9. (a) x = ¯2; y is any real number. (b) x is any real number;
y = 1. (c) x > 0 and y < 0; x and y are real numbers.
10. Perimeter = 12 units, Area = 8 sq units
11. (a) x = 3 (b) y = ¯2 (c) y = 5 (d) x = ¯4
12. Answers vary. For example:
(a) Using (60, 18) and (50, 8), the slope of the line is
$(18 - 8)/(60 - 50) = 1$. So C = T + b. Plug in the point (50, 8)
to see b = ¯42. Thus C = T − 42. (b) C = 90 − 42 = 48
(c) N = 4C, so N = 4T − 168.
13. (a) Answers vary. One possible answer is y = 1.97x + 6.13.

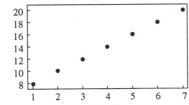

(b) Approximately $\sqrt{203.1}$
14. (a) Answers vary: (0, ¯5/3); (5/2, 0); (1, ¯1); (2, ¯1/3)
(b)   (c)

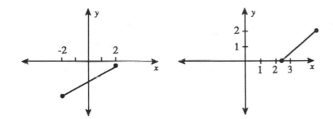

15. (a) (2, 5), unique solution (b) No solution (c) (1, ¯5);
unique solution (d) No solutions (e) (0, 0); unique solution
(f) (4/11, 1/11); unique solution
16. Equations of lines: y = 8x − 40; y = (¯4/7)x + 40/7;
y = (1/2)x. Unique common solution is (16/3, 8/3).
17. 4000 gal of gasoline and 1000 gal of kerosene
18. (a) $2000 (b) 6% annual interest or 0.5% per month
19. 17 quarters, 10 dimes
20. (a) The answers are the same. (b) Answers vary.

For example: $\left.\begin{array}{l}10x + 11y = 12 \\ 13x + 14y = 15\end{array}\right\}$ The expected solution is x = ¯1,

y = 2. (c) nx + (n + 1)y = n + 2; (n + 3)x + (n + 4)y = n + 5.
The solution to this system is x = ¯1, y = 2.

Communication
21. The intersection point gives the solution of the system
$\left.\begin{array}{l}C = F \\ C = 5/9(F - 32)\end{array}\right\}$ The solution of this system tells when C = F,
that is, when the temperature measured in degrees Celsius
equals the temperature measured in degrees Fahrenheit.
22. Answers will vary.
Explanation 1: If two distinct lines have the same slope m,
then the equations are y = mx + b and y = mx + c for some
real numbers b and c (with b ≠ c). To show that the lines are
parallel, it is sufficient to show that the lines do not intersect;
that is, that the system of equations has no solution. Indeed, if
we try to solve the equations we get mx + b = mx + c.
Because b ≠ c, this equation has no solution.
Explanation 2: With y = mx + b and y = mx + c, each is a
vertical shift of the same line, y = mx.
23. Tell Jonah that 5 − 5x is not equal to 0 (his order of
operations is incorrect). We have 5 − 5x = 5 · 1 − 5x = 5(1− x)
which is not 0.
24. Lines with undefined slopes are vertical lines and hence
parallel.

Open-ended
25. Answers vary.
26. Answers vary.
27. Answers vary.
28. Answers vary.

Cooperative Learning
29. Answers vary.

Review Problems
30. 25 years
31. 253, 255, 257, 259
32. 110 ft × 330 ft

ONGOING ASSESSMENT 7-4

1. (a) 5:21 (b) Answers vary. For example, minor.
2. (a) 30 (b) ¯3$\frac{1}{3}$ (c) 23$\frac{1}{3}$ (d) 10$\frac{1}{2}$
3. 36 lbs
4. 2469
5. $1.19
6. 270 mil
7. 64
8. 72 min for 30 in.
9. (a) 42, 56 (b) 24, 32
10. 500 ft × 900 ft
11. $14,909.09, $29,818.18, $37,272.73
12. $77 and $99
13. 135
14. (a) 5/7 (b) 6 ft
15. 120 ft
16. 8 days
17. (a) 27 (b) 20
18. Approximately 34 cm
19. 312 lbs
20. (a) 2:5. Because the ratio is 2:3, there are 2x boys and 3x
girls; hence, the ratio of boys to all students is 2x/(2x + 3x) =
2/5. (b) m : (m + n)

21. (**a**) 2/3 tsp mustard seeds, 1 c scallions, $2\frac{1}{6}$ c beans.

(**b**) 2/3 tsp mustard seeds, 2 c tomato sauce, $2\frac{1}{6}$ c beans.

(**c**) 7/13 tsp mustard seeds, $1\frac{8}{13}$ c tomato sauce, $\frac{21}{26}$ c scallions.

22. 15.12 Ω

23. (**a**) 1/3 (**b**) 10 lb (**c**) A = 7.5, B = 2.5 lbs

24. 35 ft

25. 74.6 cm

26. (**a**) y = x
(**b**) y = x
(**c**)

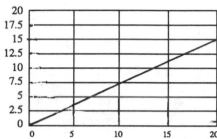

(**d**) y = 6 lb

27. 3 ft

28. (**a**)

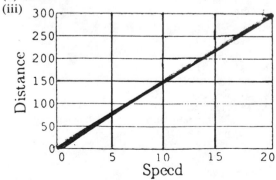

(**b**) WL = 10
(**c**) Inverse
(**d**) W = 10/L
(**e**) L = 10/W

29. (**a**) (i) d = 15t
(ii) direct
(iii)

(**b**) (i) wt = 4000
(ii) Inverse
(iii)

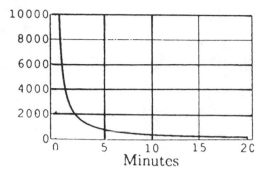

(**c**) (i) L = 25s
(ii) direct
(iii)

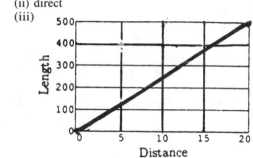

(**d**) (i) W = 100 − L
(ii) neither
(iii)

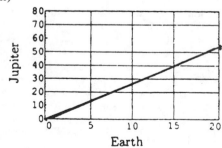

(**e**) (i) J = 2.64E
(ii) direct
(iii)

30. (**a**) directly (**b**) directly (**c**) inversely (**d**) inversely
(**e**) neither (**f**) neither

31. (a) $\frac{1}{2}$ (b) Let $\frac{a}{b} = \frac{c}{d} = \frac{e}{f} = r$.

Then $a = br$

$\quad\quad c = dr$

$\quad\quad e = fr$

So, $a + c + e = br + dr + fr$

$\quad\quad a + c + e = r(b + d + f)$

$\quad\quad a + c + e = r$

32. (a) $\frac{a}{b} = \frac{c}{d}$ implies $\frac{a}{b} + 1 = \frac{c}{d} + 1$, which implies

$\frac{a+b}{b} = \frac{c+d}{d}$. (b) By inverting (Problem 27) $\frac{b}{a} = \frac{d}{c}$ and by

part (a), $\frac{b+a}{a} = \frac{d+c}{c}$. Then inverting again gives

$\frac{a}{a+b} = \frac{c}{d+c}$. (c) $\frac{a}{b} = \frac{c}{d}$ implies $\frac{a}{b} - 1 = \frac{c}{d} - 1$, which

implies $\frac{a-b}{b} = \frac{c-d}{d}$. From part (a) and this last result, we

have $\frac{a+b}{b} + \frac{a-b}{b} = \frac{c+d}{d} + \frac{c-d}{d}$, which implies

$\frac{a+b}{a-b} = \frac{c+d}{c-d}$.

Communication

33. (a) 40/700 or 4/70 or 2/35 (b) 525 cm (c) For the first

set, $\frac{\text{footprint length}}{\text{thighbone length}} = \frac{40}{100} = \frac{20}{50}$; i.e., a 50-cm thighbone

would correspond to a 20-cm footprint. Thus it is not likely that the 50-cm thighbone is from the animal which left the 30 cm

footprint. $\left(\text{Notice that } \frac{20}{50} \neq \frac{30}{50}\right)$.

34. No, the ratio of the prices is proportional to the ratio of the areas and not to the ratio of the diameters.

35. The ratio between the mass of the gold in the ring and the mass of the ring is 18/24. If x is the number of ounces of pure gold in the ring that weighs 0.4 oz we have $18/24 = x\ /0.4$. Hence $x = (18 \cdot 0.4)/24$ or 0.3 oz. Consequently the price of the gold in the ring is $0.3 \cdot \$300$ or $90.

36. Yes. From $\frac{H}{M} = \frac{M}{S}$ and $M^2 = HS = (2.9 \cdot 10^{32})(1.7 \cdot 10^{-29})$

$= 4.93 \cdot 10^3$ kg. But then M is approximately 70 kg.

37. (a) Watch for the lightning and measure the time until you hear the thunder.

(b) Yes, because $d = t/c = (1/c) \cdot t$ and $1/c$ is a constant.

(c) $\frac{t_1}{d_1} = \frac{t_2}{d_2} = c$ This can be justified as follows: $t_1 = cd_1$,

hence $c = t_1/d_1$. Also $t_2 = cd_2$, and therefore $c = t_2/d_2$.

Open-ended

38. Answers vary.

39. Answers vary.

40. (a) 57.6 lb per sq in. (b) Both are examples of inverse variation. (c) Answers vary.

Cooperative Learning

41. Answers vary.

42. Answers vary. A possible formulation is as follows: Two or more weights (or forces) on a lever balance if and only if the sum of the products of the weights which are to the right of the fulcrum and the corresponding distances to the fulcrum equals the sum of the products of the weight which are to the left of the fulcrum and the corresponding distances to the fulcrum. If the products are not equal, the lever will tilt in the direction of the weights that correspond to the greater product.

Review Problems

43. The sum is $x + (x + 2) + (x + 4) = 3x + 6$, and $(3x + 6 - 6)/3 = x$.

44. (a) $x = 0$ (b) 15.5 (c) $x \doteq 0.019$ (d) 4 (e) $x < 6/5$

(f) $x \geq \sqrt{2}$, or $x \leq {}^-\sqrt{2}$

ONGOING ASSESSMENT 7-5

1. (a) 789% (b) 3.2% (c) 19,310% (d) 20% (e) $83\frac{1}{3}\%$

(f) 15% (g) 12.5% (h) 37.5% (i) 62.5% (j) $16\frac{2}{3}\%$

(k) 80% (l) 2.5%

2. (a) 0.16 (b) 0.045 (c) 0.002 (d) $0.00\overline{285714}$ (e) $0.13\overline{6}$

(f) 1.25 (g) $0.00\overline{3}$ (h) 0.0025

3. (a) 4 (b) 2 (c) 25 (d) 200 (e) 12.5

4. It depends on the calculator.

5. (a) 2.04 (b) 50% (c) 60 (d) 3.43 (e) 300% (f) 40

6. 63 boxes

7. $16,960

8. $14,500

9. (a) Bill sold 221. (b) Joe sold 90%. (c) Ron started with 265.

10. 20%

11. Approximately 17.65%

12. 18.4%

13. Approximately 61% increase

14. 100%

15. $22.40

16. $5.10

17. 50

18. $336

19. 35%

20. $3200

21. 1200

22. Approximately 23.5%

23. $10.37 per hour

24. 11.1%

25. $440

26. $33\frac{1}{3}\%$

27. Approximately $9207.58

28. (a) $3.30 (b) $24.00 (c) $1.90 (d) $24.50

29. (a) 4% (b) 32% (c) 64%

30. (a) Approximately 4.94%, 34.57%, 60.49%

(b) Approximately 6.25%, 37.50%, 56.25%

(c) Approximately 8.16%, 40.82%, 51.02%

(d) Apprximately 2.78%, 27.78%, 69.44%

31. (a) Answers vary. (b) (i) 0.366 sec between beats (ii) 0.0061 min between beats

32. (a) 25% (b) 20%

33. 20%

34. 25%

35. Apprentice makes $700. Journeyman makes $1400. Master makes $2100.

36. (a) 4% (b) (i) 44 (ii) 8.8%

37. $82,644.63

38. (a) 90% (b) $6\frac{2}{3}\%$ (c) 48% (d) 60.4% (e) Mental Health, Adult & Family Services, and Senior Services (f) Yes

39. $399,375

Communication

40. If they spend $40 then a 15% tip would amount to a $6 tip (since 10% of $40 is $4 and 5% of $40 is half that much). Hence they can spend approximately $40.

41. Let x be the amount invested. The first stock option will yield $(1.15x) \cdot 0.85$ after two years. The second stock will yield $(0.85x) \cdot 1.15$. Because each yield equals $(1.15 \cdot 0.85)x$, the investments are equally good.

Open-ended
42. Answers vary.
43. Answers vary.
44. Answers vary.

Cooperative Learning
45. Answers vary.

Review Problems
46. Approximately 873 ft^2
47. They are the same.
48. Boys: approximately 42.9%; girls: approximately 57.1%.

Brain Teaser (p. 399)
Let C = amount of crust
  P = amount of pie
  x = percent of crust to be reduced
  C = 25% of P, so
  $Cx/100 = (20/100)P$. Hence: $x = 20\%$.

ONGOING ASSESSMENT 7-6

1.

	Int. Rate per Period	No. of Periods	Amt. of Int. Paid
(a)	3%	4	$125.51
(b)	2%	12	$268.24
(c)	$\frac{10}{12}\%$	60	$645.31
(d)	$\frac{12}{365}\%$	1460	$615.95

2. $5,460.00
3. $24.45
4. 3.5%
5. Invest $32,040.82
6. $64,800
7. $23,720.58
8. $1944
9. (iii) at 13.2%
10. Approximately $2.53
11. Approximately $23,673.64
12. Approximately $3592.89
13. Approximately $12.79%
14. Approximately $7.026762 \cdot 10^8$
15. $4416.35
16. $81,628.83
17. The Pay More Bank offers a better rate.
18. $10,935

Communication
19. Let a be the original value of the house. Because it depreciates 10% each year for the first three years, using compound depreciation the price after three years will be $a(1 - 0.10)^3$ or $a \cdot 0.9^3$. Because of compound appreciation, after another three years the value of the house will be $a(0.9^3) \cdot 1.1^3$ or $a(0.9^3 \cdot 1.1^3)$, which equals approximately $a \cdot 0.9703$. Because $a \cdot 0.9703 < a$, the value of the house decreased after six years. The value of the house decreases by approximately 3%.
20. If we want our money doubled, then $2 = 1(1 + 0.10)^n$, or $2 = 1.1^n$ and we are looking for n. By trial and error, we can find that $1.1^{7.3} = 2.005$, so it would take about 7.3 years to double an investment at 10% compounded annually.

21. No. The percentages cannot be added because each time the percent is of a different quantity. The 15% is a savings of the original price of the fuel. The second savings of 35% is of the new price after the first savings. We could find the percent of savings as follows. For each $100 of the cost of fuel, the new cost after a 15% savings will be $85. When the second device is installed, an additional 35% is saved and the new cost is $(65/100) \cdot 85$. After the third device is installed an additional 50% is saved and the new cost is $(50/100) \cdot (65/100) \cdot 85$. The savings on a $100 initial cost is $100 - (50/100) \cdot (65/100) \cdot 85$ or $72.375. Because the savings were based on a $100 initial cost, the percent of total savings with all three devices is 72.375%.

Open-ended
22. (**a**) Answers vary. (**b**) Let a be an initial cost of an item that depreciates at a rate of p% each period of time. If n is the number of periods and C(n) is the cost (as a function of n) after n periods, then $C(n) = a(1 - P/100)^n$.
23. Answers vary.
24. Answers vary.

Cooperative Learning
25. (**a**) Answers vary. (**b**) When a person takes a loan of $a at an annual rate of p%, a loaning institution often adds on other costs to the loan (processing and other fees). Suppose all the additional costs for the loan are $b. Then the customer would have to pay interest and fees in the amount $ap/100 + b$. The percent of the original amount that equals this total is the APR. If the APR is x%, then $ax/100 = ap/100 + b$. Hence $ax = ap + 100b$, and $x = (ap + 100b)/a$.

Chapter Review
1. (**a**) $t = d/65$ (**b**) $C = 15 + 8(t - 1)$ in cents (**c**) $C = 0.6(0.14t) = 0.084t$ (**d**) $S = 50(2x - 99)$ (**e**) $V = (88/100)m$ (**f**) $E = (1.05)(1.10)(1.15)S = 1.32825S$
2. (**a**) $x \le 42/25$ (**b**) $x \le 3/2$ (**c**) $x = 8/9$ (**d**) $x = 3/2$
3. 35 1–kg packages, 115 2–kg packages
4. 7 nickels, 17 dimes
5. 1790 freshmen, 2020 sophomores, 895 juniors, and 1010 seniors
6. 42 gal
7. $1\frac{7}{9}$ oz
8. (**a**) 6 mi (**b**) 5.2 mi
9. 560 fish
10. No. The ratio depends on how many chips came from each plant.
11. (**a**)   (**b**)

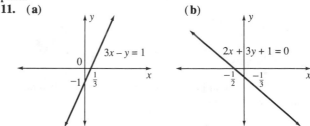

12. Hoover, 15,957,537; Roosevelt, 22,521,525
13. (**a**) $y = {}^-(4/3)x - 1/3$ (**b**) $x = {}^-3$ (**c**) $y = 3$
14. (**a**) $(4.2, {}^-0.6)$ (**b**) $\left(\frac{10}{9}, \frac{4}{3}\right)$ (**c**) no solution, parallel lines
15. (**a**) 25% (**b**) 192 (**c**) $56.\overline{6}$ (**d**) 20%
16. (**a**) 12.5% (**b**) 7.5% (**c**) 627% (**d**) 1.23% (**e**) 150%
17. (**a**) 0.60 (**b**) $0.00\overline{6}$ (**c**) 1

18. $9280
19. 3.3̄%
20. 88.6%
21. $5750
22. It makes no difference.
23. $80
24. $15,000
25. $15,110.69

CHAPTER 8

ONGOING ASSESSMENT 8-1

1. (a) 56/80 or 7/10 (b) 24/80 or 3/10 (c) Probably not. In an experiment with only a relatively small number of tosses, the outcome will probably not be identical. Experimental probability is based only on the number of times the experiment is repeated, not on what will happen in the long run. (d) You would probably obtain the same approximate results but experimental probability does not guarantee the exact results.
2. (a) {0, 1, 2, 3, 4, 5, 6, 7, 8, 9} (b) {0, 1, 2, 3, 4} (c) {1, 3, 5, 7, 9} (d) {0, 1, 3, 4, 5, 6, 7, 8, 9} (e) (b) 5/10, or 1/2 (c) 5/10, or 1/2 (d) 9/10
3. (a) 3/8 (b) 2/8 or 1/4 (c) 4/8 or 1/2 (d) 2/8 or 1/4 (e) 0 (f) 3/8 (g) 1/8
4. (a) 26/52 or 1/2 (b) 12/52 or 3/13 (c) 28/52 or 7/13 (d) 4/52 or 1/13 (e) 48/52 or 12/13 (f) 22/52 or 11/26 (g) 3/52 (h) 30/52 or 15/26
5. (a) 4/12 or 1/3 (b) 8/12 or 2/3 (c) 0 (d) 6/12 or 1/2
6. (a) 5/26 (b) 21/26
7. 0.8
8. (a) 1/6 (b) 4/6 or 2/3
9. (a) 8/36 or 2/9 (b) 4/36 or 1/9 (c) 24/36 or 2/3 (d) 6 and 8 both have 5/36 probability. (e) 0 (f) 1 (g) 10 times
10. 70%, P (No Rain) = 1 − P (Rain) = 1 − 0.30 = 0.70
11. (a) 18/38 or 9/19 (b) 2/38 or 1/19 (c) 26/38 or 13/19 (d) 20/38 or 10/19
12. 10 times
13. (a) No (b) Yes (c) Yes (d) Yes (e) No (f) Yes (g) No (h) No
14. 45/150 or 3/10
15. (a) 2/4 or 1/2 (b) 3/4 (c) 3/4
16. 350/1380 or 35/138
17. (a)

(b)

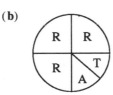

18. (a) 20/52 or 5/13 (b) 40/52 or 10/13 (c) 0
19. The answers may vary depending on how the 6, 7, and 9 are formed. The following answers are based on a Casio digital watch. (a) 8/10 (b) 8/10 (c) 7/10 (d) 10/10 or 1
20. (a) The probability of students taking Algebra or Chemistry (b) The probability of students taking Algebra and Chemistry (c) This represents 1 minus the probability of a student taking Chemistry or the probability of a student not taking Chemistry.
21. 0.7
22. (a) 45/80 or 9/16 (b) 10/80 or 1/8 (c) 60/80 or 3/4 (d) 30/80 or 3/8

Communication
23. All probabilities are less than or equal to 1 and greater than or equal to 0. If events are mutually exclusive, then P(A ∪ B)

= P(A) + P(B). Therefore, if A and B are mutually exclusive, P(A ∪ B) = P(A) + P(B) = 0.8 + 0.9 = 1.7 which is impossible. Therefore, events A and B are not mutually exclusive.
24. Bobbie's reasoning is not correct unless her theoretical probability of making a basket is really 1/2. The outcomes of making a basket or missing it are probably not equally likely, so this definition does not apply. To calculate her experimental probability of making a free throw, divide the number of shots made by the number attempted.
25. Joe's conjecture is incorrect. Each of the numbers 1 through 4 has probability 1/4 of occurring because each angle where the arrow is located measures 90 degrees and the spinner has the same chance of landing in any of the regions.

Open-ended
26. Answers vary, for example, tossing an even number and tossing an odd number are mutually exclusive.
27. Answers vary depending on the book selected.
28. Answers vary, for example, batting averages are really probabilities that a hitter will get a hit, or a free-throw shooting percentage is really a probability that a basketball player will make a free throw. Insurance companies use probabilities to determine rates.
29. Answers vary, for example, Event A is an impossible event such as rolling a 10 on a single roll of a standard die. Event B has low probability such as the chance of rain being 20%. Event C is around 0.5 so this might be something like obtaining a head when tossing a fair coin. Event D has a high probability of happening but it is not certain, for example, tossing a number less than 6 on a toss of a standard die. Event E has probability 1 so it has to happen, for example, tossing either head or a tail on the toss of a fair coin. Event F has probability greater than 1 and this cannot happen so no event is possible.

Cooperative Learning
30. This will depend on the number of each color cube in the bag. The experimental probability of each color can be obtained by finding the number of times that a color is drawn and dividing this number by 50. We can then use this probability to guess the number of cubes of each color. For example, if (20/50) of the draws were red, then a guess for the number of red is (20/50)(8) = 3.2 or 3 are red.
31. (b) 1 and 2 and then 0 and 3 (c) Answers vary. (d) The theoretical probabilities for the differences are P(0) = 6/36, P(1) = 10/36, P(2) = 8/36, P(3) = 6/36, P(4) = 4/36, P(5) = 2/36, P(6) = 0/36. (e) Using the probabilities from part (d), the 18 markers should be distributed from left to right as 3, 5, 4, 3, 2, 1, and 0.
32. (b) The person who receives four times the value of the number on the die wins when 1, 2, and 3 are tossed. The person who receives the square of the number showing wins when a 5 or a 6 is tossed. When a 4 is tossed, the game is a draw. The person who receives four times the value of the die has a greater chance of winning and therefore the game is not fair.

ONGOING ASSESSMENT 8-2

1. (a)

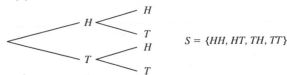

$S = \{HH, HT, TH, TT\}$

(b)

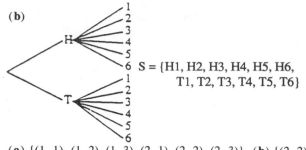

$S = \{H1, H2, H3, H4, H5, H6, T1, T2, T3, T4, T5, T6\}$

2. (a) {(1, 1), (1, 2), (1, 3), (2, 1), (2, 2), (2, 3)} (b) {(2, 2)}
(c) {(1, 2), (2, 1), (2, 2), (2, 3)} (d) {(1, 2), (2, 1), (2, 3)}
3. (a) 1/216 (b) 1/120
4. (a) 1/24 (b) 1/64 (c) 1/84 (d) 7/36
5. 1/30
6. (a) Box 1, with probability 1/3 (Box 2 has probability 1/5)
(b) Either, with probability 4/27
7. (a) 64/75 (b) 11/75
8. 0.0005
9. (a) 1/5 (b) 4/5 (c) 11/15 (d) 8/15
10. 5/16
11. 1/16
12. (a) 1/4 (b) 5/8 (c) 1/8
13. (a) 8/20 or 2/5 (b) Yes, now P(Even) = 18/20 or 9/10
14. 2/16 or 1/8
15. (a) 1/320 (b) 63/4000 (c) 0 (d) $\dfrac{171}{320}$
16. 1/32
17. (a) 16/81 (b) 8/27
18. 1/256
19. 1/34,650
20. (a) 1/25 (b) 8/25 (c) 16/25
21. (a) 100 square units
(b) P(Region A) = 4/100, or 1/25
P(Region B) = 12/100, or 3/25
P(Region C) = 20/100, or 1/5
P(Region D) = 28/100, or 7/25
P(Region E) = 36/100, or 9/25
(c) 1/625 (d) 36/100, or 9/25
22. 0.7
23. 1/12
24. 271/1000
25. 2/5
26. 25/30 or 5/6
27. 2/28 or 1/14
28. 69/3000 or 23/1000
29. Billie-Bobby-Billie because the probability of winning two in a row is greater this way. Note, it does not say win two out of three.
30. She should serve the first one hard and then it does not matter what she does on the second serve.

Communication
31. If the die is fair, the probability that Jim will roll a 3 on the next roll is 1/6, which is the same probability of rolling any one of the other numbers. The results of the first three rolls should have no effect on the next roll.
32. Finding a witness with blond hair and blue eyes has a greater probability. The probability of a red car introduces another number that is less than 1 to the product. When you multiply a, the probability that you have for blond hair and blue eyes, by a number less than 1 and greater than 0, the probability becomes smaller.
33. If the wheel was fair, the probability of a black on the next spin was the same on the 27th spin as it was on the previous 26 spins. A fair wheel has no memory.

Open-ended
34. Answers vary, for example, car insurance companies study accident rates for different age groups and different sexes. They study accident rates and costs to fix various models of cars. Life insurance companies study mortality rates.
35. Answers vary depending on how complex the game is. The game could be as simple as player A wins if the sum of the digits is even and player B wins if the sum of the digits is odd.
36. One possibility is that one die has the numbers 0, 0, 0, 3, 3, 3, and the other die has the numbers 1, 2, 3, 7, 8, 9. The probability of each outcome is 3/36 or 1/12.
37. Answers vary, but 3/5 of the area of the board must be labeled in a certain way.

Cooperative Learning
38. The probabilities of winning the game are summarized below:

		First Player's Choice			
		H H	H T	T H	T T
Second	H H	—	0.50	0.75	0.50
Player's	H T	0.50	—	0.50	0.25
Choice	T H	0.25	0.50	—	0.50
	T T	0.50	0.75	0.50	—

Of the 12 possible games, only eight result in choices with equally likely probabilities. Therefore, the game is not fair.
39. (a) The game is not fair. You should choose spinner A.
(b) The game is not fair. You should choose spinner C. It has a winning probability of 35/99.

Review Problems
40. (a) v (b) iii (c) ii (d) i (e) iv
41. (a) 1/30 (b) 0 (c) 19/30

Brain Teaser (p. 438)
The probability that at least two people share the same birthday is one minus the probability that no two people share the same birthday. We calculate the latter probability first. Let's pick a first person. Since there are 364 birthdays that a second person can have which are different from the first person's birthday, the probability that the second persons' birthday differs from the first is $\dfrac{364}{365}$. In order for the third person to have a birthday different from the first and the second person, he or she must have been born on one of the 363 days which are different from the first two person's birthdays. Thus the probability that the third person's birthday differs from the first and second is $\dfrac{363}{365}$. Hence the probability that the first three people have different birthdays is $\dfrac{364}{365} \cdot \dfrac{363}{365}$. Continuing in this way we find the probability that all n people have different birthdays is $\dfrac{364}{365} \cdot \dfrac{363}{365} \cdot \dfrac{362}{365} \cdots \dfrac{365-(n-1)}{365}$. To find the value of n for which the above product is less than $\dfrac{1}{2}$, we can use a calculator and try various values of n. For n = 23 the above product is slightly less than $\dfrac{1}{2}$. Hence if there are 23 people in the room, the probability that no two people share the same birthday is slightly less than $\dfrac{1}{2}$; therefore the complementary probability that at least two people share the same birthday is slightly greater than $\dfrac{1}{2}$.

ONGOING ASSESSMENT 8-3

1. Answers vary, for example, a black card might represent the birth of a boy and a red card might represent the birth of a girl. Choose a card to represent a birth.

2. (a) Answers vary, for example, you could use a random digit table. The numbers 1 through 9 could represent rain, and 0 could represent no rain. (b) Answers vary but should be close to 0.48. (c) Approximately 0.52.

3. Answers vary depending on the simulation.

4. (a) Let 1, 2, 3, 4, 5, and 6 represent the numbers on the die and ignore the numbers 0, 7, 8, 9. (b) Number the persons 01, 02, 03, ..., 18, 19, 20. Go to the random digit table and mark off groups of two. The three persons chosen are the first three whose numbers appear. (c) Represent Red by the numbers 0, 1, 2, 3, 4; Green by the numbers 5, 6, 7; Yellow by the number 8; and White by the number 9.

5. Mark off 30 blocks of three digits in a random digit table. Disregard 000 or any numbers that are greater than 500. These are the numbers of the 30 students who will be chosen for the trip.

6. To simulate Monday, let the digits 1 through 8 represent rain and 0 and 9 represent no rain. If rain occured on Monday, repeat the same process for Tuesday. If it did not rain on Monday, let the digits 1 through 7 represent rain and 0, 8, and 9 represent dry. Repeat a similar process for the rest of the week.

7. Answers vary, for example, mark off blocks of two digits and let the digits 00, 01, 02, ..., 13, 14 represent contracting the disease and 15 to 99 represent no disease. Mark off blocks of six digits to represent the three children. If at least one of the numbers is in the range 00 to 14, then this represents a child in the three-child family having strep.

8. 3/10

9. 1200 fish

10. (a) 7 (b) Answers vary, for example, let the digits 0, 1, 2, 3, 4 represent a victory by team A and the digits 5, 6, 7, 8, 9 represent a victory by team B. Then go to the random digit table, pick a starting place, and count the number of digits (games) it takes for one of the teams to win. Repeat this experiment a number of times for four games and for seven games and use the definition of probability to compute the experimental probability.

Communication

11. Answers vary, but the paragraph should point out that probability only tells what happens over the long run and not what will happen on the next trial or on a small number of trials. A small sample could give very biased results. For example, suppose we were simulating the toss of a coin and heads is represented by even numbers. If only 10 numbers were chosen and 2, 2, 3, 8, 6, 2, 7, 4, 8, 2 appeared, the simulation would suggest that P(H) = 8/10.

12. This problem could be simulated using even numbers for the birth of boys and odd numbers for the birth of girls for many families. If this is done, the number of boys and girls should remain about the same. This might become more clear by considering what happens for 32 women giving birth. Half the births are boys and half are girls. There are now 16 boys and 16 girls. The half with boys stop and the half with girls have another child of which half are boys and half are girls. Now there are 16 + 8 = 24 boys and 16 + 8 = 24 girls. The half with boys stop and the 8 with girls have another child, four of which are boys and four are girls. Now there are 24 + 4 = 28 boys and 24 + 4 = 28 girls. By symmetry this will continue. Also this argument holds for a different number of women initially giving birth.

13. Answers vary, for example, suppose we use a random digit table and let 1, 2, or 3 represent a hit and 0, 4, 5, 7, 8, and 9 represent no hit. We could then pick a random starting point in the table and mark off blocks of four digits. Each of the digits 1, 2, or 3 in the block represents a hit. Now, count the number of times at least three of these digits appear in the block and calculate the experimental probability.

14. Answers vary, one could use a random digit table with blocks of two digits, or a spinner could be designed with 12 sections representing the different months. The spinner could be spun five times to represent the birthdays of five people. We could then keep track of how many times at least two people have the same birthday.

15. Answers vary, for example, use a random digit table. Let the digits 1 – 8 represent a win and the digits 0 and 9 represent losses. Mark off blocks of three. If only the digits 1– 8 appear then this represents three wins in a row.

16. Let the 10 ducks be represented by the digits 0, 1, 2, 3, ..., 8, 9. Then pick a starting point in the table and mark off 10 digits to simulate which ducks the hunters shoot at. Count how many of the digits 0 through 9 are not in the 10 digits and this represents the ducks that escaped. Do this experiment many times and take the average to determine an answer. See how close your simulation comes to 3.49 ducks.

Cooperative Learning

17. (d) The probability of two boys and two girls is 6/16 or 3/8.

18. (d) $(1/2)^{10} = 1/1024$

19. Answers depend on the simulation.

20. Pick a starting spot in the table and count the number of digits it takes before all the numbers 1 through 9 are obtained. Repeat this experiment many times and find the average number of boxes.

Review Problems

21. No, you will win about 6/16 or 3/8 of the games.

22. (a) 1/4 (b) 1/52 (c) 48/52 or 12/13 (d) 3/4 (e) 1/2 (f) 1/52 (g) 16/52 or 4/13 (h) 1

23. (a) 15/19 (b) 56/361 (c) 28/171

ONGOING ASSESSMENT 8-4

1. (a) 12 to 40 or 3 to 10 (b) 40 to 12 or 10 to 3

2. 30 to 6 or 5 to 1

3. 15 to 1

4. (a) 1/2 (b) $(1/2)^{10}$ or 1/1024 (c) 1023 to 1

5. 5/8

6. 1 to 1

7. 4 to 6 or 2 to 3

8. 20 to 18 or 10 to 9

9. 1/27

10. 3 hours

11. E = 1/6 (10) + 5/6 (−2) = 10/6 + (−10/6) = 0. Therefore, you should come out about even if you play a long time.

12. (a) 1/38 (b) 37 to 1 (c) −2/38 or −1/19 dollars

13. Approximately 8¢

14. $10,000

15. (a) Because Al's probability of winning at this point was 3/4 and Betsy's was 1/4, Al should get $75 and Betsy should get $25. (b) 3 to 1 (c) Al gets about $89 and Betsy gets about $11. (d) 57 to 7

16. Yes

17. No

Communication

18. Odds are determined from probabilities. The *odds in favor* of an event, E, are determined by $P(E)/P(\overline{E})$. The *odds against* an event are determined by $P(\overline{E})/P(E)$.

19.   Don't believe it. If the odds of getting AIDS are 68,000 to 1, then the probability of getting AIDS is 68,000/68,001. Therefore the probability of getting AIDS is almost certain. The article should have talked about the odds against getting AIDS.

20.   25¢, because P(HH) = 1/4 so E = 1/4($1) = $.25.

Open-ended
21.   Answers vary, the premium would have to cost at least (47/100,000) ($50,000) = $23.50. Then the cost of overhead would have to be taken into account along with the desired amount of profit.

Cooperative Learning
22.   Games and rules will vary, as will the odds and expected values of the game.

Review Problems
23.   (a) {1, 2, 3, 4} (b) {Red, Blue} (c) {(1, Red), (1, Blue), (2, Red), (2, Blue), (3, Red), (3, Blue), (4, Red), (4, Blue)} (d) {(Blue, 1), (Blue, 2), (Blue, 3) (Blue, 4), (Blue, 5), (Blue, 6), (Red, 1), (Red, 2), (Red, 3), (Red, 4), (Red, 5), (Red, 6)} (e) {(1, 1), (1, 2), (1, 3), (1, 4), (2, 1), (2, 2), (2, 3), (2, 4), (3, 1), (3, 2), (3, 3), (3, 4), (4, 1), (4, 2), (4, 3), (4, 4)} (f) {(Red, Red), (Red, Blue), (Blue, Red), (Blue, Blue)}

24.   The blue section must have 300°; the red has 60°.

25.   25/676

ONGOING ASSESSMENT 8-5
1.   13,860
2.   224
3.   32
4.   10,000
5.   1352 with three-letter call letters; 35,152 with four-letter call letters
6.   180
7.   (a) True (b) False (c) False (d) False (e) True (f) True (g) True
8.   40,320
9.   15
10.   (a) 12 (b) 210 (c) 3360 (d) 34,650 (e) 3780
11.   (a) 24,360 (b) 4060
12.   792
13.   1/120
14.   45
15.   1260
16.   (a) 6 (b) 36
17.   eight people
18.   (a) 1/13 (b) 8/65
19.   2,598,960 different five-card hands (Order within the hand is not important.)
20.   11,232,000
21.   1/25,827,165
22. 10^9 or 1,000,000,000
23.   13440/59049 or approx. 0.228
24.   3840

Communication
25.   Answers vary, for example, the Fundamental Counting Principle (FCP) says that to find the number of ways of making several decisions in a row, multiply the number of choices that can be made for each decision. The FCP can be used to find the number of permutations. A permutation is an arrangement of things in a definite order. A combination is a selection of things in which the order is not important. We could find the number of combinations by using the FCP and then dividing by the number of ways in which the things can be arranged.

26.   Answers vary, for example, for the formula $_nP_r = n!/(n - r)!$ to work for $_nP_n$, then $_nP_n = n!/(n - n)! = n!/0!$. To make this equation true we must define 0! to be 1.

27.   (a) There are 10 choices for the number on the first reel, 10 choices for the number on the second reel, and 10 choices for the number on the third reel. By the Fundamental Counting Principle, there are 10 · 10 · 10 or 1000 choices for the combination of the lock. (b) The correct name should probably be "permutation" locks, since the order in which the three numbers are entered makes a difference, and so this is a permutation rather than a combination.

Open-ended
28.   (a) 10^6 or 1,000,000 (b) Yes, Montana, Wyoming, Alaska, Delaware, North Dakota, South Dakota, Vermont (c) Answers vary, for example, you would first find the population of California and then experiment with using letters in the license plates. This would help because the choice is for 26 letters in a slot rather than 10 numbers.

Cooperative Learning
29.   (a) Answers vary, the first and last numbers in every row are ones. Every other number is obtained by adding the numbers immediately above. The next two rows are 1, 7, 21, 35, 35, 21, 7, 1 and 1, 8, 28, 56, 70, 56, 28, 8, 1. (b) Answers vary, for example, the diagonal 1, 3, 6, 10, 15 are triangular numbers. (c) The sums of the numbers in the rows are 1, 2, 4, 8, 16, 32, 64. The sum in the 10th row is $2^{10} = 1024$. (d) Yes, a similar relationship holds in all the rows for the entries in Pascal's triangle. (e) The entries in the nth row are given by $_nC_r$ where n is the number of the row and r = 0 to n. For example, the first three entries in the sixth row are $_6C_0, _6C_1, _6C_2$.

Review Exercises
30.   (a) 396/2652 or 33/221 (b) 1352/2652 or 26/51
31.   3/36 or 1/12
32.   E = $0 so the game is fair.

Brain Teaser (p. 464)
(a) The probability of a successful flight with two engines is 0.9999 (b) The probability of a successful flight with four engines is 0.99999603.

Chapter Review
1.   (a) {Monday, Tuesday, Wednesday, Thursday, Friday, Saturday, Sunday} (b) {Tuesday, Thursday} (c) 2/7
2.   There's at least one other colored bean, besides red and blue; there are 800 blue ones; there are 125 red ones.
3.   (a) Approximately 0.501 (b) Approximately 0.499 (c) 34,226,731 to 34,108,157
4.   (a) 5/12 (b) 9/12 or 3/4 (c) 5/12 (d) 9/12 or 3/4 (e) 0 (f) 1
5.   (a) 13/52 or 1/4 (b) 1/52 (c) 22/52 or 11/26 (d) 48/52 or 12/13
6.   (a) 64/729 (b) 24/504 or 1/21
7.   6/25
8.   14/80 or 7/40
9.   7/45
10.   4 to 48 or 1 to 12
11.   3 to 3 or 1 to 1
12.   3/8
13. $.30
14.   33 1/3¢ or 34¢
15.   900
16.   120
17.   5040
18.   2/20, or 1/10

19. (a) 5 · 4 · 3 or 60 (b) 3/60 or 1/20 (c) 1/60
20. 15/36
21. 2/5
22. 0.027
23. 63/80
24. Answers vary.
25. (a) 1/8 (b) 1/4 (c) 1/16
26. 8/20 or 2/5

CHAPTER 9

ONGOING ASSESSMENT 9-1

1.

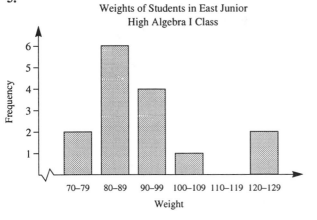

Glasses of Lemonade Sold

represents 10 glasses

2. (a) 225 million (b) 375 million (c) 550 million

3.

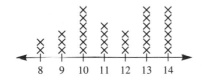

Student Ages at Washington School

4. (a) 72, 74, 81, 81, 82, 85, 87, 88, 92, 94, 97, 98, 103, 123, 125 (b) 72 lbs (c) 125 lbs

5.

Weights of Students in East Junior
High Algebra I Class

6. Answers will vary. For example,
(a) A line plot will have two columns of x's, one for Heads and one for Tails.
(b) A histogram will have two bars, one for Heads and one for Tails. The vertical axis will be partitioned to show frequencies of each.

7. (a) November, 30 cm (b) 50 cm

8. (a)

Ages of HKM Employees

6	332
5	8224
4	8561511
3	474224
2	14333617301365396
1	898

3 | 4 represents
34 years old

(b) There are more employees in their 40s. (c) 20 (d) 17.5%

9. (a) Approximately 3800 km (b) Approximately 1900 km

10.

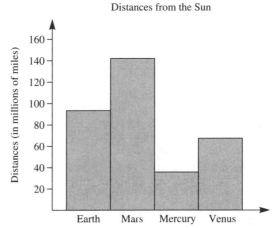

Distances from the Sun

11.

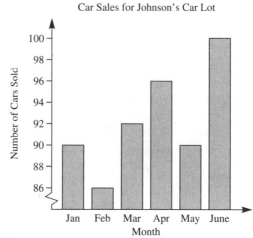

Car Sales for Johnson's Car Lot

12.

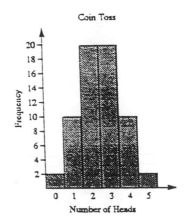

Coin Toss

13. (**a**)

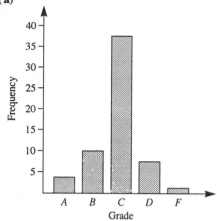

(**b**) Course Grades for Elementary Teachers

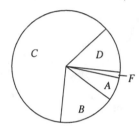

14. (**a**) Fall Textbook Costs

```
1 | 6
2 | 3 3
3 | 0 3 5 7 7 9 9
4 | 0 1 2 2 5 8 9
5 | 0 0 1 3 8
6 | 0 2 2        2|3 represents $23
```

(**b**) Fall Textbook Costs

Classes	Tally	Frequency	Classes	Tally	Frequency
$15–19	I	1	$45–49	III	3
$20–24	II	2	$50–54	IIII	4
$25–29		0	$55–59	I	1
$30–34	II	2	$60–64	III	3
$35–39	IIII	5			25
$40–44	IIII	4			

(**c**) (**d**) Frequency polygon and histogram on same graph.

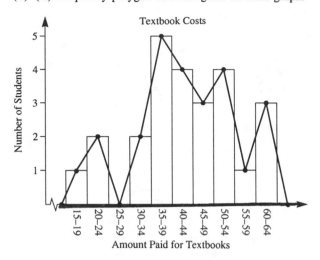

(**e**) A frequency polygon is not appropriate to use here. This is not a continuous set of data. There is no time involved.

15. (**a**) Chicken (**b**) 10 mph (**c**) Cheetah (**d**) Yes

16. (**a**) Women (**b**) Approximately one year (**c**) Approximately 7.5 years

17. (**a**) Approximately $8400 (**b**) $14,000 (**c**) Approximately $7000 (**d**) Right after two years

18. (**a**) Asia (**b**) Africa (**c**) It is about 2/3 as large. (**d**) Asia and Africa (**e**) 5:16 (**f**) Approximately 58.6 million square miles

19. (**a**)

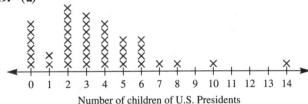

Number of children of U.S. Presidents

(**b**)

Number of Children	Tally	Frequency
0	HHT I	6
1	II	2
2	HHT III	8
3	HHT II	7
4	HHT I	6
5	IIII	4
6	IIII	4
7	I	1
8	I	1
9		0
10	I	1
11		0
12		0
13		0
14	I	1
		41

(**c**) 2 (**a**) The range of data is too diverse to lend itself to a stem-andleaf plot.

(**b**) The numbers of deaths in 1992 are significantly greater than the numbers of deaths in each category in 1983.

20. (**a**) The range of data is too diverse to lend itself to a stem-and-leaf plot. (**b**) The number of deaths in 1992 are significantly greater than the number of deaths in each age category in 1985.

Communication
21. Answers may vary. However, a circle graph would be more appropriate when it is desired to emphasize proportions.
22. Answers may vary. However, a line graph is preferable when data are continuous.
23. Answers may vary. However, a stem-and-leaf plot is more informative when exact data are needed.
24. Answers may vary. The line graph is more helpful, since we can approximate the point midway between 8:00 and 12:00 noon and then draw a vertical line upward until it hits the line graph. An approximation for the 10:00 temperature can be obtained from the vertical line.

Open-ended
25. Answers may vary. A good source of graphs is *U.S.A. Today*.
26. Answers may vary. The federal budget is usually depicted as a circle graph. This is probably to show the proportion of total budget each category has for funding.
27. (**a**) A line graph is more appropriate since we have continuous data changing over time.

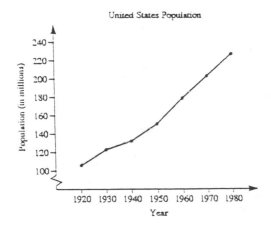

(**b**) The data falls into distinct categories and is not continuous, so we use a bar graph.

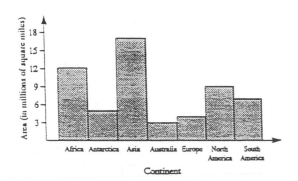

Cooperative Learning
28. Answers will vary. Students may find not only packages in stores but also may find shareware at low costs or free software on the Internet.

29. Answers will vary. Students may not be able to make definitive decisions other than for their class. You may want to check in department stores to see if they can determine the desired size.

Technology Corner (p. 472)
The answers will vary depending on the packages available to students. Teachers may choose to have students examine graphing calculators to see if statistical packages are available there.

Brain Teaser (p. 506)
The mean speed for the total six-mile run is 6 divided by the total time it took to drive six miles. The total time is the sum of the times spent on the first 3 miles, the next $1\frac{1}{2}$ miles, and the last $1\frac{1}{2}$ miles. On the first 3 miles, he averaged 140 miles per hour. Thus his time was $\frac{3}{140}$ hours. Similarly, the times on the next two segments were $\frac{1.5}{168}$ hours and $\frac{1.5}{210}$ hours. His total time was therefore $\frac{3}{140} + \frac{1.5}{168} + \frac{1.5}{210} = 0.0375$ hours. Consequently, the mean speed was $\frac{6}{0.375} = 60$ miles per hour.

ONGOING ASSESSMENT 9-2
1. (**a**) Mean = 6.625, median = 7.5, mode = 8 (**b**) Mean $= 13.\overline{4}$, median = 12, mode = 12 (**c**) Mean $\doteq$ 19.9, median = 18, modes = 18 and 22 (**d**) Mean = 81.4, median = 80, mode = 80 (**e**) Mean = $5.8\overline{3}$, median = 5, mode = 5
2. (**a**) The mean, median, and mode are all 80. (**b**) Answers may vary. One set is {70, 80, 80, 80, 90}.
3. 1500
4. 150 pounds
5. 78.3
6. (**a**) $\bar{x}$ = 18.4 years (**b**) 23.4 years (**c**) 28.4 years (**d**) The mean in (b) is equal to the mean in (a) plus five years. The mean in (c) is equal to the mean in (a) plus ten years or the mean in (b) plus five years.
7. Mode, answers vary.
8. Approximately 2.59
9. Approximately 215.45 lbs
10. $1880
11. (**a**) $41,275 (**b**) $38,000 (**c**) $38,000
12. (**a**) Balance beam—Olga (9.575); Uneven Bars—Lisa (9.85); Floor—Lisa (9.925) (**b**) Lisa (29.20)
13. $19\frac{2}{3}$ mpg
14. 30 mph
15. $5\frac{4}{5}$ hr
16. 58 years old
17. (**a**) A (**b**) B and C (**c**) C
18. s $\doteq$ 7.3 cm
19. (**a**) s = 0 (**b**) Yes
20. (**a**) Approximately 76.8 (**b**) 76 (**c**) 71 (**d**) Approximately 156.8 (**e**) Approximately 12.5
21. 91
22. 96, 90, and 90
23. 2

24.

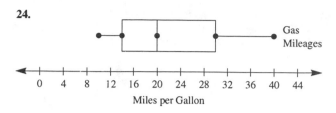

25. (a) A—$25, B—$50 (b) B (c) $80 at B (d) Answers vary. There is more variation at theater B; also there are higher prices at Theater B.

26.

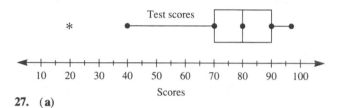

27. (a)

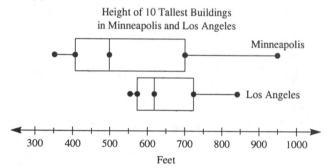

(b) There are no outliers.

28. (a) (i) Increase by $1000 (ii) Increase by $1000 (iii) Increase by $1000 (iv) Increase by $1000 (v) Stays the same (b) (i) Increase by 5% (ii) Increase by 5%

29. (a) (i) $\bar{x} = 5$, median = 5 (ii) $\bar{x} = 100$, median = 100 (iii) $\bar{x} = 307$, median = 307 (b) The mean and median of an arithmetic sequence are the same.

30. One might use the mode. If you collect the data of all states and consider the most common age at which one could get a license, that would be the mode. Both the mean and median might be decimals, and no state would worry about a decimal age for a driver's license.

31. The answers must be the mode. One cannot compute the mean and median on non-numerical data without a numerical coding.

32. The government probably uses the mean of data collected over a period of time.

Communication

33. (a) Mean = 90; Median = 90; Mode = 90 (b) Median or Mode (c) Mean

34. (a) For example, 10, 30, 70, and 90. (b) Choose four numbers whose mean is 50. (c) The mean of the new numbers is 50.

35. No. To find the average speed we divide the distance traveled by the time it takes to drive it. The first part of the trip took $\frac{5}{30}$ or $\frac{1}{6}$ of an hour. The second part of the trip took $\frac{5}{50}$

or $\frac{1}{10}$ of an hour. Therefore, to find the average speed we

compute $\dfrac{10}{\dfrac{1}{6}+\dfrac{1}{10}}$ to obtain 37.5 mph.

36. The mean increases by the number which has been added. The standard deviation remains the same.

37.
$$v = \frac{\left(x_1 - \bar{x}\right)^2 + \left(x_2 - \bar{x}\right)^2 + \cdots + \left(x_n - \bar{x}\right)^2}{n}$$

$$= \frac{\left(x_1^2 - 2\bar{x}x_1 + \bar{x}^2\right) + \left(x_2^2 - 2\bar{x}x_2 + \bar{x}^2\right) + \cdots + \left(x_n^2 - 2\bar{x}x_n + \bar{x}^2\right)}{n}$$

$$= \frac{\left(x_1^2 + x_2^2 + \cdots + x_n^2\right) - 2\bar{x}\left(x_1 + x_2 + \cdots + x_n\right) + n\bar{x}^2}{n}$$

$$= \frac{\left(x_1^2 + x_2^2 + \cdots + x_n^2\right)}{n} - \frac{2\bar{x}\left(x_1 + x_2 + \cdots + x_n\right)}{n} + \frac{n\bar{x}^2}{n}$$

$$= \frac{\left(x_1^2 + x_2^2 + \cdots + x_n^2\right)}{n} - 2\bar{x}^2 + \bar{x}^2$$

$$= \frac{\left(x_1^2 + x_2^2 + \cdots + x_n^2\right)}{n} - \bar{x}^2$$

Open-ended

38. Answers will vary depending on student choice. Probably a good choice might be a box plot with two sets of data depicted so that comparisons could be easily seen.

Cooperative Learning

39. Answers will vary. Students should be able to predict the approximate age of each level of student based on the data collected. This assumes that next year's students are approximately in the same age ranges as this year's students.

40. Answers will vary. To do this problem, the class will have to be divided in such a way that the choice of newspapers does not overlap. A teacher may want to discuss how one might do a random sample of newspapers.

Review Problems

41. Most of the equipment would probably be exercise walking equipment for women and swimming, fishing, and biking equipment for males. Arguments could be made for other types of equipment using the graph as well.

42. (a) Education—191°; General fund—97°; Cities—25°; Senior citizen programs—25°; other—25° (b) Students should recognize that the graph depicts more than 100% of the distribution of state lottery proceeds.

43. (a) Everest, approximately 8500 m (b) Aconcagua, Everest, McKinley

44. (a)

History Test Scores

5	5
6	48
7	2334679
8	0255567889
9	00346

7 | 2 represents a score of 72

(b)

History Test Scores

Classes	Tally	Frequency
55-59	I	1
60-64	I	1
65-69	I	1
70-74	IIII	4
75-79	III	3
80-84	II	2
85-89	HHT III	8
90-94	IIII	4
95-99	I	1

(c)

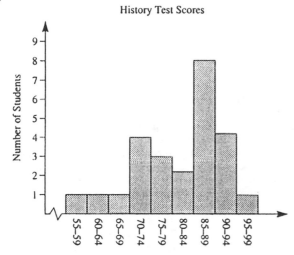

(d)

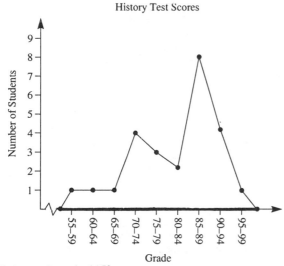

(e) Approximately 115°

Technology Corner (p. 511)
The mean is 46, the standard deviation is approximately 8.85; the variance is approximately 78.32

Brain Teaser (p. 510)
Let n be the sum of ages of the first seven people in the room. Because the mean is 21, we have n /7 = 21, and n = 147. When Jeff arrived, there were eight people in the room with

the sum of the ages equal to 147 + 29 or 176. To find the effect of Mary's age on the mean, we add her age, 29, to the sum of the other ages in the room, 176, and divide by 9, the number of people in the room. Therefore the mean with Mary in the room is (176 + 29)/9 = 205/9 = 22.8. When Elmer entered the room, the mean age became 30. If we let E be Elmer's age, then (205 + E)/10 = 30, and E = 95. Therefore Elmer is 95 years old on his birthday.

ONGOING ASSESSMENT 9-3

1. (a) 1020 (b) 1425 (c) 1.5, so 1 or 2 people
2. 97.5%
3. 0.68
4. (a) Verbal, 0.6; Quantitative, 0.83; Logical reasoning, 1 (b) (i) Logical reasoning (ii) Verbal (iii) Holly has a composite score of 0.81.
5. 16%
6. (a) 47.5% (b) 16%
7. (a) 1.07% (b) 95.54% (c) 2.27%
8. 1.4%
9. 84% (all values LESS than 125 oz.)
10. 8
11. 90
12. Between 60.5 in. and 70.5 in.
13. 50
14. 1600
15. (a)

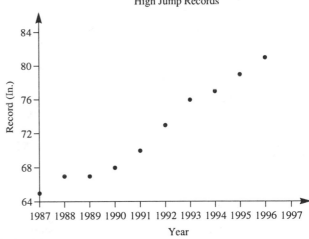

(b) Positive
16. (a) Negative (b) Approximately 10 (c) 22 years old

Communication
17. They are equal. The normal distribution has a symmetric graph.
18. Answers may vary. For example, in reality the curve is not smooth. If we are showing student scores, then the graph should be a series of points, not a continuous curve.
19. Answers may vary. For example, the Central Limit Theorem may be interpreted as follows: As the size of the data increases, the normal curve comes closer to approximating the data.

Open-ended
20. (a) If two different normal curves depicting scores on a nationally standardized test have the same mean, but one has twice as many students taking it, then on the same graph the height of the normal curve with the most students taking it should be greater than the height of the other. (b) The curves

are still normal curves, but the one with more students will be taller than the other. (**c**) The percents under the curves will not change, but the standard deviations in the two curves will not be placed in exactly the same places.
21. Answers will vary depending on the choice of scores. Each student may have a different scoring scheme.

Cooperative Learning
22. This problem is a take-off on deciding what letter is used most in the English language using a sample of writing. This is somewhat easier than that one. One thing that might be observed is that individual students may have strange data, but the entire collection should be more typical of the population.

Review Problems
23. (**a**) 74.17 (**b**) 75 (**c**) 65 (**d**) 237.97 (**e**) 15.43
24. 27.74
25. 76.6
26.

Men's Olympic
100 meter Run Times
1896–1964

```
1 0 | 0 2 3 3 3 4 5 6 8 8 8 8
1 1 | 0 0
1 2 | 0            10|0 represents
                    10.0 seconds
```

27.

From examining the box plot, we can see that the times on the 100-m butterfly are much greater (relatively speaking) than are the times on the 100-m freestyle.

ONGOING ASSESSMENT 9-4

1. Answers may vary in all parts of this question.
(**a**) A question to ask is whether or not the car is running. If it is not running, then there is no sound and the car would be quieter. (**b**) One question is how many motorcycles were sold in the recent years. All of them could have been. (**c**) 11% more fruit solids than 10% is very little. (**d**) Any time there is a percentage involved, one should ask "Percentage of what?" (**e**) "Up to" is very indefinite and the conditions under which the 30 was obtained. (**f**) "Brighter" than what? (**g**) How many dentists responded? (**h**) Most accidents occur in the home because a majority of time is spent in the home. The argument is specious. (**i**) A question to ask is whether or not there is another airline flying to the city.
2. Answers may vary. One possibility is that the temperature is always 25 °C.
3. She could have taken a different number of quizzes during the first part of the quarter than the second part.
4. When the radius of a circle is doubled, the area is quadrupled, which is misleading since the population has only doubled.
5. The horizontal axis does not have uniformly-sized intervals and both the horizontal axis and the graph are not labeled.

6. There were more scores above the mean than below, but the mean was affected more by low scores.
7. It could very well be that most of the pickups sold in the last 10 years were actually sold during the last two years. In such a case most of the pickups have been on the road for only two years, and therefore the given information would not imply that the average life of a pickup is around ten years.
8. Answers vary; however, he is assuming that there are no deep holes in the river where he crosses.
9. The three-dimensional drawing distorts the graph. The result of doubling the radius and the height of the can is to increase the volume by a factor of 8.
10. No labels, so we cannot compare actual sales. Also, there is no scale on the vertical axis.
11. One would need more information; for example, is the graph in percentages or actual numbers?
12. (**a**) False, prices vary only by $30. (**b**) False, the bar has four times the area but this is not true of prices. (**c**) True
13. (**a**) This bar graph could have perhaps 20 accidents at the point where the scale starts. Then 38 in 1996 would appear to be almost double the 24 of 1988, when in fact it is only 58% higher. (**b**) This bar graph would have 0 accidents at the point where the scale starts.
14. Answers may vary, but one such would be 5, 5, 5, 5, 5, 5, 100, 100. The mean would be 28.75 and the median 5.
15. You could not automatically conclude correctly that the population of the coastal West has increased since 1790. However, based on the westward movement of the mean center of population, there would be strong suspicion that was the case.
16. Answers will vary. The mean moved approximately 4 cm during the first 100 years, 3.5 cm during the next 100 years. One could expect it to move 5.5 cm during the next 200 years (3 cm in the first 100 and 2.5 cm in the next 100). If this pattern continued, then at the end of 400 years, the mean would have moved yet another 3.5 cm.
17. Answers will vary. One such line has equation $y = {}^-0.017x + 44.164$. (**a**) Using the linear regression, the expectation in 1992 is 10.3. That is truly unexpected by looking at the data. (**b**) Students should look up the winning time in an encyclopedia. (**c**) Using the equation above, the expectation is ${}^-6.77$ sec in 2996. (**d**) Because a negative time is impossible, you know the equation is not accurate. In any event, the times are decreasing. You can be sure that the times can never reach 0.
18. The homeowner may be looking at a scattergram of years versus interest rates. The rates are dropping in the 90s. Whether or not the pattern continues is dependent upon the economy.
19. A student would need to know the highest possible score that a person could make. Also the scores of other students would be important.
20. You would need to know the standard deviation of the number of students in the classes. You could not answer the overcrowding condition on the one number alone.
21. You could report the mode of a selected number of spots if enough spots were chosen at random. It is also possible that the mode would not exist. A median might be misleading, depending on the number of data points given. Also the mean would not be sufficient. A report of the mean, median, and standard deviation would be the most helpful of all "averages" studied.
22. It is possible. Such a country might be the Netherlands. The country has dikes to help keep out the sea.

23. Answers may vary. A sample size is needed. Then, one way to pick a random sample of adults in the town is to use the telephone book or a voter registration list. These methods will not list all adults in the town, but these are probably the most accessible sets of data. To pick the sample, one might roll a die and consider the number n that appears on it. Then starting at some point in the adult list, choose every nth person after the start on the list.

24. One of the primary reasons that this statement could be true is that the cost of replacing defective chips is less expensive than attempting to correct the problems that caused the disks to be defective in the first place. The claim seems impossible, but it is true.

25. Answers may vary. The writers of the *Standards* may have based the statement only on their own interactions with students. They may also have observed magazines and television show ratings, etc.

Brain Teaser (p. 530)

To average 60 mph for 2 mi, it would take 2/60 hr, or 2 min. However, we used the entire 2 min to drive the first lap. Therefore, no matter how fast we drive the second lap, we can never reach an average speed of 60 mph. The greater the speed on the second lap, the closer we can come to an average speed of 60 mph, but we can never reach it.

Chapter Review

1. If the average is 2.41 children, then the mean is being used. If the average is 2.5, then the mean or the median might have been used.

2. 23

3. (a) Mean = 30, median = 30, mode = 10 (b) Mean = 5, median = 5, modes = 3, 5, 6

4. (a) Range = 50, variance $\doteq$ 371.4, standard deviation $\doteq$ 19.3
(b) Range = 8, variance $\doteq$ 5.2, standard deviation = 2.28

5. (a)

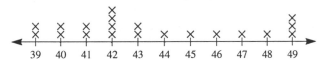

Miss Rider's Class
Masses in Kilograms

(b)

Miss Rider's Class
Masses in Kilograms

```
3 | 99
4 | 001122223345678999   4 | 0 represents
                              40 kg
```

(c)

Miss Rider's Class
Masses in Kilograms

Mass	Tally	Frequency
39	II	2
40	II	2
41	II	2
42	IIII	4
43	II	2
44	I	1
45	I	1
46	I	1
47	I	1
48	I	1
49	III	3
		20

(d)

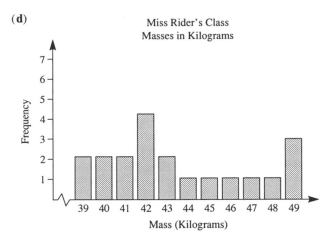

Miss Rider's Class
Masses in Kilograms

6. (a)

Test Grades

Classes	Tally	Frequency
61 – 70	ЖH I	6
71 – 80	ЖH ЖH I	11
81 – 90	ЖH II	7
91 – 100	ЖH I	6
		30

(b) and (c) are on the same graph.

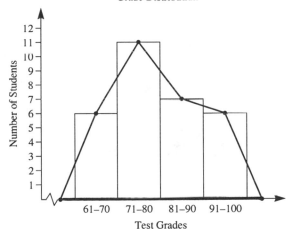

Grade Distribution

7.

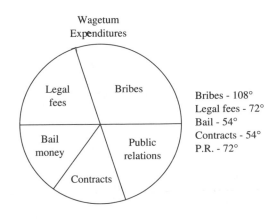

Wagetum
Expenditures

Bribes - 108°
Legal fees - 72°
Bail - 54°
Contracts - 54°
P.R. - 72°

8. The widths of the bars are not uniform and the graph has no title.

9. $2840

10.

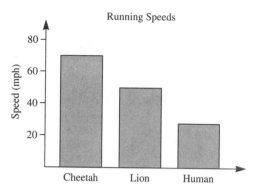

Running Speeds

11. (**a**)

Life Expectancies
of Males and Females

Females		Males
	67	1446
	68	28
	69	156
	70	0049
	71	0223458
	72	
	73	
7	74	
9310	75	
86	76	
88532	77	
54332211	78	
	79	

7 |74| represents |67| 1 represents
74.7 years old   67.1 years old

(**b**)

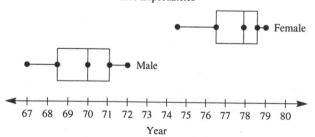

Life Expectancies

12. Larry was correct because his average was $3.2\overline{6}$ while Marc's was $2.7\overline{3}$.

13. (**a**) 360 (**b**) none (**c**) 350 (**d**) s $\doteq$ 108.22

14. (**a**) 67 (**b**) UQ = 74, LQ = 64

(**c**)

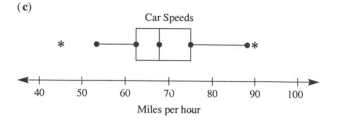

Car Speeds

(**d**) 50% (**e**) 30% (**f**) No, there are fewer speeds close to 67 in the third quartile than in the second quartile.

15. (**a**) 25 (**b**) 475 (**c**) 0.16

16. 475

17. $1.\overline{6}$

18. Answers may vary. For example, with 95% certainty, Company A's products will have a life of between 130 hr and 170 hr; Company B's products will have a life of between 141 and 149 hr. One's chances of knowing how long the product will really last would seem to be better with Company B.

19. (**a**) Positive (**b**) 170 (**c**) 67 (**d**) 64 (**e**) 50

20. Answers may vary. (**a**) One way would be to leave the television on, even if no one is watching. (**b**) They show very popular shows during "ratings sweeps" periods.

21. Answers may vary. For example, graphs may show area or volume instead of relative size; another is to select a horizontal baseline that will support the point trying to be made.

22. Answers will vary. If your state is one of the darker graphs, then you would probably want to use this type of graph because it shows that your state has greater than 105% of the national average for hourly earnings.

23. One way to obtain the line labeled "Total" is to sum the "y-values" for corresponding points on the other graphs and to plot the sum as the y-value on the "Total" line.

24. The advertisement is not reasonable. One would expect the snow to be okay, but with reports like those given, there is little information about the snow in the middle of the mountain. If it is cold enough to have 23 in. at the bottom of a hill, one would expect there to be snow all the way to the top. However, if the bottom and the top are shaded, then there could be much variation if a part of the hill were sunny.

CHAPTER 10

ONGOING ASSESSMENT 10-1

1. No. The symbol is a finite collection of points.

2. (**a**) For example: $\overleftrightarrow{BC}$ and $\overleftrightarrow{DH}$ or $\overleftrightarrow{AE}$ and $\overleftrightarrow{BD}$ (**b**) Parallel (**c**) No (**d**) Empty set (since $\overleftrightarrow{BD}$ and plane EFG have no points in common) (**e**) Point H (**f**) Planes BFC and EFG, or planes BFD and EFG (**g**) For example: $\overleftrightarrow{BF}$ and $\overleftrightarrow{DH}$ (**h**) ∠EFB (**i**) 90°

3. (**a**) ∅ (**b**) Plane E-BD-A (**c**) {C} (**d**) {A} (**e**) Answers vary (**f**) $\overleftrightarrow{AC}$ and $\overleftrightarrow{DE}$ or $\overleftrightarrow{AD}$ and $\overleftrightarrow{CE}$ (**g**) Plane BCD or plane BEA

4. 20 pairs

5. Answers vary

6. (**a**) 110° (**b**) 40° (**c**) 20° (**d**) 130°

7. (**a**) Approximately 36° (**b**) Approximately 120°

8. (a) (i) 41°31'10" (ii) 79°48'47" (b) (i) 54' (ii) 15°7'48"
9. (a) (i) 90° (ii) 12°30' (iii) 205° (b) 52°30'
(c) Approximately 32 min and 43.1 sec after 12 noon.
10. 2:27
11. (a) 4 (b) 6 (c) 8 (d) 2(n − 1)
12. (a) 3 (b) 6 (c) 10 (d) $\dfrac{n(n-1)}{2}$

13. (a)

Number of Intersection Points

	0	1	2	3	4	5
2	⟷	✕	Not Possible	Not Possible	Not Possible	Not Possible
3	⟷	✳	⟷	✕	Not Possible	Not Possible
4	⟷	✳	Not Possible	⟷	✕	✕
5	⟷	✳	Not Possible	Not Possible	⟷	✕
6	⟷	✳	Not Possible	Not Possible	Not Possible	⟷

Number of lines

(b) n(n − 1)/2
14. Answers vary.
15. (a) 3 (b) 4 (c) 4 (d) 6 (e) 2n
16. b, d, e, and g

17. Suppose α ∥ β and γ intersect α in $\overset{\leftrightarrow}{AB}$, and γ intersects β
in $\overset{\leftrightarrow}{CD}$. If $\overset{\leftrightarrow}{AB} \cap \overset{\leftrightarrow}{CD}$ is Q, then Q is a point of both plane α and
plane β. This cannot happen, so $\overset{\leftrightarrow}{AB} \parallel \overset{\leftrightarrow}{CD}$.
18. Answers vary. For example:
(a)   TO ANGLE :SIZE
        FD 100 BK 100
        RT :SIZE FD 100
        BK 100 LT :SIZE
      END
(b)   TO SEGMENT :LENGTH
        FD :LENGTH BK :LENGTH
      END
(c)   TO PERPENDICULAR :LENGTH1 :LENGTH2
        FD :LENGTH1 BK :LENGTH2
        RT 90 FD :LENGTH2
        BK :LENGTH2 LT 90
        BK :LENGTH1/2
      END
(d)   TO PARALLEL :LENGTH1 :LENGTH2
        DRAW
        FD :LENGTH1 PENUP
        RT 90 FD 10 RT 90
        PENDOWN FD :LENGTH2
        PENUP HOME
        RT 180 PENDOWN
      END
(In LCSI, replace DRAW with CLEARSCREEN)

Communication
19. (a) Answers vary. (b) The fire is located near the
intersection of the two bearing lines. (c) Answers vary.
20. Three points determine a single plane, and a plane
determines a level surface. Four points may not all lie in a
plane and hence may not determine a level surface.

21. (a) No. If ∠BCD were a right angle, then both $\overset{\leftrightarrow}{BD}$ and $\overset{\leftrightarrow}{BC}$
would be perpendicular to $\overset{\leftrightarrow}{DC}$ and thus be parallel. (b) No.
The angle formed by $\overset{\leftrightarrow}{PD}$ and $\overset{\leftrightarrow}{PC}$ must have a measure less

than a right angle. Otherwise, $\overset{\leftrightarrow}{DP}$ would be parallel to either
$\overset{\leftrightarrow}{DC}$ or $\overset{\leftrightarrow}{PC}$. This is impossible. (c) Yes. Use the definition of
perpendicular planes.
22. No. If the four points are collinear, there is one line; if three
are collinear, there are four lines; and if no three are collinear,
there are six lines.

Cooperative Learning
23. (a) An angle of 20° can be drawn by tracing a 50° angle
and a 30° angle, as shown in the following figure. Another 20°
angle adjacent to the first 20° angle can be drawn in a similar
way, thus creating a 40° angle.

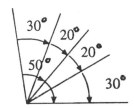

(b) Answers vary. (c) Answers vary.

24.

Points	Lines	Planes
3	3	1
4	6	4
5	10	10
n	$\dfrac{n(n-1)}{2}$	$\dfrac{n(n-1)(n-2)}{6}$

Open-ended
25. Answers vary.
26. Answers vary.

ONGOING ASSESSMENT 10-2
1. (a) 1, 2, 5, 6, 7, 8, 10 (b) 1, 6, 7, 8 (c) 1, 2, 5, 6, 7, 8
(d) 1, 6, 7, 8 (e) 6, 7 (f) 1, 8
2. D and O
3. 8 (nonconvex quadrilateral)
4. A concave polygon
5. (a) and (c) are convex, since no matter which two points in
the interior of the figure are chosen, the entire segment
connecting the points lies within the figure. (b) and (d) are
concave since two points within the figure can be chosen such
that the segment formed by the two points does not lie entirely
within the figure.
6. (d) and (e) are impossible because each angle of an
equilateral triangle has measure 60°.
7. (a) 35 (b) 170 (c) 4850
8. (a) Isosceles and equilateral (b) Isosceles (c) Scalene
9. (a) and (b) represent rhombuses and rectangles.
10. (a) T, Q, R, H, G, I, F, J (b) Y, Z, E (c) W, D, A, Z, U, E
(d) Q, J, F, G, H (e) Y
11. Answers vary.
12. (a) Answers vary; for example:
        TO SQUARE :SIDE
          REPEAT 4 [FD :SIDE RT 90]
        END
(b) Answers vary; for example:
      TO RECTANGLE :WIDTH :LENGTH
        REPEAT 2 [FD :WIDTH RT 90 FD :LENGTH
        RT 90]
      END

Communication
13. Answers vary.

Open-ended
14. Answers vary.

Cooperative Learning
15. Answers vary.
16. (**a**) 4 (**b**) Answers vary. One possible answer is,
"So that the wheels will rotate in opposite directions."
17. (**a**) 45 (**b**) n(n − 1)/2
18. ∅, 1 point, 2 points, ray
19. (**a**) False. A ray has only one endpoint. (**b**) True (**c**) False.
Skew lines cannot be contained in the single plane. (**d**) False.

$\overrightarrow{MN}$ has endpoint M and extends in the direction of point N;

$\overrightarrow{NM}$ has endpoint N and extends in the direction of point M.
(**e**) True (**f**) False. Their intersection is a line.

Brain Teaser (p. 564)
No, it is not possible.

ONGOING ASSESSMENT 10-3

1. (**a**) 0.9 cm (**b**) 0.9 cm (**c**) 8 cm (**d**) 0.5 cm (**e**) 0.7 cm
(**f**) 4.9 cm (**g**) 7.3 cm (**h**) 5.2 cm
2. (**a**) 2 7/9 (**b**) 14,400 (**c**) 100 (**d**) 31
3. Answers vary.
4. (**a**) 98 (**b**) 9.8
5. (**a**) Centimeters (**b**) Millimeters (**c**) Centimeters
(**d**) Centimeters (**e**) Centimeters (**f**) Meters (**g**) Centimeters
(**h**) Centimeters
6. (**a**) Inches (**b**) Inches (**c**) Feet (**d**) Inches (**e**) Inches
(**f**) Feet (**g**) Feet (**h**) Inches
7. (**a**) 0.35, 350 (**b**) 163, 1630 (**c**) 0.035, 3.5 (**d**) 0.1, 10
(**e**) 200, 2000
8. (**a**) 10.00 (**b**) 0.77 (**c**) 10.0 (**d**) 15.5 (**e**) 195.0 (**f**) 8.100
(**g**) 40.0
9. 6 m, 5218 mm, 245 cm, 700 mm, 91 mm, 8 cm
10. Answers vary.
11. (**a**) 8 cm (**b**) 12 cm (**c**) 9 cm (**d**) 20 cm
12. (**a**) 1 cm (**b**) 0.262 km (**c**) 3000 m (**d**) 0.03 m
(**e**) 3500 cm (**f**) 0.359 m (**g**) 64.7 cm (**h**) 1 mm (**i**) 5000 m
(**j**) 5130 cm
13. (**a**) AB + BC > AC (**b**) BC + CA > AB (**c**) AB + CA >
BC
14. Answers are a result of the Triangle Inequality: (**a**) Can be
(**b**) Cannot be (**c**) Cannot be. In (b) and (c) the numbers
cannot be the lengths of the sides of a triangle because in (b)
10 + 40 = 50 and in (c) 260 + 14 < 410, each of which
contradicts the triangle inequality.
15. No. Justification. Suppose such a square existed. Let "a" be
the length of a side of the square and "d" the length of the
diagonal. Then we would have 4a = 2d and hence 2a = d or
a + a = d. This contradicts the triangle inequality for the
triangle created by two sides of the square and a diagonal.
16. (**a**) The minimum perimeter is attained when the second
longest side is not part of the perimeter. (**b**) The maximum
perimeter is attained when the longer sides are part of the
perimeter; for example:

(**a**)

(**b**)

17. (**a**) Answers vary. (**b**) 8 squares (**c**) 20 squares

18.

Number of Toothpicks	Possible Triangles	Type of Triangle
8	2-3-3	Isosceles
9	3-3-3	Equilateral
	2-3-4	Scalene
	1-4-4	Isosceles
10	2-4-4	Isosceles
	3-3-4	Isosceles
11	1-5-5	Isosceles
	2-4-5	Scalene
	3-3-5	Isosceles
	4-4-3	Isosceles
12	4-4-4	Equilateral
	2-5-5	Isosceles
	3-4-5	Scalene

19. (**a**) 6 cm (**b**) 3/π m (**c**) 0.335/π m (**d**) 46 cm
20. (**a**) 6π cm (**b**) 6π cm (**c**) 4 cm (**d**) $6\pi^2$ cm
21. The circumference will double.
22. πr
23. (**a**) About $9.5 \cdot 10^{12}$ km (**b**) About $4.1 \cdot 10^{13}$ km
(**c**) About $6.8 \cdot 10^8$ km or about 78,000 years (**d**) 2495 hr, or
about 104 days
24. (**a**) 3096 (**b**) 1032 (**c**) Approximately Mach 4.04
25. (**a**) 6 foot longs (**b**) 10,560 foot longs
26. (50 + 6π) ft
27. Even integers greater or equal. Each time a square is added,
the perimeter either does not change, increases by 2, or
decreases by 2.

28.

Perimeter	Minimum Area	Maximum Area
4	1	1
6	2	2
8	3	4
10	4	6
12	5	9
14	6	12
16	7	16
18	8	20
20	9	25
22	10	30
24	11	36
26	12	42
2n	n−1	*

* Let q be the whole number quotient when 2n is divided
by 4. If 2n is a multiple of 4, then the maximum area is
q^2; otherwise it is q(q + 1).

Communication
29. The height is three tennisball-diameters. The perimeter is
given by the circumference of a tennis ball, πd, and is thus
about 3.14 tennisball diameters.
30. The outer curve has a greater radius and a correspondingly
greater distance (i.e., arc length) to run. To compensate for the
extra distance, the runner in the outer lane is given an apparent
head start.

Open-ended

31. (**a**) Answers vary. For example: 1-1-1 and 2-2-1 work, 2-3-6 and 1-2-3 do not. (**b**) Using the Triangle Inequality, a triangle can be constructed, if and only if a + b > c and a + c > b and b + c > a.

32. Answers vary.

Cooperative Learning

33. (**a**) Answers vary. (**b**) If the circles are the same size, then regardless of the radius of each circle the amount of wire needed is the same. (**c**) Let the radius of each circle be r cm. Then the number of circles needed for each chain is $\frac{60}{2r}$ (Why?). The circumference of each circle is $2\pi r$ and hence the amount of wire, which is the total circumference of all the circles, is $\frac{60}{2r} \cdot 2\pi r$, or 60π cm. Because this number does not depend on the value of r, the amount of wire needed for the chain is the same regardless of the radius of each circle.

Review Problems

34. (**a**) Yes, because $\overset{\leftrightarrow}{BC}$ and $\overset{\leftrightarrow}{EH}$ are parallel and determine the shaded plane shown in the following figure. (**b**) Yes. Every three points labeled are not collinear and hence they determine a unique plane. (**c**) No, because C is not in the unique plane determined by E, H, and G.

35. Answers vary.

Brain Teaser (p. 577)

The tallest person on Earth could walk under the wire. Suppose the two concentric circles represent Earth and the lengthened wire.

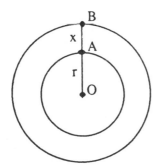

$\overline{OA}$ and $\overline{OB}$ are the radii of the respective circles and have lengths r and r + x. Since the circumference of the Earth plus 20m equals the circumference of the lengthened wire, we have $2\pi r + 20 = 2\pi(r + x)$. Consequently x = 10/π, or approximately 3.18 m.

ONGOING ASSESSMENT 10-4

1. Answers vary.

2. 20

3. (**a**) 60° (**b**) 45° (**c**) 60° (**d**) 60°

4. (**a**) Yes. A pair of corresponding angles are 50° each. (**b**) Yes. A pair of corresponding angles are 70° each. (**c**) Yes. A pair of alternate interior angles are 40° each. (**d**) Yes. A pair of corresponding angles are 90° each.

5. 70° and 20°

6. (**a**) 20 (**b**) 162°

7. (**a**) 70° (**b**) 70° (**c**) 65° (**d**) 45°

8. (**a**) x = 40° and y = 50° (**b**) x = 18° and 4x = 72° (**c**) x = 50° and y = 60° (**d**) x = 83°

9. (**a**) 60° (**b**) 90°

10. (**a**) 360° (**b**) 360° (**c**) 360°

11. a = 118°, b = 152°

12. 60, 84, 108, 132, 156

13. 90°

14. 111°

15. m(∠1) = 60°, m(∠2) = 30°, m(∠3) = 110°

16. 135°

17. Answers vary.

18. (**a**) 100° (**b**) The measure of the exterior angle equals the sum of the remote interior angles. Since ∠1 and ∠ACB are supplementary, then m(∠1) + m(∠ACB) = 180°. We also know that the sum of the measures of the angles of a triangle equals 180°. m(∠A) + m(∠B) + m(∠C) = 180°. So m(∠1) = m(∠A) + m(∠B). (**c**) m(∠ACB) = 40°, m(∠ABD) = 40°, m(∠DBC) = 50° (**d**) m(∠ACB) = 90 − α, m(∠ABD) = 90 − α, m(∠DBC) = α.

Communication

19. Place a long ruler or board so that it touches all the stairs and the ground. The angle α that the board makes with the ground measures the steepness of the stairs.

20. (**a**) No. Two or more obtuse angles will produce a sum of more than 180°. (**b**) Yes. For example, each angle may have measure 60°. (**c**) No. The sum of the measures of the three angles would be more than 180°. (**d**) No. It may have an obtuse or right angle as well.

21. No, it is not possible. The sum of all the measures of the angles in ∆ABC must equal 180°, but m(∠ABC) + m(∠ACB) + m(∠BAC) = 90° + 90° + m(∠BAC) > 180°. Hence, the situation shown in the diagram is not possible.

22. (**a**) Five triangles will be constructed in which the sum of the angles of each triangle is 180°. The sum of the measures of the angles of all the triangles equals 5(180°), from which we subtract 360° (the sum of all the measures of the angles of the triangles with vertex P) . Thus 5(180°) − 360° = 540°. (**b**) Here, n triangles are constructed, so we have n(180°) from which we subtract 360° (the sum of all the measures of the angles of the triangles with vertex P). Thus we obtain n(180°) − 360°, which is the same answer stated in section 10-4.

23. x = 30°. Possible explanation: The ladder makes an isosceles triangle with base angles of 60° (since the angle supplementary to 120° is 60°, as shown in the following figure). The bar across the ladder is parallel to the ground and hence creates corresponding angles formed by the bar, the ground, and the side of the ladder. Consequently, the angle formed by the bar and the side of the ladder is 60°. Since the line from the apple is perpendicular to the bar crossing the ladder, we have x = 90° − 60° = 30°. Hence x = 30°.

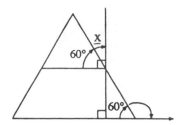

24. (**a**) Choose a vertex and fold the triangle at that vertex so that the other two vertices fall on top of each other. Two angles of the triangle should fall on top of each other. Repeat at the other vertex. (**b**) Fold the trapezoid so that its sides fall on top of each other and check that the base angles fall on top of each other as well.

25. (**a**) Divide the quadrilateral into two triangles: $\triangle ABC$ and $\triangle ACD$. The sum of the measures of the interior angles of each triangle is $180°$, so the sum of the measures of the interior angles of the quadrilateral is $2(180°)$, or $360°$. (**b**) This is also true for nonconvex polygons. (**c**) Any concave pentagon can be divided into three triangles and a concave hexagon can be divided into four triangles. In general, it seems that any concave n-gon can be divided into $n - 2$ triangles so that the sum of the measures of the angles of the triangles is the sum of the measures of the interior angles of the n-gon.

26. No. Regular hexagons fit because the measure of each vertex angle is $120°$, three hexagons fit to form $360°$, and the plane can be filled. For a regular pentagon, the measure of each vertex angle is $108°$, so pentagons cannot be placed together to form $360°$ (360 is not divisible by 108) and the plane cannot be filled.

27. POLY will draw a polygon if and only if the input for ANGLE is $360/N$, where N is an integer and $N \geq 3$. (Justification: The sum of the measures of all exterior angles of a polygon is $360°$. Hence, each exterior angle in a regular polygon measures $360°/N$.)

28. Answers vary. For example:
(**a**) TO PARALLELOGRAM :L :W :A
    REPEAT 2 [FD :L RT 180- :A FD :W RT :A]
    END
(**b**) TO RECTANGLE :L :W
    PARALLELOGRAM :L :W 90
    END
(**c**) TO RHOMBUS :L :A
    PARALLELOGRAM :L :L :A
    END
(**d**) Execute PARALLELOGRAM 50 50 90
(**e**) Execute RHOMBUS 50 90

Open-ended
29. Answers vary.
30. Answers vary. The following are some properties of figures in a plane and corresponding properties on a sphere:

Property in a Plane	Property on a Sphere
Two lines in a plane may intersect in one point or may be parallel.	Two great circles (lines on a sphere) always intersect in two points.
Two points determine a unique line.	Two points do not always determine a unique great circle.
A line has no length, and any point on the line separates it into two parts.	A great circle has a finite length ($2\pi r$ where r is the radius of the sphere) and is not separated into two parts by a point on the circle.

Cooperative Learning
31. (**a**) If $m(\angle A) = \alpha$ and $m(\angle B) = \beta$, then $m(\angle D) = 180 - \dfrac{\alpha}{2} + \dfrac{\beta}{2}$.
(**b**) If $m(\angle C)$ is always the same, no matter what the measures of $\angle A$ and $\angle B$ are, then $m(\angle D)$ is always the same.
(**c**) Answers vary. The following is a possible solution. From (**a**):
$$m(\angle D) = 180 - \left(\frac{\alpha + \beta}{2}\right) = \frac{360 - (\alpha + \beta)}{2}.$$ Because $\alpha + \beta = 180 - m(\angle C)$, we get the following:
$$m(\angle D) = \frac{360 - (180 - m(\angle C))}{2}$$
$$= \frac{360 - 180 + m(\angle C)}{2}$$
$$= 90 + \frac{1}{2} m(\angle C).$$
Because the answer for $m(\angle D)$ depends only on $m(\angle C)$, the conjecture is justified.

32. (**a**) Because congruent supplementary angles are formed (**b**) The theorem concerning the sum of the measures of the angles of a triangle (**c**) When A and C are folded, congruent supplementary angles are formed and hence, each is a right angle. When B is folded along $\overline{BB'}$, the crease $\overline{DE}$ formed is perpendicular to $\overline{BB'}$ (again because congruent supplementary angles are formed), consequently, $\overline{DE} \parallel \overline{GF}$. Thus D and E are also right angles. (**d**) GF = GB' + B'F = 1/2 AB' + 1/2 B'C = 1/2 (AB' + B'C) = 1/2 AC. Hence GF = 1/2 AC.

Review Problems
33. (**a**) 10 cm (**b**) 104 mm (**c**) 0.35 m (**d**) 40 mm (**e**) 8000 m (**f**) 6.504 km
34. (**a**) $(2\pi + 4)$mm (**b**) $(5\pi + 6)$mm
35.

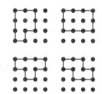

36. (**a**) All angles must be right angles, and all diagonals are the same length. (**b**) All sides are the same length, and all angles are right angles. (**c**) This is impossible because all squares are parallelograms.

ONGOING ASSESSMENT 10-5

1. (**a**) Quadrilateral pyramid (**b**) Quadrilateral prism; possibly a trapezoidal prism (**c**) Pentagonal pyramid
2. (**a**) A, D, R, W (**b**) $\overline{AR}, \overline{RD}, \overline{AD}, \overline{AW}, \overline{WR}, \overline{WD}$ (**c**) $\triangle ARD, \triangle AWD, \triangle AWR, \triangle WDR$ (**d**) {R}
3. Answers vary.
4. (**a**) 5 (**b**) 4 (**c**) 4
5. (**a**) True (**b**) False (**c**) True (**d**) False (**e**) False (**f**) False (**g**) False (**h**) True
6. All are possible.
7. Answers vary.

8.

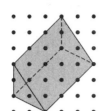

9. (**a**) Hexagonal pyramid (**b**) Quadrilateral (square) pyramid
(**c**) Cube (**d**) Rectangular prism (**e**) Hexagonal prism
10. (**a**) iv (**b**) ii
11. (**a**) i, ii, and iii (**b**) ii, iii, iv

12.

Vertices per Base	Diagonals per Vertex	Total Number of Diagonals
4	1	4
5	2	10
6	3	18
7	4	28
8	5	40
.	.	.
.	.	.
.	.	.
n	$(n-3)$	$n(n-3)$

13. (**a**) (**b**)

14. (**a**) (2) (**b**) (4)
15. (**a**) (**d**)

Cube

Remainder of unseen figure completes the cube

(**b**) (**e**)

Sphere

Right pentagonal prism

(**c**) (**f**)

Right circular cone
(plane parallel to base)

Right circular cylinder
(plane not parallel to base)

16. (**a**) Rectangle, square, triangle (**b**) Rectangle, parallelogram, circle, ellipse

17. (**a**) $10 + 7 - 15 = 2$ (**b**) $9 + 9 - 16 = 2$
18. (**a**) 6 (**b**) 48 (**c**) 11
The suggested relationship is $V + F - E = 2$.

19.

	Pyramid	Prism
(**a**)	$n + 1$	$n + 2$
(**b**)	$n + 1$	$2n$
(**c**)	$2n$	$3n$
(**d**)	$(n + 1) + (n + 1) - 2n$ $= 2$	$(n + 2) + 2n - 3n$ $= 2$

Communication
20. (**a**) Yes. A prism with bases that are 11-gons will have exactly 33 edges because there are 11 edges on each of the bases and 11 edges that connect each vertex of the top base to each vertex of the bottom base. (**b**) No because a pyramid will have only an even number of edges.
21. 3. Each pair of parallel faces could be considered as bases.
22. Answers vary.
23. Both could be drawings of a quadrilateral pyramid. In (**a**), we are directly above the pyramid, and in (**b**), we are directly below the pyramid.

Open-ended
24. Answers vary.
25. Answers vary.

Cooperative Learning
26. Answers vary.
27. Answers vary.
28. (**a**) Parallelogram, rectangle, square, scalene triangle, isosceles triangle, equilateral triangle (**b**) Triangle, quadrilateral

Review Problems
29. Yes because the sum of the angles of a triangle is 180°.
30. m(∠BCD) = 60°
31. 140°
32. (**a**) True (**b**) True (**c**) False (e.g., equilateral triangle)
33. Lines in the same plane and perpendicular to the same line are parallel. This is because corresponding angles are right angles and hence are congruent.

Brain Teaser (p. 601)
Read Hoffer's article listed in the bibliography.

ONGOING ASSESSMENT 10-6
1. (a), (b), (c), (e), (g), (h), and (j) are traversable.
(**a**) (**b**)

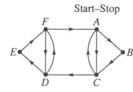 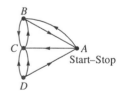

Path:
ABCACDEFDFA;
any point can be a
starting point.

Path:
DACDCBABC;
any point can be a
starting point.

(c)

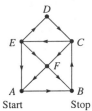

Start   Stop

Path:
ABCFAEDCEFB;
only points *A* and *B*
can be starting points.

(e)

Start

Path:
ABCBDCAD;
only points *A* and *D*
can be starting points.

(g)

Start   Stop

Path:
FADABCBGFEDCHEHG;
only points *F* and *G*
can be starting points.

(h)

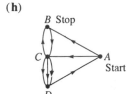

Path:
ACBCDCDAB;
only points *A* and *B*
can be starting points.

(j)

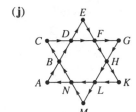

Path:
EFHKLNABDFGHLMNBCDE;
any point can be a
starting point.

2. All of them
3.

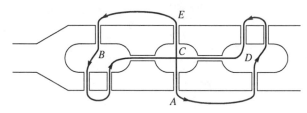

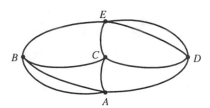

4. (a)

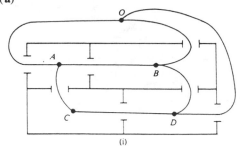

(i)

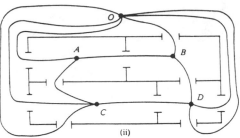

(ii)

(b) Network (i) is not traversable because it has four odd
vertices. Network (ii) has two odd vertices, so it is traversable,
as shown in the following figure:

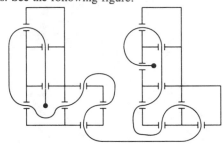

5. Yes. See the following figure:

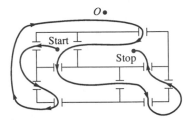

6. It is not possible.
7.

Network	R	V	A	R + V − A
(a)	6	6	10	2
(b)	6	4	8	2
(c)	6	6	10	2
(d)	4	4	6	2
(e)	5	4	7	2
(f)	8	8	14	2
(g)	9	8	15	2
(h)	6	4	8	2
(i)	7	7	12	2
(j)	8	12	18	2

8.

All vertices are even, so the trip is possible. It makes no
difference where she starts.

Communication
9. Answers vary. Possibilities are as follows:

  (a)   **(b)**   **(c)** Answers vary.

10. The bridge could be built anywhere and we would have two odd vertices. Thus the network is traversable.

Open-ended
11. Answers vary; for example:

12. Answers vary.
13. Answers vary.

Cooperative Learning
14. Answers vary.

Chapter Review
1. Answers vary.
2. (a) $\overleftrightarrow{AB}$, $\overleftrightarrow{BC}$, and $\overleftrightarrow{AC}$ (b) $\overrightarrow{BA}$ and $\overrightarrow{BC}$ (c) $\overline{AB}$ (d) $\overline{AB}$
3. (a) Answers may vary. (b) Planes APO and BPQ (c) $\overleftrightarrow{AQ}$
(d) No. $\overleftrightarrow{PQ}$ and $\overleftrightarrow{AB}$ are skew lines, so no single plane contains them.
4. Answers vary.
5. (a) No. The sum of the measures of two obtuse angles is greater than 180°, which is the sum of the measures of the angles of any triangle. (b) No. The sum of the measures of the four angles in a parallelogram must be 360°. If all the angles are acute, the sum would be less than 360°.
6. 18°, 36°, 126°
7. (a) Given any convex n-gon, pick any vertex and draw all possible diagonals from this vertex. This will determine n − 2 triangles. Because the sum of the measures of the angles in each triangle is 180°, the sum of the measures of the angles in the n-gon is (n − 2) 180°. (b) 90 sides
8. Answers vary.
9. Answers vary, but the possibilities are a point, a segment, a triangle, a quadrilateral, or an empty set.
10. m(∠3) = m(∠4) = 45°
11. 35°8'35"
12. (a) 60° (b) 120° (c) 120°
13. (a) The sum of the measures of the angles in a triangle is 180°. Also the fact that the measure of an exterior angle of a triangle equals the sum of the measures of the two other angles that are not supplementary to the exterior angle. (b) Construct ∠BAD = ∠B. This implies that AD ∥ BC. (Why?) Consequently, ∠DAE = ∠BCA (corresponding angles formed by the parallels $\overline{BC}$ and $\overline{AD}$ and the transversal $\overrightarrow{AC}$.) If we mark the measure of the angles as shown in the figure, we have b = b' and c = c'. Consequently, a + b + c = a + b' + c' = 180.

14. (a) Not possible because q + r > p, which contradicts the Triangle Inequality. (b) Not possible because q + r = p.
15. (a) 16 2/3 yd (b) approximately 0.5381 mi (c) 3960 ft (d) approximately 9.6944 yd
16. (a) The angles at O of each of the triangles is 360°/6, or 60°. Because all the sides that meet at O are radii, all the triangles are isosceles. Consequently, the angles at A and B in

ΔOAB are congruent. The sum of their measures must be 180° − 60°, or 120°. Hence, each angle measures 60°. Because all the angles of ΔABC measure 60°, all the sides of the triangle are congruent. Hence, AB = r. An identical argument applies to each of the remaining triangles. Thus, the length of each side of the hexagon is r. (b) The perimeter of the hexagon is 6r, and the circumference of the circle is 2πr. The error is 2πr − 6r or (2π − 6)r. The error is

$$\frac{(2\pi - 6)r}{2\pi r} \text{ or } \frac{2\pi - 6}{2\pi}$$

of the actual circumference, which is $\frac{(2\pi - 6)}{2\pi} \cdot 100\%$ or

approximately 4.5%.
17. Sketches may vary, but the possibilities are the empty set, a single point, a segment, a quadrilateral, a triangle, a pentagon, and a hexagon. There are various types of quadrilaterals possible.
18. 8
19. 48°
20. (a) (i), (ii), and (iv)
(b)

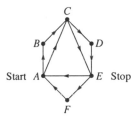

Path:
ABCDEFACEA;
any point can be used
as a starting point.

(i)

Path:
ABCDAEDBE;
points *A* and *E* are
possible starting points.

(ii)

Path:
BDEABAEDBCD;
points *B* and *D* are
possible starting points.

(iv)

CHAPTER 11

Technology Corner (p. 622)
(g) The lengths respectively are equal. (h) The angles respectively are congruent. (i) The two triangles are congruent.

ONGOING ASSESSMENT 11-1
1. (a) m(∠A) > m(∠B) (b) The side of greater length is opposite the angle of greater measure.
2. (c) Scalene right (d) No triangle is possible.
3. (b) The triangle is unique by SSS. (c) The triangle is unique by SSS. (d) There is no triangle because of the Triangle Inequality. (e) The triangle is unique by SSS. (f) The triangle is unique by SAS. (g) The triangle is not unique. (h) The triangle is unique by SAS. (i) The triangle is unique by SAS.
4. 22 triangles

5. (a) Yes; SAS (b) Yes; SSS (c) No

6. The purpose of the diagonals is to form congruent triangles. Triangles are rigid structures and hence make the gate stronger. They also prevent the cows from squeezing through.

7. The lengths of the wires must be the same because they are congruent parts of the congruent triangles formed.

8. Such a construction tells us that $\triangle BDC \cong \triangle BAC$ by SAS. Therefore, DB = AB. By measuring DB, we know AB.

9-10. Constructions

11. (a) $\triangle ABC \cong \triangle ABC$ $\triangle ABC \cong \triangle ACB$
$\triangle ABC \cong \triangle BAC$ $\triangle ABC \cong \triangle BCA$
$\triangle ABC \cong \triangle CAB$ $\triangle ABC \cong \triangle CBA$
(b) Because $\triangle ABC \cong \triangle BCA$, $\angle A \cong \angle B$ and $\angle B \cong \angle C$. Hence $\angle A \cong \angle B \cong \angle C$.

12. (a) Answers may vary. Some objects are tins of food and floor tiles. (b) Answers may vary. Photographs and their enlargements, an original and its projected image in an overhead projector, and a slide and its image are examples.

13. (a) One method of placing the six points on the circle is to use a compass with opening the length of a radius of the circle. (c) The triangles are congruent by SSS. The sides are the same length as a radius of the circle.

14. (a) F is the midpoint of both diagonals. We can show $\triangle ABD \cong \triangle CBD$ by SSS and then $\angle BDC \cong \angle BDA$ by CPCTC. $\triangle AFD \cong \triangle CFD$ by SAS, so $\overline{AF} \cong \overline{FC}$; thus F is the midpoint of $\overline{AC}$. A similar argument will show $\overline{BF} \cong \overline{FD}$. (b) 90°. Because $\angle AFD$ and $\angle CFD$ are both supplementary and congruent, each has measure 90°. Because m($\angle AFD$) = 90°, m($\angle BFA$) = 90°.

15. (a) A parallelogram. Let ABCD be the quadrilateral, with E the intersection point of its diagonals. Show that $\triangle AED \cong \triangle CEB$ and that $\triangle BEA \cong \triangle DEC$. Use congruent alternate interior angles to show $\overline{BC} \parallel \overline{AD}$ and $\overline{AB} \parallel \overline{CD}$. (b) Rectangle (c) Rhombus

16. (a) The angles formed by the diagonals of a rhombus are right angles. (b) Let the rhombus be ABCD with O as the point of intersection of the diagonals. First show that $\triangle ABO \cong \triangle CDO$ and conclude that $\overline{AO} \cong \overline{OC}$. Then show that $\triangle ABO \cong \triangle CBO$ by SSS. Hence, conclude that $\angle AOB \cong \angle COB$ and consequently that each angle is a right angle.

17. (a) A parallelogram. In quadrilateral ABCD let $\overline{AB} \cong \overline{CD}$ and $\overline{BC} \cong \overline{AD}$. Prove that $\triangle ABC \cong \triangle CDA$ and conclude that the $\overline{BC} \parallel \overline{AD}$. Similarly show $\triangle ABD \cong \triangle DCB$ and conclude that $\overline{AB} \parallel \overline{DC}$.

18. Congruent arcs are arcs of a circle whose central angles have the same measure.

19. The side of one cube is congruent to a side of the other cube.

20. The least number is two; for example, the length of a side of the base and the height.

21. (a) 6 (b) 24 (c) $n(n-1)(n-2) \cdots 3 \cdot 2 \cdot 1$

22. The triangles are congruent by SAS.

23. The perimeters are equal because the sides are congruent making the measures equal.

24. Answers may vary. For example,
TO EQUITRI :SIDE
   REPEAT 3 [FD :SIDE RT 120]
END

25. Execute the procedure.

26. (a) A triangle is constructed because the computer does not know the difference between an angle measure and a compass heading. (b) No. A triangle cannot have an angle with measure 190°. (c) Add the following:
IF NOT (:ANGLE <180) PRINT [NO TRIANGLE IS POSSIBLE.] STOP

Communication

27. Two triangles can be proved to be similar using SSS and SAS type of properties. If the corresponding sides of two triangles are proportional, the triangles are similar. Also is the corresponding sides of two triangles are proportional and the included angles are congruent, the triangles are similar.

28. The arguments might be as follows:
(a) By the definition of an isosceles triangle, $\overline{AB} \cong \overline{AC}$. Since congruence is an equivalence relation, we have the symmetric statement $\overline{AC} \cong \overline{AB}$. Also $\overline{BC} \cong \overline{CB}$. Hence by SSS, $\triangle BAC \cong \triangle CAB$ and by CPCTC, $\angle ABC \cong \angle ACB$. (b) Use Theorem 11-1 part (a) to show that the base angles of the isosceles triangle formed are congruent. The two triangles formed by the altitude are congruent by AAS. Then use corresponding parts of congruent triangles are congruent.

Theorem 11-2 may be proved by forming two triangles and proving them congruent using SAS. Then use corresponding parts of congruent triangles are congruent.

29. A brick wall of building might be considered a rep-tile if the wall is similar to a brick in the wall and the wall is used to construct larger walls also similar to the brick.

30. Most quilts contain congruent pieces in order that seams may be made to align and so that the quilt pieces can be fitted together to form the whole quilt.

Open-ended

31. Answers may vary. One possible pattern is the stamp-block quilt that is a quilt constructed entirely of squares.

32. Answers may vary. However, the answer must include at least three sides and one angle of each general quadrilateral in order to have them congruent.

Cooperative Learning

33. Student answers may vary. Without having the correspondence among vertices, students can have selected congruent sides and all congruent angles and have similar figures that are not necessarily congruent.

ONGOING ASSESSMENT 11-2

1. (d) Infinitely many triangles are possible.

2. (a) No; by ASA, the triangle is unique. (b) No; by AAS, the triangle is unique. (c) No; by ASA, the triangle is unique. (d) Yes; AAA does determine a unique shape but not size.

3. (a) Yes; ASA (b) Yes; AAS (c) No; SSA does not assure congruence. (d) No; AAA does not assure congruence.

4. When the parallel ruler is open at any setting, the distance BC = BC. It is given that AB = DC and AC = BD. So $\triangle ABC \cong \triangle DCB$ by SSS. Hence $\angle ABC \cong \angle DCB$ by CPCTC. Because these angles are alternate interior angles formed by lines $\overleftrightarrow{AB}$ and $\overleftrightarrow{CD}$ with transversal line $\overleftrightarrow{BC}$, then $\overline{AB} \parallel \overline{DC}$.

5. (a) Parallelogram (b) None (c) None (d) Rectangle (e) Rhombus (f) Square (g) Parallelogram

6. The trapezoid is an isosceles trapezoid and the angles formed with one base as a side are congruent, as are the angles formed on the other base. Those angles are sometimes referred to as the base angles of the isosceles trapezoid.

7. The third angles of the triangles must also be congruent because the sum of the measures of the three angles of a triangle must be 180°.

8. (a) If one leg and an acute angle of one right triangle are congruent, respectively, to a leg and an acute angle of another right triangle, the triangles are congruent.

Also if the hypotenuse and an acute angle of a right triangle are congruent, respectively, to the hypotenuse and an acute angle of another right triangle, the triangles are congruent. (b) See part (a).

9. (a) True (b) Truc (c) True (d) True (e) True (f) False; A counter example can be seen in a trapezoid in which two consecutive angles are right angles but the other two are not. (g) True (h) False; A square is both a rectangle and a rhombus. (i) False; A square is a trapezoid. (j) True

10. (a) Answers may vary. (b) If a quadrilateral has three right angles, then the fourth must also be a right angle. (c) No; any parallelogram with a pair of right angles must have right angles as its other pair of angles and hence be a rectangle.

11. There are five possibilities: one parallelogram and four kites.

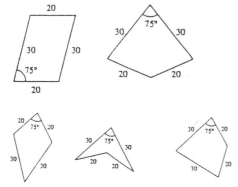

12. The quadrilateral formed must be a rhombus because all the sides are congruent.

13. The polygons must have the same number of sides and the length of one side of one polygon must be the same as a length of a side of the other.

14. The minimal conditions are that the measures of the central angles of the sectors must be the same.

15. Make one of the quadrilaterals a square and the other a rectangle.

16. (a) $\triangle ABC \cong \triangle ADC$ by SSS. Hence $\angle BAC \cong \angle DAC$ and $\angle BCM \cong \angle DCM$ by CPCTC. Therefore $\overleftrightarrow{AC}$ bisects $\angle A$ and $\angle C$. (b) The angles formed are right angles. By part (a), $\angle BAM \cong \angle DAM$. Hence $\triangle ABM \cong \triangle ADM$ by SAS. $\angle BMA \cong \angle DMA$ by CPCTC. Since $\angle BMA$ and $\angle DMA$ are adjacent congruent angles, each must be a right angle. Since vertical angles formed arc congruent, all four angles formed by the diagonals are right angles. (c) By part (b), $\overline{BM} \cong \overline{MD}$; CPCTC.

17. (a) The sides of opposite congruent angles in an isosceles trapezoid are congruent. (b) The diagonals are congruent. (c) In isosceles trapezoid ABCD, draw $\overline{BX}$ and $\overline{CY}$ perpendicular to $\overline{AD}$.

BCYX is a rectangle. (Why?) $\overline{BX} \cong \overline{CY}$; opposite sides of a rectangle are congruent. $\triangle BAX \cong \triangle DCY$; AAS. Thus $\overline{AB} \cong \overline{DC}$; CPCTC. $\triangle ABD \cong \triangle DCA$; SAS. Thus $\overline{AC} \cong \overline{DB}$; CPCTC.

18. Construction. Answers may vary.

19. (a) Rhombus (b) Use SAS to prove that $\triangle ECF \cong \triangle GBF \cong \triangle EDH \cong \triangle GAH$. (c) Parallelogram. (d) Suppose ADCB in part (a) is a parallelogram. Use SAS to show that $\triangle EDH \cong \triangle GBF$ and conclude that $\overline{EH} \cong \overline{GF}$. Similarly, show that $\triangle ECF \cong \triangle GAH$ and hence that $\overline{EF} \cong \overline{GH}$. Next use SSS to prove that $\triangle EFG \cong \triangle GHE$. Now conclude that $\angle GEH \cong \angle EGF$ and consequently that $\overline{FG} \parallel \overline{EH}$. Similarly, show that $\overline{EF} \parallel \overline{HG}$. (e) Parallelogram.

20. (a) The lengths of one side of each square must be equal. (b) The lengths of the sides of two perpendicular sides of the rectangles must be equal (c) Answers vary. One solution is the lengths of two adjacent sides of the parallelograms must be equal and the angles between them must have equal measure.

21. (a) Use the definition of a parallelogram and ASA to prove that $\triangle ADB \cong \triangle CDB$ and $\triangle ADC \cong \triangle CBA$. (b) Use a pair of triangles from (a). (c) Hint: Prove that $\triangle ABF \cong \triangle CDF$. (d) Hint: Extend $\overline{AB}$ and look for corresponding angles.

22. (b) (i) Two intersecting line segments (ii) Three segments that do not close into a triangle (c) Add the following line:
IF NOT (ALLOF (:ANGLE1 + :ANGLE2 < 180) (:ANGLE1 > 0) (:ANGLE 2 > 0) PRINT [NO TRIANGLE IS POSSIBLE.] STOP
(In LSCI, use the following line:
IF NOT (AND (:ANGLE1 + :ANGLE2 < 180) (:ANGLE1 > 0) (:ANGLE2 > 0)) [PRINT [NO TRIANGLE IS POSSIBLE.] STOP])

23. (a) Answers may vary.
  TO RHOMBUS :SIDE :ANGLE
   REPEAT 2 [FD :SIDE RT (180 - :ANGLE) FD :SIDE RT :ANGLE]
  END
(b) They are congruent.
(c) TO SQ. RHOM :SIDE
  RHOMBUS :SIDE 90
  END

24. Answers may vary. Students have to consider carefully the inputs for :ANGLE.
  TO ISOTRI :SIDE :ANGLE
  HOME FD :SIDE
  RIGHT (2* :ANGLE)
  FD :SIDE RIGHT :ANGLE
  HOME
 END

Communication

25. Mathematical congruence is exact. Two objects are congrucnt if they have exactly the same size and shape. In manufacturing the best that can happen is two items are congruent if they are within some tolerance of each other.

26. The triangle formed by Stan's head, Stan's feet, and the opposite bank is congruent to the triangle formed by Stan's head, Stan's feet, and the spot just obscured by the bill of his cap. These triangles are congruent by ASA since the angle at Stan's feet is 90° in both triangles, Stan's height is the same in both triangles, and the angle formed by the bill of his cap is the same in both triangles. The distance across the river is approximately equal to the distance he paced off, since these distances are corresponding parts of congruent triangles.

27. One way is to make both legs of the ironing board the same length and fasten them together with a hinge at their centers. If one of these legs is attached to the board at a fixed spot and the other leg can be attached at various spots, then the height of the ironing board can be adjusted. Since the legs form the diagonals of a rectangle, the board will always be parallel to the floor. (It can be shown that a quadrilateral whose diagonals are the same length and bisect each other is a rectangle.) In most commercially available ironing boards, the legs are designed to form the diagonals of a trapezoid. The fact that the surface is always parallel to the floor follows from properties of similar triangles discussed in section 11-4.

Open-ended

28. (**a**) All rolls of wallpaper are not congruent. They come in different widths and lengths. Typically with the same pattern, they are congruent. (**b**) Answers may vary. Wallpaper books give the exact drop length. Drop length is the length before a pattern repeats. (**c**) If rolls were congruent and there was a zero drop length in the pattern, then there would be less waste in cutting and matching patterns.

29. The United States Postal Service tries to make all of a single variety of stamps congruent. There have been some notable examples where errors were made and the stamps of one type were not congruent. Probably the most famous of the non-congruent stamps was the upside down "flying jenny." There have been many others. The result is that the anomalies are rare and become very valuable collector's items.

Cooperative Learning

30. (**a**) In many secondary school and middle school geometry books, kites are not defined. For many of these books, a trapezoid is a quadrilateral with exactly one set of parallel sides. (**c**) The definition used in this text allows a structure among the quadrilaterals that does not exist with the definition in part (a), namely the subset relationships among the quadrilaterals. The one in this text does cause some difficulty in the definition of an isosceles trapezoid. It must be defined in terms of its base angles not its sides.

Review Problems

31. The triangles that are congruent to triangle ABC are triangles AED and CDE. They are all congruent by SAS. Students may need to cut these triangles out and compare shapes.

32.-33. Constructions

34. (**a**) Yes: SAS (**b**) Yes: SSS (**c**) No

Technology Corner (p. 640)

The altitudes of an acute triangle meet at a point inside the triangle. The altitudes of a right triangle meet at the vertex of the right angle. The altitudes of an obtuse triangle meet at a point outside the triangle.

ONGOING ASSESSMENT 11-3

1. Construction

2. Constructions. The advantages and disadvantages of each may be discussed. The Mira is easy to use when the paper on which the constructions are to be performed may not be altered. The compass and straightedge is the classical way to do constructions. Paperfolding adds a tactile approach to the problem. The geometric drawing utility demands that exact measurements must be used on the screen unless you want similar figures.

3. (**a**) A right triangle is formed. (**b**) The altitude of the triangle is along the cable.

4. (**a**) The perpendicular bisectors of the sides of an acute triangle meet inside the triangle. (**b**) The perpendicular bisectors of the sides of a right triangle meet at the midpoint of the hypotenuse. (**c**) The perpendicular bisectors of the sides of an obtuse triangle meet outside the triangle.

5. (**a**) The point on the perpendicular bisector of a segment is equidistant from the endpoints of the segment. (**b**) This point is equidistant from all vertices because it is on all three perpendicular bisectors. Being on one perpendicular bisector makes the point equidistant from two of the vertices. Being at the intersection of two of the perpendicular bisectors forces the point to be equidistant from all three vertices. (**c**) The answer is the same. (**d**) Construction. The circle must pass through every vertex.

6. Construction

7. (**a**) The distances are equal. (**b**) Construction (**c**) Construction (**d**) Construction. The constructed circle is tangent to each of the sides of the triangle.

8. (**a**) The perpendicular bisector of a chord of a circle contains the center of the circle. (**b**) Choose an arbitrary chord $\overline{AB}$ on the circle with center 0. Then $\overline{OA} \cong \overline{OB}$ since both are radii. Construct the angle bisector of $\angle AOB$ and let P be the point of intersection with chord $\overline{AB}$. Then $\triangle AOP \cong \triangle BOP$ by SAS, and $\angle OPB$ is a right angle since it is both congruent and supplementary to $\angle OPA$. Since $\overline{AP} \cong \overline{PB}$ and $\angle OPB$ is a right angle, $\overline{OP}$ is the perpendicular bisector of $\overline{AB}$, and therefore the perpendicular bisector of an arbitrary chord contains point O. (**c**) Hint: Construct two non-parallel chords and find their perpendicular bisectors. The intersection of the perpendicular bisectors is the center of the circle.

9. Construction

10. Answers may vary. One possibility is: Draw a line segment. (10¢)
Draw two intersecting arcs (20¢) to construct a perpendicular segment. (10¢)
With compass point at the intersection of the two segments, sweep a wide arc (10¢) intersecting both segments.
Maintain the same compass setting and measure an arc from each of these points to determine the fourth point. (20¢) Draw the two segments to complete the square. (20¢) The sum is 90¢.

11. Construction.

12. (**a**) $\overrightarrow{PQ}$ is the perpendicular bisector of $\overline{AB}$. (**b**) Q is on the perpendicular bisector of $\overline{AB}$ because $\overline{AQ} \cong \overline{QB}$. Similarly, P is on the perpendicular bisector of $\overline{AB}$. Because a unique line contains two points, the perpendicular bisector contains $\overrightarrow{PQ}$. (**c**) $\overrightarrow{PQ}$ is the angle bisector of $\angle APB$; $\overrightarrow{QC}$ is the angle bisector of $\angle AQB$. (**d**) Show that $\triangle APQ \cong \triangle BPQ$ by SSS; then $\angle APQ \cong \angle BPQ$ by CPCTC. Show that $\triangle AQC \cong \triangle BQC$ and conclude that, $\angle AQC \cong \angle BQC$.

13. The figure is a non-convex kite.

14. (**a**) See Problem 9. (**b**) Construct two perpendicular segments bisecting each other and congruent to the given diagonal. (**c**) There is no unique rectangle. The endpoints of two segments bisecting each other and congruent to the given diagonal determine a rectangle. Since the segments may intersect at any angle, there are infinitely many such rectangles. (**d**) Without the angle between the sides being given, there is no unique parallelogram. (**e**) Construct two perpendicular segments bisecting each other and congruent to the given diagonals. (**f**) This is impossible because the sum of the measures of the angles would be greater than 180°. (**g**) This is impossible because the fourth angle must be a right angle also. (**h**) The kite would not be unique without knowing the lengths of some sides. (**i**) The kite would not be unique but would be a square. (**j**) Consider $\triangle ABC$ and the angle bisector $\overline{CD}$. Since $\overline{AC} \cong \overline{BC}$, then $\overline{CD} \perp \overline{AB}$. It is possible to construct $\triangle ADC$, since $\overline{AD}$ is half as long as the base and m($\angle DAC$) = 90° − 1/2m($\angle ACB$) .

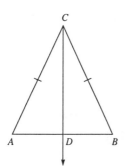

(**k**) There is no unique trapezoid unless two sides are designated as parallel; if this is the case, consider the trapezoid ABCD. Through B, construct $\overline{BE} \parallel \overline{CD}$. It follows that $\overline{BE} \cong \overline{CD}$. (Why?) Also, AE = AD − ED = AD − BC. Hence, $\triangle ABE$ can be constructed by SSS. Now extend $\overline{AE}$ so that $\overline{ED} \cong \overline{BC}$ and through B draw $\overline{BC}$ parallel to $\overline{AE}$. The construction is not always possible. If the four given sides are such that $\triangle ABE$ cannot be constructed, the trapezoid cannot be constructed either.

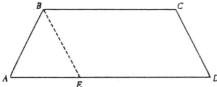

15. (**a**)-(**e**) Construction
16. Construction. See Problem 12 for a hint.
17. (**a**) Since the triangles are congruent, the acute angles formed by the hypotenuse and the line are congruent. Since the corresponding angles are congruent, the hypotenuses are parallel (the line formed by the top of the ruler is the transversal). (**b**) Construction.
18. Make the edge of the ruler coincide with ℓ. Let one of the legs of the right triangle slide along the edge of the ruler until the other leg goes through P. The line along the edge containing P is the required perpendicular.
19. Connecting the points with the center of the circle forms six congruent equilateral triangles. Thus all interior angles of the polygon may be proved congruent and all the sides are congruent. The polygon is a regular hexagon.
20. An equilateral triangle may be formed by connecting every other vertex of the regular hexagon.
21. Construction
22. Hint: Construct two perpendicular diameters. The ends of the diameters are the vertices of the square.
23. Hint: Bisect the angles formed by the diagonals of the square. The angle bisectors, if extended, intersect the circle in four of the vertices. The other vertices are the vertices of the square.
24. Answers may vary.
   TO ALTITUDES
      REPEAT 3 [RT 30 FD 60 RT 90 FD 110 BK 130 FD
      20 LT 90 FD 60 RT 90]
   END
25. Answers may vary.
   (**a**) TO ANGBIS :MEAS
      REPEAT 3 [FD 75 BK 75 RT :MEAS/2]
   END
   (**b**) TO PERBIS :SIZE
      FD: SIZE/2 RT 90 FD :SIZE BK :SIZE LT 90 FD
      :SIZE/2
   END

(**c**) TO PARALLEL :SEG1 :SEG2
      FD :SEGI PENUP RT 90
      FD 20 RT 90 PENDOWN
      FD :SEG2
   END

Communication
26. Fold the circle onto itself along two diameters. The intersection of the diameters is the center of the circle. Using a Mira, reflect the circle onto itself using two different diameters as the reflecting lines.
27. Given $\angle BAC$, put one strip of tape so that an edge of the tape is along $\overline{AB}$ and another strip of the tape so that so that one of its edges is on $\overline{AC}$ as shown. Two edges of the strips of tape intersect in the interior of the angle at D. Connect A with D. $\overline{AD}$ is the angle bisector. Because the diagonals of a rhombus bisect its angles, this construction can be justified by showing that AEDF is a rhombus. (E and F are the points of intersection of the tops of the tape pieces and the opposite sides.) AEDF is a parallelogram. (Why?) It remains to be shown that $\overline{AF} \cong \overline{AE}$. For that purpose, we show that $\triangle FAG \cong \triangle EAH$. We have $\overline{FG} \cong \overline{HE}$ because the two strips of tape have the same width. $\angle A \cong \angle A$, and the angles at H and G are right angles. Thus the triangles are congruent by AAS.

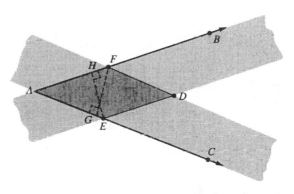

28. The lines along the side of the highway appear to intersect and the middle line appears to bisect the angle formed.
29. Answers may vary. Most students will probably lobby to have other tools included as construction tools.

Open-ended
30. Most students will say that there are more perpendiculars from a point to a line using the North Pole as a point and the equator as a line. All lines of longitude intersect at the North Pole and all are perpendicular to the equator.
31. There are no parallels on a sphere. All great circles (that represent lines) intersect in two points.
32. This depends totally on the geometry utility.

Cooperative Learning
33. The three classical problems of antiquity are to duplicate a cube (or construct a cube with twice the volume of a given cube), to square a circle (or to construct a square and a circle with equal areas), and to trisect any angle. Descriptions of these problems are given in most geometry books and in any encyclopedia.

Review Problems
34. $\triangle ABC \cong \triangle DEC$ by ASA. ($\overline{BC} \cong \overline{CE}$, $\angle ACB \cong \angle ECD$ as vertical angles, and $\angle B \cong \angle E$ as alternate interior angles

formed by the parallels $\overline{AB}$ and $\overline{ED}$ and the transversal $\overleftrightarrow{EB}$.)
$\overline{AC} \cong \overline{DC}$ by CPCTC.

35. Construction

36. (a) No (b) (1) $\triangle LYC \cong \triangle UCY$ by SAS. $\overline{LY} \cong \overline{UC}$ is given; $\overline{YC} \cong \overline{CY}$. To show $\angle LYC \cong \angle UCY$, construct $\overline{UV} \parallel \overline{LY}$. Now LUVY is a parallelogram; $\overline{UV} \cong \overline{LY}$ and, by transitivity, $\overline{UV} \cong \overline{UC}$. $\angle LYC \cong \angle UVC$ (corresponding angles formed by $\overline{LY} \parallel \overline{UV}$ and transversal $\overleftrightarrow{YC}$). $\angle UVC \cong \angle UCV$ (base angles of isosceles triangle UVC). $\angle LYC \cong \angle UCY$ by transitive property. (2) $\triangle ULY \cong \triangle LUC$ by SAS; $\overline{LY} \cong \overline{UC}$ is given; $\overline{UL} \cong \overline{LU}$. To show $\triangle ULY \cong \triangle LUC$, use supplementary pairs of angles $\angle ULY$ and $\angle LYC$, $\angle LUC$ and $\angle UCY$, and $\angle LYC$ and $\angle UCY$ from part (1). (3) $\triangle LOY \cong \triangle UOC$ by SAS. $\overline{LY} \cong \overline{UC}$ is given. $\angle YLC \cong \angle CUY$ by CPCTC from part (1). $\angle LYU \cong \angle UCL$ by CPCTC from part (2).

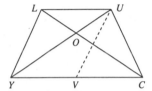

37. $\overline{AB}$

38. $\angle ABC$

39. If $\angle A$ is not the right angle the triangles are congruent. If $\angle A$ is the right angle, the triangles are not necessarily congruent.

Technology Corner (p. 644)

1. (c) m($\angle BOC$) = 2m ($\angle BPC$)

2. The angle is a right angle.

Brain Teaser (p. 655)

It can be shown that the fence post must be 6 ft high regardless of how far apart the flag poles are.

ONGOING ASSESSMENT 11-4

1. (a) Yes; AAA (b) Yes; sides are proportional and angles are congruent. (c) No (d) No (e) Yes; radii are proportional. (f) No (g) Yes; sides are proportional and angles are congruent.

2. This illustration is one possibility.

(a)

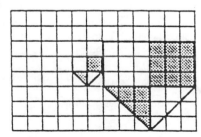

(b)

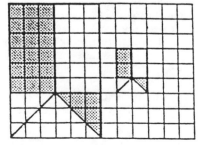

(c)

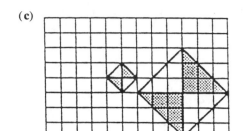

(d)

3. (c) The triangles are similar if the corresponding sides are proportional.

4. (c) The triangles are similar if, for example, in $\triangle ABC$ and $\triangle DEF$, we have AB/DE = AC/DF and $\angle A \cong \angle D$.

5. Answers may vary. (a) Two rectangles, one of which is a square and the other is not. (b) Two rhombuses, one of which is a square and the other is not but the sides are all the same length.

6. The ratio of the perimeters is the same as the ratio of the sides.

7. (a) (i) $\triangle ABC \sim \triangle DEF$ by AA (ii) $\triangle ABC \sim \triangle EDA$ by AA (iii) $\triangle ACD \sim \triangle ABE$ by AA (iv) $\triangle ABE \sim \triangle DBC$ by AA (b) (i) 2/3 (ii) 1/2 (iii) 3/4 (iv) 3/4

8. (a) 7 (b) 24/7 (c) 3 (d) 96/13

9. Construction

10. (a) (1) $\triangle ABC \sim \triangle ACD$ by AA since $\angle ADC$ and $\angle ACB$ are right angles, and $\angle A$ is common to both. (2) $\triangle ABC \sim \triangle CBD$ by AA since $\angle CDB$ and $\angle ACB$ are right angles and $\angle B$ is common to both. (3) Using (1) and (2), $\triangle ACD \sim \triangle CBD$ by the transitive property. (b) (1) AC/AB = CD/CB = AD/AC (2) CB/AB = CD/AC = DB/CB (3) AC/CB = AD/CD = CD/DB

11. No. The maps are similar and even though the scales may change, the actual distances do not.

12. 15 m

13. 9 m

14. (a) In $\triangle ABC$ let AB = BC and let $\overline{BD}$ be the angle bisector of $\angle B$. Then $\overline{BD} \perp \overline{AC}$ (why?) and we have $\alpha + \beta = 90°$. $\alpha = \beta$. Hence $\alpha = 45°$ and $2\beta = 90°$. Consequently, the angles of the triangle are 45°, 45°, 90°. Next suppose the angle bisector is the bisector of one of the base angles. If the measure of each of the base angles is 2α then $\triangle AEC$ is isosceles if and only if m($\angle AEC$) = 2α. Then in $\triangle AEC$: $\alpha + 2\alpha + 2\alpha = 180°$ or $5\alpha = 180°$. Hence $\alpha = 36°$ and $2\alpha = 72°$. Now m($\angle B$) = $180° - 2 \cdot 72° = 36°$. Hence the angles of $\triangle ABC$ are 72°, 72°, and 36°.

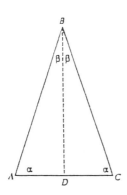

(**b**) In the first triangle, the angle bisector of the right angle partitions the original triangle into two congruent isosceles right triangles with base angles measuring 45°. The new triangles are similar to the original triangle. In the second triangle, the angle bisector of one of the 72° base angles partitions the original triangle into two isosceles triangles, which are neither congruent nor similar to each other. One of the new triangles, however, is similar to the original triangle.

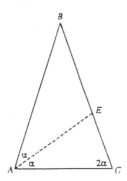

15. 232.6 in. or 19.4 ft
16. Place the projector so that the slide is 23 ft 9 in. from the screen.
17. (**a**) 1/3 (**b**) 1/9 (**c**) 0 (**d**) No slope (**e**) 20,000
(**f**) 1 if a ≠ b
18. (**a**) y − 3 = (1/3)(x − 4) (**b**) y − 1 = (1/9) (x + 4)
(**c**) y = 2 (**d**) x = ¯3 (**e**) y − 12 = 20,000(x − 1.0001)
(**f**) y = x
19. Answers may vary. (**a**) (¯3,2) (5,2), ... (**b**) (¯1,7), (¯1,¯5), ...
(**c**) (2,0), (4,0), ... (**d**) (0,¯1), (0,6), ... (**e**) (3,3), (2,2), ...
20. All regular octagons have side lengths proportional and all interior angles are congruent.
21. The perimeters have ratio 1/k, because all sides are in this proportion. The sum must be in the same proportion.
22. The cross-sections are all circles. They have exactly the same shape but not necessarily the same size. They must be similar.
23. The answer is no. The cross-sections may be circular if cut parallel to bases but could also be oval or elliptical.

24. Answers may vary.
(**a**) TO RECTANGLE :LEN :WID
    REPEAT 2 [FD :LEN RT 90 FD :WID RT 90]
END
TO SIM.RECT :LEN :WID
    RECTANGLE :LEN*2 :WID*2
END

(**b**) TO SIM.RECTANGLE :LEN :WID :SCALE
    RECTANGLE :LEN* :SCALE :WID* :SCALE
END
(**c**) TO PARALLELOGRAM :LEN :WID :ANGLE
    REPEAT 2 [FD :LEN RT 180- :ANGLE FD :WID RT
    :ANGLE]
END
TO SIM.PAR :LEN :WID :ANGLE :SCALE
    PARALLELOGRAM :LEN* :SCALE :WID* :SCALE
    :ANGLE
END
25. Answers may vary.
(**a**) TO TRISECT :LEN
    REPEAT 3 [MARK FD :LEN/3]
END
TO MARK
RT 90 FD 5
BK 5 LT 90
END
(**b**) TO PARTITION :LEN :NUM
    REPEAT :NUM [MARK FD :LEN/:NUM]
END

Communication
26. Any two cubes are similar because they have the same shape.
27. In theory the real product is similar to the model. In reality, this is rarely the case because of changes in the building once the building has been started.
28. Lay the licorice diagonally on the paper so it spans a number of spaces equal to the number of children. (See the figure.) Cut on the lines. Equidistant parallel lines will divide any transversal into congruent segments.

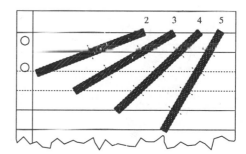

Open-ended
29. (**a**) They should have the same shape. (**b**) The answers may vary depending upon the construction. (**c**) The perimeters of the bases should be in the same ratio as the heights in part (**b**). (**d**) Answers will vary depending upon the construction. (**e**) The ratio of the volumes should be the cube of the ratio found in part (**b**). (**f**) See the above answers.
30. Babies and adults are not similar in body shape. Student answers may vary, though.

Cooperative Learning
31. (**b**) The following are two different size triangles with the given data. The triangles are similar but not congruent. (The ratio of the corresponding sides is $\frac{80}{100}$ or $\frac{4}{5}$.) Hence, the surveyor and the architect could both have been correct in their conclusions.

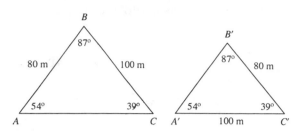

(c) One way for them to avoid their confusion is to specify which sides are opposite which angles.

Review Problems

32. No; the image is two-dimensional while the original person is three-dimensional.

33. Construction

34. Construction

35. Answers may vary. Students may suggest that angles of measure 45° be constructed with the endpoints of the hypotenuse as vertices of the 45° angles and the hypotenuse as one of the sides of the angles. Both angles need to be constructed on the same side of the hypotenuse.

36. Yes. Use the vertical angles to justify this result.

37. Answers may vary.
```
TO TRI30 :HYPOT
    DRAW
    FD :HYPOT/2 RT 120
    FD :HYPOT RT 120
    HOME
END
```
(*In LCSI Logo, replace DRAW with CLEARSCREEN.*)

38. Answers may vary from the one given.
```
TO RTISOS :HYPOT
    DRAW
    FD :HYPOT RT 135
    CHECK
END
```
(*In LCSI Logo, replace DRAW with CLEARSCREEN.*)
```
TO CHECK
    FORWARD 1
    SETHEADING TOWARD 0 0
    IF ABS (HEADING - 225) < 2
        HOME STOP
    SETHEADING - 135
    CHECK
END
```
(*In LCSI Logo, replace SET HEADING TOWARD 0 0 with SETHEADING TOWARD [0 0] and IF ABS (HEADING-225)<2 HOME STOP with IF ABS (HEADING-225<2) [HOME STOP].*)
```
TO ABS :VALUE
    IF :VALUE <0 OUTPUT  – :VALUE ELSE
    OUTPUT :VALUE
END
```
(*In LCSI Logo, replace IF :VALUE<0 OUTPUT – :VALUE ELSE OUTPUT :VALUE with IF :VALUE <0 [OUTPUT – :VALUE] [OUTPUT :VALUE].*)

Technology Corner (p. 659)

The perimeter of the S_1 is 3; the perimeter of S_2 is 4; and the perimeter of S_3 is 48/9. Students may have trouble thinking about the perimeters of the snowflake curves.

Brain Teaser (p. 661)

Use similar triangles and set up the ratio 20/30 = AG/15. AG = 10 cm, and AG = CE.

Technology Corner (p. 663)

1. All trigonometric ratios are approximated by the technology used. The sines and cosines are all greater than 0 and less than 1. They do approach a limit, but students will not know this. The tangents are greater than 0 but may get extremely large.

2. It is not necessary to measure the sides of the triangles if the technology is available.

ONGOING ASSESSMENT 11-5

1. (a) 13.12 m (b) 43.59 m (c) 9.53 m (d) 11.94 m

2. Approximately 5.13 ft

3. Regardless of the size of the tile, sin 45° is equal to the cos 45° is approximately equal to 0.707; tan 45° is 1.

4. 8.34 m

5. The vertical component is approximately 8.62 lb; the horizontal component is approximately 11.03 lb.

6. (a) The angle should be approximately 35.7° (b) The length of the lake is approximately 99.27 ft.

7. Approximately 63.9 ft.

8. (a) Approximately 561.9 ft. (b) Approximately 1390.78 ft.

9. Approximately 41.4 ft.

10. 8.44 mi

11. Decimals are truncated at three places.

Angle Measure	Sine	Cosine	Square of Sine	Square of Cosine	Sum of Columns 4 and 5
10°	0.174	0.985	0.030	0.970	1
20°	0.342	0.940	0.117	0.884	1.01
30°	0.500	0.866	0.250	0.750	1
40°	0.643	0.766	0.413	0.587	1
50°	0.766	0.643	0.587	0.413	1
60°	0.866	0.500	0.750	0.250	1
70°	0.940	0.342	0.884	0.117	1.01
80°	0.985	0.174	0.970	0.030	1

(b) The sum of the squares of the sines and cosines of various angles is 1.

12. Approximately 297 ft.

13. The tangent is the rise over the run. The tangent is also related to the slope of a line.

14. The tangent. The rise is a vertical distance while the run is a horizontal distance.

15. Approximately 63.59 ft horizontally and approximately 101.77 ft vertically

16. (a) 121.8° (b) 40.2° (c) 1.68 m

17. (a) 0.669 (b) 0.743 (c) 0.900

18. The program draws a square with one diagonal.

Chapter Review

1. (a) △ADB ≅ △CDB by SAS (b) △GAC ≅ △EDB by SAS (c) △ABC ≅ △EDC by AAS (d) △BAD ≅ △EAC by ASA (e) △ABD ≅ △CBD by ASA or by SAS (f) △ABD ≅ △CBD by SAS (g) △ABD ≅ △CBE by SSS (h) △ABC ≅ △ADC by SSS; △ABE ≅ △ADE by SSS or SAS; △EBC ≅ △EDC by SSS or SAS

2. A parallelogram. △ADE ≅ △CBF by SAS. Hence, ∠DEA ≅ ∠CBF. Since ∠DEA ≅ ∠EAF (alternate interior angles between the parallels $\overleftrightarrow{DC}$ and $\overleftrightarrow{AB}$ and the transversal $\overleftrightarrow{AE}$), it follows that ∠EAF ≅ ∠CFB. Consequently, $\overline{AE} ≅ \overline{AE}$. Also, $\overline{EC} ≅ \overline{EC}$ (Why?), and therefore AECF is a parallelogram.

3. Construction

4. (a) x = 8 cm; y = 5 cm (b) x = 6 m

5. Construction

6. a/b = c/d because a/b = x/y and x/y = c/d

7. Hint: Find the intersection of the perpendicular bisector of $\overline{AB}$ and line ℓ.

8. (**a**) $\triangle ACB \sim \triangle DEB$ by AA. $x = 24/5$ in. (**b**) $\triangle ABC \sim \triangle ADE$ by AA. $x = 55/6$ ft and $y = 4/3$ ft

9. (**a**) False: A chord has its endpoints on the circle.

10. 12 m high

11. (**a**) (iii) and (iv) (**b**) Any regular convex polygon can be inscribed in a circle.

12. 6 m

13. 256/5 m

14. True in some cases and false in others: If the diagonals do not bisect each other, then it is not a square. Quadrilateral ABCD is not a square. However, its diagonals are perpendicular and congruent.

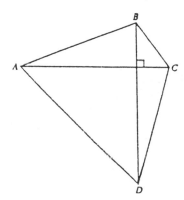

15. (**a**) $y - 1 = (^-4/3)(x + 1)$ (**b**) $y - 2 = (1 + 3)(x - 3)$

16. There is no single line through the points with the given coordinates because using two of the points the slope is 3/4 while using one of those points with the third, the slope is $^-4/7$.

17. Approximately 5.20 cm

18. 45°

19. You might draw an altitude of the triangle forming two right triangles, one of which has an acute angle of 72°. Then one can measure sides and find the ratio to approximate the sine.

20. Approximately 3.46 cm

21. The measures of the angles of elevation and depression are equal because they are alternate interior angles formed by a transversal cutting parallel lines.

CHAPTER 12

ONGOING ASSESSMENT 12-1

1. (**a**) cm², in². (**b**) cm², in². (**c**) cm², in². (**d**) m², yd²
(**e**) m², yd² (**f**) km², mi²

2. Answers vary, for example, (**a**) 1.5 m² (**b**) 1400 cm²
(**c**) 2500 cm² (**d**) 3 m²

3. (**a**) 0.0588 m², 58,800 mm² (**b**) 0.000192 m², 1.92 cm²
(**c**) 15,000 cm², 1,500,000 mm² (**d**) 0.01 m², 10,000 mm²
(**e**) 0.0005 m², 500 mm²

4. (**a**) 444.$\overline{4}$ yd² (**b**) 0.32 mi² (**c**) 6400 acres (**d**) 130,680 ft²

5. (**a**) 4900 m² (**b**) 98 (**c**) 0.98 ha

6. (**a**) 3 sq. units (**b**) 3 sq. units (**c**) 2 sq. units (**d**) 5 sq. units
(**e**) 6 sq. units (**f**) 4 1/2 sq. units

7. They all check; i.e., $I + (1/2)B - 1 = A$

8. (**a**) 20 cm² (**b**) 900 cm², or 0.09 m² (**c**) 7.5 m² (**d**) 39 cm²
(**e**) 600 cm²

9. (**a**) 9 cm² (**b**) 96 cm² (**c**) $\left(2\sqrt{21} - 2\sqrt{5}\right)$cm² or approx.
4.69 cm² (**d**) 20 cm² (**e**) 84 cm² (**f**) 105 cm²

10. (**a**) (i) 1.95 km² (ii) 195 ha (**b**) (i) 0.63 mi²
(ii) 402.89 acres (**c**) Answers vary, for example, the metric system is easier because you only have to move the decimal point to convert units within the system.

11. (**a**) True (**b**) Don't know (**c**) Don't know (**d**) Don't know

12. (1/2)ab

13. (**a**) $405.11 (**b**) $550

14. (**a**) 25π cm² (**b**) (8/3)π cm² (**c**) (18/5)π cm²
(**d**) (9/2)π cm² (**e**) 100 cm²

15. 1200 tiles

16. 8 bags of seed

17. (**a**) $24\sqrt{3}$ cm² (**b**) $9\sqrt{3}$ cm²

18. In the first picture the wasted space is $\pi r^2 - 2r^2$ or about $1.14\ r^2$. The wasted space for the circle in the square is $4r^2 - \pi r^2$ or about $0.86\ r^2$. Therefore the circle in the square has less wasted space.

19. (**a**) 16π cm² (**b**) $r = s/\sqrt{\pi}$

20. (**a**) 2π cm² (**b**) (π/2 + 2) cm² (**c**) 2π cm² (**d**) (50π − 100) cm² (**e**) (1/4)πr² (**f**) (1/8)πr² (**g**) (1/16)πr²

21. 7π m²

22. (**a**) 48 cm (**b**) 64 cm²

23. (**a**) The area is quadrupled. (**b**) 1:25

24. (**a**) The area is quadrupled. (**b**) The area is 1.1² or 1.21 times as great. (**c**) The area is increased by a factor of 9.

25. 40 m

26. The first is a better buy at 10 ft² per dollar versus 9.375 ft² per dollar.

27. (320 + 64π) m²

28. 1 in.

29. P should be connected to the point that is 2 units above P and 1 1/2 units to the right of P.

30. (**a**)

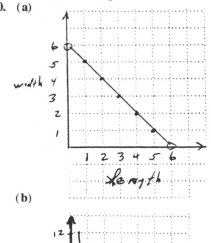

(**b**)

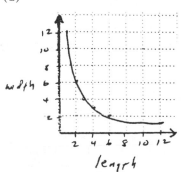

31. The area of the crosshatched portion is the same as the area as of the shaded region, 9π in.².

32. (a)

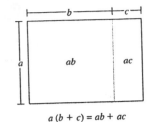

$$a(b + c) = ab + ac$$

(b)

$$(a + b)(c + d) = ac + ad + bc + bd$$

33. (a) 4:9; $A_1/A_2 = S_1^2/S_2^2$, and $S_1/S_2 = 2/3$; hence, $A_1/A_2 = (2/3)^2 = 4/9$ (b) 4:9 (Hint: $A = d^2/2$ where d is the length of a diagonal.)

34. (a) 4:1 (b) The former is the square of the latter. (c) Answers vary, for example, if two similar triangles have ratio x:y then the ratio for their bases and heights is xb:yb and xh:yh respectively. The ratio of the areas is $\frac{1}{2}$(xb)(xh):

$$\frac{1}{2}(yb)(yh) = x^2\left(\frac{bh}{2}\right) : y^2\left(\frac{bh}{2}\right) = x^2 : y^2.$$

35. (a) As seen in previous problems, the ratio of the areas of the two screens is $20^2:27^2$ or 400:729. This ratio is less than 400:600, so the larger set is the better buy. (b) Approx. 28.3 in.

36. Draw altitudes $\overline{BE}$ and $\overline{DF}$ of triangles BCP and DCP, respectively. $\triangle ABE \cong \triangle CDF$ by AAS. Thus $\overline{BE} \cong \overline{DF}$. Because $\overline{CP}$ is a base of $\triangle BCP$ and $\triangle DCP$, and because heights are the same, the areas must be equal.

Communication

37. Answers vary, for example, the circle can be cut up into pie-shaped pieces and reassembled in the shape of a parallelogram-shaped figure with height equal to the radius and the base equal to C/2. Another technique might be to inscribe and circumscribe polygons about the circle and continue to squeeze the area of the circle between the areas of the inner and outer polygons.

38. (a) The area of the 10-in. pizza is 25π in.^{2} The area of the 20-in. pizza is 100π in.^{2}. Because the area of the 20-in. pizza is four times as great, this pizza might cost four times as much, or $40. However, this is not the case because other factors are considered rather than just the area of the pizza. (b) If the price is based only on the area of pizza, then the ratio between prices should be 1: k^2.

39. The area of each triangle is 10 cm^2 because the base of each triangle is $\overline{AB}$ and the height of each triangle is the perpendicular distance between the two lines. Because each triangle has the same base and height, the areas of the triangles are the same.

40. (a) Rotate the shaded region 180° about point E. The area of the triangle is the same as the area of the parallelogram that is formed. The area of the parallelogram is (h/2) b. (b) Use paper cutting and try it.

41. After the rotations, a rectangle is formed. The area of the rectangle is length times width which in the case of the parallelogram is the same as the base times the height.

Open-ended

42. Answers vary, for example, a rectangle that is 3 cm by 4 cm has perimeter 14 cm and area 12 cm^2. A rectangle that is 5 cm by 2 cm also has perimeter 14 cm but it has area 10 cm^2.

43. (a) Answers vary depending on the size of the hand. (b) Answers vary, for example, many people will trace their hands on square centimeter paper and then count the number of squares that are entirely contained in the outline. Next, they count the number of squares that are partially contained in the hand outline and multiply this number by 1/2. The final estimate is the sum of the two numbers.

44. (a) 5 square units (b) 12 units (c) (i) 3 (ii) 15 (iii) 20 (d) Answers vary depending on chosen shape. (e) Answers vary depending on chosen shape.

45. (a) (i) 12, 10 (ii) 14, 10 (iii) 62, 22 (b) (i) 9, 5 (ii) 42, 12 (c) 2(n + 1) (d) n − 1

Brain Teaser (p. 696)

(1) 64 (2) 65 (3) Although the pieces look like they should fit together, they do not really. To see this, assume the pieces do fit. We then obtain the figure.

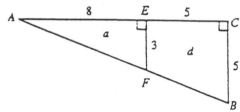

Since $\triangle AEF \sim \triangle ACB$, we have $\frac{8}{13} = \frac{3}{5}$ which is a contradiction. This implies that pieces like those in the figure cannot fit together in order to form a triangle. In order for the pieces to fit together, the measure of $\overline{EF}$ must be given as: $\frac{8}{13} = \frac{EF}{5}$; hence $EF = \frac{40}{13} = 3\frac{1}{13}$. Since $3\frac{1}{13}$ is close to 3, the discrepancy is small and the pieces only appear to fit. Other pieces which appear to fit should be analyzed.

ONGOING ASSESSMENT 12-2

1. (a) No, in order for it to be a square the sides must be the same length and the angles must be right angles. The sides are of different lengths. (b) The diagonal is $\sqrt{45}$ units long which is about 6.7 units. (c) The length of the diagonal is doubled.

2. (a) 6 (b) 5a (c) 12 (d) $s\sqrt{3}/2$ (e) 9 (f) 13 (g) $2\sqrt{2}$ (h) $3\sqrt{5}$ (i) $3\sqrt{3}$ (j) 5/3

3. $6\sqrt{5}, 12\sqrt{5}$

4. (a) No (b) Yes (c) Yes (d) Yes (e) Yes (f) Yes

5. $\sqrt{450}$ or $15\sqrt{2}$

6. About 2622 km

7. $\sqrt{125}$ mi or about 11.2 mi

8. $6\sqrt{6}$ or about 14.7 ft

9. 9.8 m approx.

10. (a) $(s^2\sqrt{3})/4$ (b) $s^2/2$

11. (a) x = 8, y = $2\sqrt{3}$ (b) x = 4, y = 2

12. 1.5 m approx.

13. 12.5 cm; 15 cm

14. 8 cm

15. We are not clear how she will saw it. If she saws straight across, we get $8 - \sqrt{34}$ or about 2.17 ft.

16. $90\sqrt{2}$ or about 127.28 ft

17. The longest piece of straight spaghetti will be $\sqrt{116}$ in. or approximately 10.77 in.

18. (a)   **(b)** Not possible

(c)

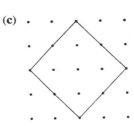

(d) Not possible **(e)** Not possible

19. $\triangle ACD \sim \triangle ABC$; $AC/AB = AD/AC$ implies $b/c = x/b$ which implies $b^2 = cx$; $\triangle BCD \sim \triangle ABC$; $AB/CB = CB/DB$ implies $c/a = a/y$ which implies $a^2 = cy$; $a^2 + b^2 = cx + cy = c(x + y)$ $= cc = c^2$

20. $\sqrt{10}$ or approximately 3.16 m

21. Approximately 16.97 in.

22. Approximately 99.5 ft.

23. Approximately 10.6 mi.

24. The area of the trapezoid is equal to the sum of the areas of the three triangles. Thus,

$$1/2(a + b)(a + b) = (1/2)ab + (1/2)ab + (1/2)c^2$$
$$1/2(a^2 + 2ab + b^2) = ab + (1/2)c^2$$
$$a^2/2 + ab + b^2/2 = ab + c^2/2$$

Subtracting ab from both sides and multiplying both sides by 2, we have $a^2 + b^2 = c^2$. The reader should also verify that the angle formed by the two sides of the length c has measure $90°$.

25. The area of the large square is equal to the sum of the areas of the small square and the four right triangles. Therefore, $(a + b)^2 = c^2 + 4(ab/2)$. Thus, $a^2 + 2ab + b^2 = c^2 + 2ab$ which in turn implies that $c^2 = a^2 + b^2$. It must also be shown that the inside quadrilateral is really a square.

26. Yes

27. Yes

28. (a) 4 **(b)** 5 **(c)** $2\sqrt{13}$ **(d)** $\dfrac{\sqrt{365}}{4}$ or approx. 4.78 **(e)** 5

29. $10 + \sqrt{10}$

30. The sides have lengths $\sqrt{45}$, $\sqrt{180}$, and $\sqrt{225}$. Because $\left(\sqrt{45}\right)^2 + \left(\sqrt{180}\right)^2 = \left(\sqrt{225}\right)^2$, the triangle is a right triangle.

31. The side lengths are $5, 7\sqrt{2}$, and 5 and so the triangle is isosceles.

32. $x = 9$ or $^-7$

33. $c\sqrt{3}/4$

Communication

34. (a) Let the length of the side of the square be s. Draw the diagonal of the square and make the new square have side lengths equal to the diagonal. Then the area is $\left(\sqrt{2}\,s\right)^2 = 2s^2$.

(b) Make the lengths of the new square 1/2 the length of the diagonal, or $\left(\sqrt{2}\,s/2\right)$; then the area of the new square is

$\left(\sqrt{2}\,s/2\right)^2 = s^2/2$.

35. A 6% grade means that there is a six-unit vertical rise for every 100-unit horizontal distance.

36. Yes, because they are right triangles the third legs must be equal and these legs could be found using the Pythagorean

Theorem. Then the two triangles must be congruent by SSS (or SAS).

37. Yes, she had a right-triangle because the converse of the Pythagorean Theorem implies that if $13^2 = 12^2 + 5^2$, then the triangle is a right triangle. Because this is true, she has a right triangle and therefore a right angle.

Open-ended

38. Areas vary depending on the triangles drawn, but the Pythagorean Theorem works only for the right triangles.

39. Answers vary, for example, many students will discuss applications involving designing or building a construction project.

40. (a) Answers vary, for example, 6-8-10, and 12-16-20.

(b) Yes, we know that if a-b-c is a Pythagorean Triple, then $a^2 + b^2 = c^2$. This implies that $4(a^2 + b^2) = 4c^2$, and that $(2a)^2 + (2b)^2 = (2c)^2$. **(c)** No, for example consider adding 2 to 3-4-5 which results in 5-6-7 which is not a Pythagorean Triple.

(d) $a^2 + b^2 = (2uv)^2 + (u^2 - v^2)^2$
$= 4u^2v^2 + u^4 - 2u^2v^2 + v^4$
$= u^4 + 2u^2v^2 + v^4$
$= (u^2 + v^2)^2$
$= c^2$

Cooperative Learning

41. Answers vary depending on the proof chosen.

42. Answers vary depending on the triangles that are formed.

43. 0.032 km, 322 cm, 3.2 m, 3.020 mm.

44. (a) 33.25 cm^2 **(b)** 30 cm^2 **(c)** 32 m^2

45. (a) 10 cm, 10π cm, 25π cm^2 **(b)** 12 cm, 24π cm, 144π cm^2 **(c)** $\sqrt{17}$ m, $2\sqrt{17}$ m, $2\pi\sqrt{17}$ m **(d)** 10 cm, 20 cm, 100π cm^2

46. $25/\pi$ m^2

Brain Teaser (p. 710)

The room can be thought of as a box, which can be opened up so that A and C lie on the same plane. Then the shortest path is the line segment connecting A and C.

Thus $AC = \sqrt{2^2 + 6^2} = \sqrt{40} = 2\sqrt{10}$ m.

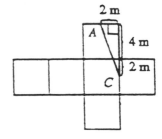

ONGOING ASSESSMENT 12-3

1. (a) 96 cm^2 **(b)** 216π cm^2 **(c)** 236 cm^2 **(d)** 64π cm^2 **(e)** 24π cm^2 **(f)** 90 cm^2 **(g)** 1500π ft^2 **(h)** $(32\pi + 16\pi\sqrt{5})$ cm^2

2. 2.5 L

3. 2688π mm^2

4. $162,307,600\pi$ km^2

5. 4:9

6. (a) They have equal lateral surface areas. **(b)** The one with radius 6

7. $(108\sqrt{21} + 216\sqrt{3})$ m^2

8. Approx. 32.97 in.^{2}

9. $\left(100 + \dfrac{50}{\pi}\right)$ or 115.92 cm^2 approx.

10. Approx. 91.86 ft^2

11. $l = 11$ cm, $w = 8$ cm, $h = 4$ cm

12. (a) The surface area is multiplied by 4. (b) The surface area is multiplied by 9. (c) The surface area is multiplied by k^2.

13. (a) The lateral area is multiplied by 3. (b) The lateral area is tripled. (c) The lateral area is multiplied by 9.

14. (a) The surface area is multiplied by 4. (b) The surface area is multiplied by 9.

15. $(100 + 100\sqrt{17})$ cm^2

16. (a) 44 (b) 38 (add the cube to the center hole) (c) Yes, for example, place five cubes in the shape of a C. Then adding a cube to the center of the C would add no surface area.

17. (a) 1.5π m^2 (b) 2.5π m^2

18. (a) $100\pi(1 + \sqrt{5})$ cm^2 (b) 1350π cm^2 (c) 2250π cm^2

19. (a) Approx. 42 cm (b) Approx. 73 cm

20. $(6400\pi\sqrt{2} + 13{,}600\pi)$ cm^2

21. 375π cm^2

Communication

22. The ice cubes would melt faster because they have a greater surface area that is exposed to the air.

23. She would need four times as much cardboard. If each face is doubled, then the area of each face is increased by a factor of 4, that is, $A_1 = lw$ and $A_2 = (2l)(2w) = 4lw = 4A_1$. Because this is true for all faces, the surface area is multiplied by 4.

24. The opposite faces of a rectangular prism are congruent rectangular regions and hence have equal areas. A triangular prism does not have opposite sides, and the widths of the rectangular regions that are faces are dependent on the shape of the triangular base. If the base is an equilateral triangle, the rectangular faces are congruent. If the base is a scalene triangle, the rectangular faces are not congruent.

25. (a) Estimates vary. (b) The height of the can is 3d or 6r, where d is the diameter of the ball. The circumference of the can is $2\pi r$. Therefore, the LSA is $(2\pi r)6r = 12\pi r^2$. The surface area of three balls is $3(4\pi r^2) = 12\pi r^2$. Therefore the surface area of the three balls is the same as the lateral surface area of the can.

Open-ended

26. (a) 2% (b) Estimates vary. (c) Estimates vary depending on the size of the person. (d) Answers vary depending on the size of the person and the desk.

27. Answers vary, for example, a regular square pyramid with square side 2 cm and slant height 1.5 cm has area 10 cm^2.

Cooperative Learning

28. (a)

NUMBER OF SIDES PAINTED	NUMBER OF PIECES
6	0
5	0
4	0
3	8
2	12
1	6
0	1

(b)

NUMBER OF SIDES PAINTED	NUMBER OF PIECES
6	0
5	0
4	0
3	8
2	24
1	24
0	8

(c) There could never be more than three sides painted. The number of pieces with three sides painted is always 8. The number of pieces with two sides painted is always a multiple of 12. The number of pieces with two sides painted is $12(n - 2)$. The number of pieces with one side painted is the number of pieces in the center square of each side. The length of the square is $(n - 2)$ so there are $(n - 2)^2$ pieces on each of the six sides. Therefore there are $6(n - 2)^2$ pieces. The number of pieces with no sides painted is the number of the interior cubes, which is two units less than the dimensions of the original cube, or $(n - 2)^3$.

Review Problems

29. (a) 100,000 (b) 1.3680 (c) 500 (d) 2,000,000 (e) 1 (f) 1,000,000

30. $10\sqrt{5}$ cm

31. $20\sqrt{5}$ cm

32. (a) 240 cm; 2400 cm^2 (b) $(10\sqrt{2} + 30)$ cm, 75 cm^2

33. Length of side is 25 cm. Diagonal $\overline{BD}$ is 30 cm.

Brain Teaser (p. 720)

The cone and the flattened region obtained by slitting the cone along a slant height are shown below.

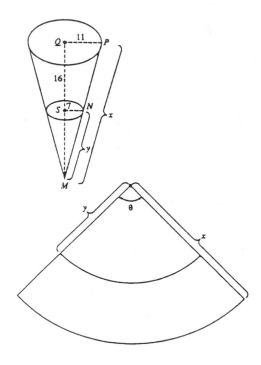

To construct the flattened ring we need to find x, y, and θ.

Because $\triangle MQP \sim \triangle MSN$ we have $\dfrac{16 + MS}{MS} = \dfrac{11}{7}$. Hence $MS = 28$ cm. In $\triangle MSN$ we have $28^2 + 7^2 = y^2$ or $y \doteq 28.86$. In $\triangle PQM: x^2 = 11^2 + 44^2$ or $x \doteq 45.35$ cm. To find θ we roll the sector with radius y and central angle θ into the cone whose base is 7 cm and whose slant height is y. Hence

$$2\pi y \cdot \frac{\theta}{360} = 2\pi \cdot 7 \text{ or } \theta = \frac{7 \cdot 360}{28.86} \doteq 87°19'.$$

ONGOING ASSESSMENT 12-4

1. (a) 8000 (b) 0.0005 (c) 0.000675 (d) 3,000,000 (e) 7 (f) 2000 (g) 0.00857 approx. (h) 675 (i) 345.6 (j) 0.694

2. 32.4 L

3. (**a**) 64 cm^3 (**b**) 120 cm^3 (**c**) 216 cm^3 (**d**) 50 cm^3
(**e**) 21π cm^3 (**f**) 432π cm^3 (**g**) (4000/3)π cm^3 (**h**) 22,800 ft^3
(**i**) (20,000/3)π ft^3 (**j**) 76,200 ft^3 (**k**) (256/3)π cm^3
4. (**a**) 2000, 2, 2000 (**b**) 0.5, 0.5, 500 (**c**) 1500, 1.5, 1500
(**d**) 5000, 5, 5 (**e**) 0.75, 0.75, 750 (**f**) 4.8, 4.8, 4800
5. (**a**) 200.0 (**b**) 0.320 (**c**) 1.0 (**d**) 5.00
6. 1680π mm^3
7. 8/27
8. It is multiplied by 8
9. (**a**) 2000, 2, 2 (**b**) 6000, 6, 6 (**c**) 2 dm, 4000, 4 (**d**) 2.5 dm, 7500, 7.5
10. 253,500π L
11. 64 to 1
12. 1.62 L
13. 2,500,000 L
14. π mL
15. (**a**) It is multiplied by 8. (**b**) It is multiplied by 27.
(**c**) It is multiplied by n^3.
16. The Great Pyramid has the greater volume. It is approx. 25.12 times greater.
17. Approx. 16363.62 or 16,364 apartments
18. 600 m^3
19. Approx. 35.34 L
20. No, another approx. 7.33 cm^3 would be needed.
21. 1/8 of the cone is filled.
22. It is multiplied by 2.197.
23. 260,810,575,168 m^3
24. The 2 × 2 × 4 ft freezer is a better buy at $25/ft^3
25. 66 2/3% occupied by balls, so 33 1/3% occupied by air.
26. About 21.5%
27. 16 m^3
28. They are equal.
29. Approx. 2.2 cm
30. No, it is only 1/3 of the volume for 1/2 the price.
31. The volume of the 5-cm grapefruit is approx. 523.6 cm^3 which gives a cost of 0.042 cents/cm^3. The cost for the larger grapefruit is approx. 0.034 cents/cm^3 so the larger grapefruit is the better buy.
32. The larger is the better buy. The volume of the larger melon is 1.728 times the volume of the smaller but is only 1.5 times as expensive.
33. (**a**) Answers vary (**b**) Infinitely many. Because V = 100 = (1/3)a^{2}h, where a is a side of the square base, then 300 = a^{2}h . This equation has infinitely many solutions.
34. (2/3) $\sqrt{2/(5\sqrt{5})}$ m^3, or approximately 0.28 m^3
35. (**a**) 512,000 cm^3 (**b**) Vol. = (y − 2x)^{2}x
36. Approx. 45.90 in.^{2}
37. It won't hold the cream at 10 cm tall; it would have to be 20 cm tall.
38. It is approx. 0.8 times the original radius.

Communication
39. Doubling the height will only double the volume. Doubling the radius will multiply the volume by 4. This happens because the value of the radius is squared after it is doubled.
40. Answers vary.
41. Answers vary, for example, the discussion might include how a pyramid with height h approaches the volume of a cone with height h as the number of sides in the base becomes greater. As the base of the pyramid gets more and more sides, the base approaches a circle. Therefore the formula for the volume of a pyramid should work for the volume of a cone, that is, V = 1/3 Bh.
42. Answers vary, for example, fill the shape with sand and dump the sand into a container that can be used to measure the sand.

Open-ended
43. Answers vary but should have volumes close to 24π or 75.4 in.^{3}, for example, a rectangular prism that is 6 in. long, 4 in. wide, and 3.14 in. high.
44. If the cookies are stood up so the 6-cm diameter is toward the front of the box, then the minimum surface area is obtained by having two cookies across (12 cm), two cookies high (12 cm), and 12 cookies deep (12 cm).
45. Answers vary but the volume must be 1000 cm^3. Some students will worry about shelf space while others will worry about what shape is easiest to hold.
46. Answers vary depending on the cans selected.

Review Problems
47. (**a**) 15,600 cm^2 (**b**) (100 + 200 $\sqrt{2}$) cm^2
(**c**) (1649 + (81 $\sqrt{3}$)/2) m^2, or about 1719.1 m^2
48. (**a**) 340 cm (**b**) 6000 cm^2
49. 2$\sqrt{2}$ m^2
50. 62 cm

ONGOING ASSESSMENT 12-5
1. (**a**) Kilograms or tons (**b**) Kilograms (**c**) Grams (**d**) Tons
(**e**) Grams (**f**) Grams (**g**) Tons (**h**) Kilograms or grams
(**i**) Grams or kilograms
2. (**a**) Milligrams (**b**) Kilograms (**c**) Milligrams (**d**) Grams
(**e**) Grams (**f**) Milligrams
3. (**a**) 15 (**b**) 8 (**c**) 36 (**d**) 0.072 (**e**) 4.230 (**f**) 3.007 (**g**) 5750
(**h**) 5.750 (**i**) 30 (**j**) 41.6 (**k**) 1.5625 (**l**) 3.125 (**m**) 60.8
4. (**a**) No (**b**) Possibly (**c**) Yes (**d**) Yes (**e**) Yes
5. 16 kg
6. $2.32
7. 2¢
8. Abel, because he paid 0.9¢/g while Babel paid 1.15¢/g
9. (**a**) ⁻12°C (**b**) ⁻18°C (**c**) ⁻1°C (**d**) 38°C (**e**) 100°C
(**f**) ⁻40°C
10. (**a**) No (**b**) No (**c**) No (**d**) Yes (**e**) No (**f**) Yes (**g**) Yes
(**h**) Chilly (**i**) Hot
11. (**a**) 50°F (**b**) 32°F (**c**) 86°F (**d**) 212°F (**e**) 414°F
(**f**) ⁻40°F
12. Answers vary, for example, if a heart pumps 60 beats per minute, then it pumps 36,288,000 mL or 36,288 L per week.
13. (**a**) 200,000 L (**b**) 200,000 kg or 200 t
14. Approx. 145.52 lb

Communication
15. (**a**) Yes, for example, consider boxes that are 1 cm × 5 cm × 1 cm and 1 cm × 2 cm × 3 cm. Both boxes have surface areas of 22 cm^2 but the first one has volume 5 cm^3 and the second one has volume 6 cm^3. (**b**) Yes, for example, consider boxes that are 10 cm × 10 cm × 2 cm and 20 cm × 5 cm × 2 cm. Both have volumes of 200 cm^3, but the first has SA of 280 cm^2 and the second has SA of 300 cm^2 which implies that the weights of the two are different.
16. (**i**) The volume is approx. 144.7 ft^3, the capacity is approx. 1082.45 gal., and the weight of the water is approx. 8985 lb.
(**ii**) The volume is 8 m^3, the capacity is 8000 L, and the mass is 8000 kg. The metric problem is much easier to work because the conversions are much easier. They just involve moving the decimal point. The relationships among length, volume, capacity, and mass are much easier than in the English system.
17. The air temperature increases more with a 10-degree increase on the Celsius scale because every time the air temperature increases 1 degree Celsius, it increases 1 4/5 degrees Fahrenheit.

Open-ended

18. Answers vary, for example, time could be saved by not having to teach all the conversion factors in the English system and all the units of measure. The relationships among the metric units of length, volume, capacity, and mass would save time over learning the disjoint facts in the English system. Once the prefixes and conversions are learned for metric units of length, then the same ideas and prefixes work for mass and capacity. Conversions within area and volume are also much easier to teach because of the decimal nature of the conversions.

19. Answers vary, for example, should decimals be introduced earlier and should work with complicated fractions be reduced?

Cooperative Learning

20. Answers vary, for example, you could take 1 L of water and pour it into a container with a volume of 1 dm^3. The water could then be weighed.

Review

21. (a) $(20 + 6\pi)$ cm; $(48 + 18\pi)$ cm^2 (b) 40π cm; 100π cm^2 (c) 50 m; 80 m^2

22. (a) 35 (b) 0.16 (c) 400,000 (d) 5,200,000 (e) 5200 (f) 0.0035

23. (a) Yes (b) No (c) Yes (d) No

24. $\sqrt{61}$ km

25. (a) 12,000π cm^3; 2400π cm^2 (b) 42,900 cm^3; $(6065 + 40\sqrt{5314})$ cm^2

Chapter Review

1. 16

2. (a) 8 1/2 cm^2 (b) 6 1/2 cm^2 (c) 7 cm^2

3. 252 cm^2

4. The pieces of the trapezoid are rearranged to form a rectangle with width h/2 and length $(b_2 + b_1)$. The area is $A = h/2(b_2 + b_1)$ which is the area of the initial trapezoid.

5. (a) $54\sqrt{3}$ cm^2 (b) 36π cm^2

6. (a) 12π cm^2 (b) $(12 + 4.5\pi)$ cm^2 (c) 24 cm^2 (d) 64.5 cm^2 (e) 178.5 m^2 (f) 4π cm^2

7. (a) Yes (b) No

8. (a) SA = $32(2 + \sqrt{13})$ cm^2; Vol = 128 cm^3 (b) SA = 96π cm^2; Vol = 96π cm^3 (c) SA = 100π m^2; Vol = $(500\pi)/3$ m^3 (d) SA = 54π cm^2; Vol = 54π cm^3 (e) SA = 304 m^2; Vol = 320 m^3

9. 65π m^3

10. The graph on the right has volume 8 times the volume of the figure on the left, rather than double as it should be.

11. (a) Metric tons (b) 1 cm^3 (c) 1 g (d) Same volume (e) 25 L (f) 2000 (g) 51,800 (h) 10,000,000 (i) 50,000 (j) 5.830 (k) 25,000 (l) 75,000 (m) 52.813 (n) 4.8

12. $h_1^3/h_2^3 = V_1/V_2$

13. (a) 6000 kg (b) 1.557 m

14. (a) L (b) kg (c) g (d) g (e) kg (f) t (g) mL

15. (a) Unlikely (b) Likely (c) Unlikely (d) Unlikely (e) Unlikely

16. (a) 2000 (b) 1000 (c) 3 (d) 0.0042 (e) 0.0002

CHAPTER 13

ONGOING ASSESSMENT 13-1

1. (a) 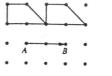 (b)

2. Reverse the translation so that the image completes a slide from X' to X (to what is called its pre-image). Then check by carrying out the given motion in the "forward" direction; i.e., see if $\overline{AB}$ goes to $\overline{A'B'}$.

(a) 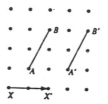 (b)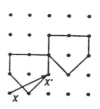

3. (a) Construct as suggested by the following figure: Trace $\overline{BC}$ and the line containing the slide arrow on the tracing paper and label the trace of B as B' and the trace of C as C'. Mark on the original paper and on the tracing paper the initial point of the arrow by P and the head of the arrow by Q. Slide the tracing paper along the line $\overset{\leftrightarrow}{PQ}$ so that P will fall on Q. Trace $\overline{BC}$. The segment $\overline{B'C'}$ is the image of $\overline{BC}$ under the translation. (b) Construct a parallellogram as in Figure 13-3.

4. (a) (3, ⁻4) (b) (0, 0) (c) (⁻3, ⁻13) (d) (10, 10)

5. (a) (3, ⁻4) (b) (0, 0) (c) (⁻3, ⁻13) (d) (10, 10)

6. (a)

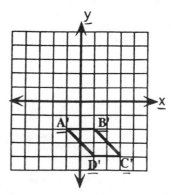

(b)

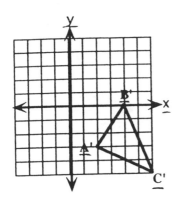

(c)

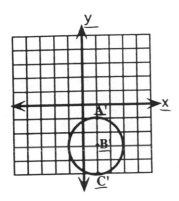

(d)

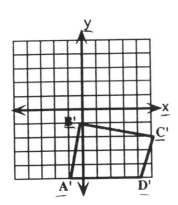

7. (a)

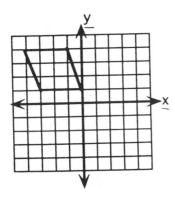

(b)

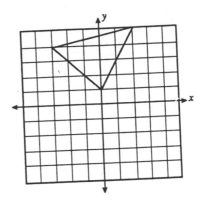

8.

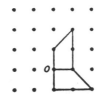

9. In each case find the images of the vertices.

10. Reverse the rotation (to the counterclockwise direction) to locate $\overline{AB}$, that is, the pre-image.

(a)

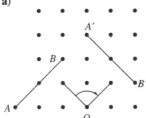

(b)

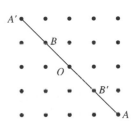

11. (a) Answers may vary, but H, I, N, O, S, X, or Z could appear in such rotational words. Examples include SOS. Variations could use M and W in rotational images; for example, MOW. **(b)** 1, 8, 11, 69, 88, 96, 101, 111, 181, 609, 619, 689, 808, 818, 888, 906, 916, 986, 1001, 1111, 1691, 1881, 1961, 6009, 6119, 6699, 6889, 6969, 8008, 8118, 8698, 8888, 8968, 9006, 9116, 9696, 9886, 9966

12. (a) When the figure is creased and folded along the perpendicular to $\overline{PP'}$, the point P falls on P′. This shows that the perpendicular also bisects $\overline{PP'}$. Alternatively, by the definition of rotation $\overline{PO} = \overline{PO'}$. This implies that O is equidistant from P and P′, and hence, it is on the perpendicular bisector of $\overline{PP'}$. **(b)** From (a), O is on the perpendicular bisector of $\overline{AA'}$ and $\overline{BB'}$ as well as $\overline{CC'}$. Consequently, O can be found by finding the point at which any two of the perpendicular bisectors intersect. $\angle AOA'$ is the angle of rotation.

13. Hints: An angle whose measure is 45° angle can be constructed by bisecting a right angle. An angle whose measure is 60° can be constructed by first constructing an equilateral triangle.

14. (a) (⁻4, 0) **(b)** (0, ⁻3) **(c)** (⁻2, ⁻4) **(d)** (2, ⁻5) **(e)** (2, 4) **(f)** (⁻a, ⁻b)

15. Hint: Find the images of the vertices.

16. (a) $\ell' = \ell$ **(b)** $\ell' \parallel \ell$ **(c)** $\ell' \perp \ell$ **(d)** ℓ' and ℓ intersect at a 60° angle.

17. (**a**) (i) A′ (⁻2, 3) (ii) A′ (⁻3, ⁻2) (iii) A′ (2, 3) (**b**) A′ (⁻b, a) (**c**) Under the rotation about the origin counterclockwise by a right angle, the image of A is A′ and the image of B is B′, as shown. Because A′B′ = AB and $\overline{OB'}$ = $\overline{OB}$, it follows that $\overline{OB'}$ = a and $\overline{A'B'}$ = b. If A is in the first quadrant, then A′ is in the second quadrant. Hence, the coordinates of A′ are (⁻b, a). A similar argument holds if A is in any quadrant.

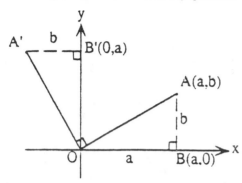

18. (**a**) First rotate ΔABC by angle α to obtain ΔA′B′C′ and then rotate ΔA′B′C′ by angle β to obtain ΔA′B′C′. (**b**) No. (**c**) Yes rotation about 0 by angle |α − β| in the direction of the larger of α and β.
19. Construct the image m′ of m under a half-turn about P. Point A is the intersection of m′ and ℓ. The intersection of $\overleftrightarrow{AP}$ with m is B.
20. $\overline{AB}$ is the west side of the park. Line ℓ represents Shady Lane and line s represents Sunny Street. $\overline{PQ}$ represents the road to be built parallel to and the same length as $\overline{AB}$. We need to find points P and Q. Choose any two points X and Y on ℓ and find their images X′ and Y′. The *line* connecting X′ and Y′ is ℓ′. Q is the intersection of ℓ′ with s, and P is the image of Q under translation from B to A, and $\overline{PQ}$ represents the road to be built.

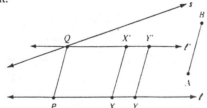

21. (**a**) Execute the program.
(**b**) TO SLIDE: DIRECTION :DISTANCE :SIDE
    EQUILATERAL :SIDE
    SETHEADING :DIRECTION
    FORWARD :DISTANCE
    PENDOWN
    SETHEADING 0
    EQUILATERAL :SIDE
  END

    TO EQUILATERAL :SIDE
      REPEAT 3 [FORWARD : SIDE RIGHT 120]
    END

22. TO ROTATE :A :SIDE
    SQUARE :SIDE
    RIGHT :A
    SQUARE :SIDE
  END

    TO SQUARE :SIDE
      REPEAT 4 [FORWARD :SIDE RIGHT 90]
  END
23. (**a**) TO TURN.CIRCLE :A
    CIRCLE
    LEFT :A
    CIRCLE
  END

    TO CIRCLE
      REPEAT 360 [FORWARD 1 RT 1]
  END
  To produce the desired transformation, execute
    TURN.CIRCLE 180.
(**b**) To produce the desired transformation, execute
    TURN.CIRCLE 90.

Communication
24. Yes. If the congruent segments are $\overline{AB}$ and $\overline{CD}$, connect A with C and B with D as shown. The perpendicular bisectors of $\overline{AC}$ and $\overline{BD}$ intersect at O. (If they do not intersect, connect A with D and B with C.) The point O is the center of the required rotation. The angle of rotation is ∠ AOC in a clockwise direction. The image of A will be C because the rotation is by ∠ AOC. To show that under this rotation the image of $\overline{AB}$ is $\overline{CD}$, we need only show that ∠AOC ≅ ∠BOD. This can be checked experimentally by performing the rotation or by measuring ∠ AOC and ∠BOD.

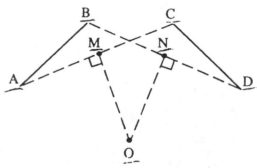

25. (**a**) Yes. If a point P and image P′ are known, the translation is determined by the slide arrow from P to P′. (**b**) No. If A and B are two points and A′ and B′ are their respective images, then the center of the rotation must be on the perpendicular bisector $\overline{AA'}$ as well as on the perpendicular bisector of $\overline{BB'}$. If $\overline{AA'}$ and $\overline{BB'}$ are not parallel, then the perpendicular bisectors intersect. The point of intersection is the center of the rotation, and ∠ AOA′ is the angle of rotation. However, if $\overline{AA'}$ and $\overline{BB'}$ are parallel, the center of the rotation cannot be determined. (**c**) Yes. If A′ is the image of A, then the half-turn is about the midpoint of $\overline{AA'}$. (**d**) Yes. If A and its image A′ are known, the center O of the rotation must be on the perpendicular bisector ℓ of $\overline{AA'}$. Because ΔAOA′ is a right isosceles triangle, m(∠ A′AO) = 45°. Thus the center O can be found as the intersection of ℓ and a line m that makes an angle of 45° with $\overline{AA'}$. Notice that there are two lines that make a 45° angle with $\overline{AA'}$. The other line (not shown) will intersect ℓ at point O₁, but the rotation about O₁, which takes A to A′, will be clockwise rather than counterclockwise. (**e**) Yes. The only point whose image under a rotation is the point itself is the center of the rotation. Thus the center of the rotation is the given point and the rotation is determined.

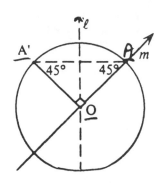

26. (**a**) A circle (**b**) The vertices A and B trace an identical path if, and only if, OA = OB; that is if and only if O is on the perpendicular bisector of $\overline{AB}$. Thus all points O for which two vertices trace an identical path are the points on the perpendicular bisectors of the sides of the triangle. (**c**) Yes. The intersection of the perpendicular bisector (center of the circumscribed circle)

27. (**a**) A parallelogram. Under a half-turn, the image of a line is parallel to the line. Thus $\overline{AB} \parallel \overline{CD}$ and $\overline{AC} \parallel \overline{DB}$; therefore ABCD is a parallelogram.

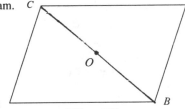

(**b**) A parallelogram. The image of $\overline{AB}$ is $\overline{FE}$ and thus $\overline{AB} \parallel \overline{EF}$. Consequently, $\overline{BF} \parallel \overline{AE}$ and ABFE is a parallelogram.

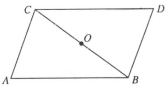

(**c**) A square. Because the image of A is C and the image of B is D, the image of ABCD is CDAB.

Open-ended
28. Answers vary.
29. Answers vary.
30. Answers vary. If rotation is by 30°, there will be 360/30, or 12, images. In general, one of the images will coincide with the original after a 360° revolution if the angle of rotation divides 360.

Cooperative Learning
31. (**a**) The path will look like the one shown in the following figure. Such a path traced by P on the circle is called a *cycloid*.

(**b**) Rotation about the center of the circle and translation by the slide arrow from A to B. (**c**) The path is not an arc of a circle. The perpendicular bisectors of all the chords (segments connecting two points on the arc) do not intersect on a single point. (**d**) The length of $\overline{AB}$ is the circumference of the circle.
32. For the particular point A, it is true that the indicated rotation and the reflection in line ℓ will produce the same image A′. However, for the reflection to be the same as the indicated rotation, the image of every point in the plane under the reflection in ℓ has to be the same under the indicated reflection (by the same angle and the same point O). This is not the case.
33. (**a**) Rotation about the center of the square and translation by the slide arrow from A to A′ (**b**) See the answer to (b) in Problem 31. (**c**) AA′ = 4AB.

Brain Teaser (p. 766)
Straight down.

ONGOING ASSESSMENT 13-2
1. Locate the image of vertices directly across (perpendicular to) ℓ on the geoboard.
(**a**)   (**b**)

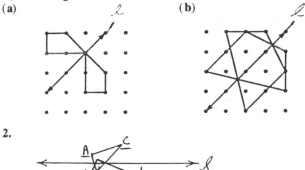

2.

3. Find the image of the center of the circle and one point on the circumference of the circle to determine the image of the circle.
4. Reflecting lines are described for each. (**a**) All diameters (infinitely many) (**b**) Pependicular bisector of the segment (**c**) The line containing the ray (**d**) Perpendicular bisectors of the sides and lines containig the diagonals (**e**) Perpendicular bisectors of pairs of parallel sides (**f**) None (**g**) Perpendicular bisector of the side that is not congruent to the other two (**h**) Perpendicular bisectors of each (**i**) None (**j**) Perpendicular bisector of parallel sides (**k**) Perpendicular bisector of the chord connecting the endpoints of the arc (**l**) The line containing the diagonal determined by vertices of the noncongruent angles (**m**) The lines containing the diagonals (**n**) Perpendicular bisectors of parallel sides and three diameters determined by vertices on the circumscribed circle (**o**) There will be n reflecting lines in all. If n is even the lines are determined as in part (n). If n is odd, the lines are the perpendicular bisectors of the sides.
5. The original figure.
6. (**a**) The final images are congruent but in different locations, and hence not the same. (**b**) A translation determined by a slide arrow from P to R is determined as follows: Let P be any point on ℓ and Q on m such that PQ $\perp$ ℓ. Point R is on $\overline{PQ}$ such that $\overline{PQ} = \overline{QR}$.

7. (a)

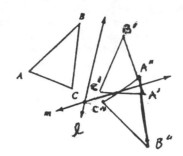

(**b**) A rotation about O by 2α, where d is the measure of the angle between ℓ and m in the direction from ℓ to m as shown
(**c**) A half-turn bout O
8. Construction
9. (a) Examples include MOM, WOW, TOOT, and HAH.
(**b**) Examples include BOX, HIKE, CODE, etc. B, C, D, E, H, I, K (depending on construction), O, and X may be used.
(**c**) 1, 8, 11, 88, 101, 181, 808, 818, 888, 1001, 1111, 1881
10. (a) The images are the same. (**b**) Yes
11. None of the images has a reverse orientation, so there are no reflections or glide reflections involved. Thus

    1 to 2 is a counterclockwise rotation.
    1 to 3 is a clockwise rotation.
    1 to 4 is a translation down.
    1 to 5 is a rotation (with an exterior point as the center of rotation).
    1 to 6 is a translation (sides are parallel to 1).
    1 to 7 is a translation (sides are parallel).

12. Reflect A in road 1 to locate A′ and B in road 2 to locate B′. Connect A′ and B′ to locate P and Q. Reflecting A and B creates the straight-line (i.e., shortest) path A′B′, which by construction is equal to the distance (AP + PQ + QB) for the actual roads.
13. In each case, find B′, the image of B under reflection in the x-axis, and use the distance formula to find AB′.
(**a**) $\sqrt{125}$ or $5\sqrt{5}$ (**b**) $\sqrt{113}$
14. (a) A′ (3, ‾4), B′ (2, 6), C′ (‾2, ‾5) (**b**) A′ (‾3, 4), B′ (‾2, ‾6), C′ (2, 5) (**c**) A′ (4, 3), B′ (‾6, 2), C′ (5, ‾2)
(**d**) A′ (‾4, ‾3), B′ (6, ‾2), C′ (‾5, 2)
15. (a) (i) (x, ‾y) (ii) (‾x, y) (ii) (y, x) (iv) (‾y, ‾x)
(**b**) (‾x, ‾y) From (a), the reason can be seen in the following figure:

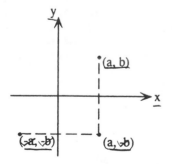

Communication
16. Find A′ the image of A under reflection in $\overline{EH}$ and B′, the image of B under reflection in $\overline{GH}$. Mark the intersections of $\overline{A'B'}$ with $\overline{EH}$ and $\overline{GH}$, respectively, by C and D. The player should aim the ball at A toward the point C. The ball will hit D, bounce off, and hit B. To justify the answer, we need to

show that the path A‾ C‾ D ‾ B is such that $\angle 1 \cong \angle 3$ and $\angle 4 \cong \angle 6$. Notice that $\angle 1 \cong \angle 2$ and $\angle 6 \cong \angle 5$ because the image of an angle under reflection is congruent to the original angle. Also $\angle 2 \cong \angle 3$ and $\angle 4 \cong \angle 5$ as each pair constitutes a vertical angle. Consequently, $\angle 1 \cong \angle 3$ and $\angle 4 \cong \angle 6$.

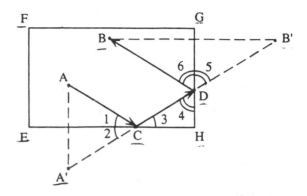

17. (a) Reflect the location P of the ball in $\overline{AB}$. The intersection of $\overline{PO'}$ with $\overline{AB}$ is the point at which the ball should be aimed. The justification is similar to the one at given in Problem 16. (**b**) Reflect P in $\overline{CB}$ and Q in $\overline{AB}$. Connect the images P′ and Q′ by a straight line. The intersection of $\overline{P'Q'}$ with $\overline{BC}$ is the point at which the ball should be aimed. The justification is similar to the one given in Problem 16.

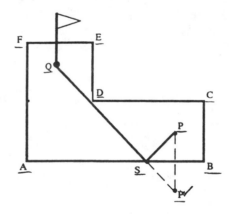

18. (a) If $\overline{AB} \cong \overline{BC}$, then the perpendicular bisector of $\overline{AC}$ is the required line. The image of B is B and the image of A is C. Hence, the image of $\triangle ABC$ is $\triangle CBA$. (**b**) Equilateral triangles. Each side could be considered a base. (**c**) No. Since no sides (or angles) are congruent, bisecting any side or angle will leave noncongruent portions of the triangle on opposite sides of the bisector. (**d**) All lines containing diameters will satisfy this situation. Diameters divide a circle into two congruent semicircles.
19. The angle of incidence is the same as the angle of reflection. With the mirrors tilted 45°, the object's image reflects to 90° down the tube and then 90° to the eyepiece. The two reflections "counteract" each other, leaving the image upright.

Open-ended
20. Answers vary.
21. Answers vary.
22. Answers vary. The follwing are some examples:
(**a**) When a scalene triangle ABC is reflected in $\overline{AB}$, its image is $\triangle AC'B$. Because a reflection preserves distance,

AC'BC is a kite. By definition of a reflection, $\overline{AB}$ is the perpendicular bisector of $\overline{CC'}$. Hence, in a kite the diagonals are perpendicular to each other. One of the diagonals bisects the other and bisects a pair of opposite angles.

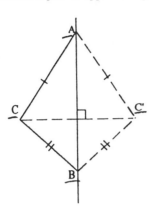

(b) If a trapezoid with a right angle is reflected in one of its legs as shown in the following figure, an isosceles trapezoid is obtained. It follows from the fact that a reflection preserves angle measure that the base angles in an isosceles trapezoid are congruent.

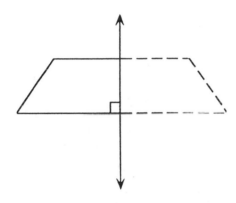

Cooperative Learning
23. (a) Constructions will vary. (b) The outgoing ray is parallel to the incoming ray. (c) Because the angle of incidence is congruent to the angle of reflection, we designate the measures of the congruent angle by α and β, as shown in the following figure. One way to show that $k \parallel \ell$ is to extend ℓ and to show that $\alpha = \gamma$ (measures of corresponding angles formed by the line k and ℓ and the transversal m.) Notice that $\beta = \beta_1$, as these are measures of vertical angles. Consequently, by ASA, $\triangle ABC \cong \triangle DBC$. Thus $\alpha = \gamma$ and hence, $k \parallel \ell$.

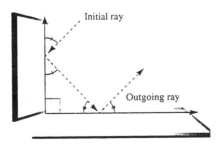

24. (a) Constructions will vary. (b) The experiment will work for rectangular tables in which the length is twice the width and for any position of B.

Review Exercises
25. For a rotation of 360°, all letters. For 180°, see Problem 26. No other rotations result in the original letter.
26. H, I, N, O, S, Z
27. A half-turn about the center of the letter O
28. (a) A rotation by any angle about the center of the circle will result in the same circle. (b) Reflections about lines containing diameters
29. (a) Rectangle (b) It equals the area of $\triangle ABC$.
(c) Because a half-turn preserves angle measure, the angles at P' and Q' are right angles and hence PP'Q'Q is a rectangle. Notice that $\triangle ABC$ and the rectangle PP'Q'Q both contain the pentagon MANQP. Because $\triangle CMP \cong \triangle AMP'$ and $\triangle AON \cong \triangle BQN$, each pair of triangles has the same area. We mark the equal areas by I and II. We mark the area of the pentagon by III and obtain the following:

Area $\triangle ABC = I + III + II$
Area of PP'Q'Q $= I + II + III$

Hence, the areas are equal.

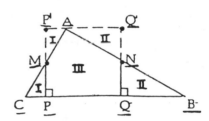

30. Construct $\overline{BE}$ perpendicular to $\overline{AD}$ as shown. Next translate $\triangle BAE$ by the slide arrow from B to C. The image of $\triangle ABE$ is $\triangle DCE'$. The rectangle BCE'E is the required rectangle.

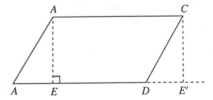

ONGOING ASSESSMENT 13-3

1. (a) Slide the smaller triangle down two units (translation). Then complete a size transformation with scale factor 2 using the top-right vertex as the center.

(**b**) Slide right 5, and up 1. Then complete the size transformation as in (a). (**c**) Rotate 90° counterclockwise with the lower-right vertex of the smaller triangle as the center of rotation. Then complete a size transformation with scale factor 2 using the same point as center.

2.

3. (**a**) Translation taking B to B' followed by a size tranformation with center B' (and scale factor 2) (**b**) Rotate 90° counterclockwise using center B, translate to take B to B', and then complete a size translation with a scale factor 1/2.

(**c**) Half-turn with the midpoint of $\overline{AA'}$ as center, followed by a size transformation with scale factor 1/2 and center A'.

(**d**) Half-turn about C followed by a size transformation with center C and scale factor 3/2.

4. (**a**) x = 6, y = 5.2. Scale factor 2/5. (**b**) x = 98/15, y = 90/7. Scale factor 7/15.

5. (**a**) The triangles are similar (**b**) Approximately 4.08$\overline{3}$ m (**c**) 17.5 mm.

6. (**a**) Scale factor 3, x = 12, y = 10 (**b**) Scale factor 10/3, x = 15/7, y = 12/7

7. (**a**) A' (6, 9), B' (9, 12), C'($^-$6, 9) (**b**) (rx, ry)

8. The size transformation with center O and scale factor 1/r

Communication

9. (**a**) It does change. For example, consider the segment whose endpoints are (0, 0) and (1, 1) and has length $\sqrt{2}$. Under the size transformation with center at (0, 0) and scale factor 2, the image of the segment is a segment whose endpoints are (0, 0) and (2, 2). That segment has length $2\sqrt{2}$. (**b**) It does not change. Under a size transformation, the image of a triangle is a similar triangle and the angles of corresponding angles of two similar triangles are congruent. (**c**) It does not change. Given two parallel lines, draw a transversal that intersects each line. Because the lines are parallel, the corresponding angles are congruent. From (b), the images of the angles will also be congruent and hence the image lines will be parallel.

10. Suppose ΔABC ~ ΔABC. If $\overline{AA'}$, $\overline{BB'}$, and $\overline{CC'}$ intersect at the same point, the required size transformation exists. The intersection point will be the center of the size transformation and A'B'/AB will be the scale factor.

11. (**a**) A single size transformation with center O and scale factor $\frac{1}{2} \cdot \frac{1}{3}$ or $\frac{1}{6}$. Let P be any point and P' its image under the first size transformation and P'' the image of P' under the second size transformation. Then $\frac{OP'}{OP} = \frac{1}{2}$ and $\frac{OP''}{OP'} = \frac{1}{3}$.

Consequently, $\left(\frac{OP'}{OP}\right) \cdot \left(\frac{OP''}{OP'}\right) = \frac{1}{2} \cdot \frac{1}{3}$ or $\frac{OP''}{OP} = \frac{1}{2} \cdot \frac{1}{3}$. Thus P' can be obtained from P by a size transformation with center O and scale factor $\frac{1}{2} \cdot \frac{1}{3}$. (**b**) The size transformation with center O and scale factor $r_1 r_2$.

12. The scale factor = $\dfrac{A'B'}{AB} = \dfrac{3}{4}$. The center must be the intersection of $\overrightarrow{BB'}$ and $\overrightarrow{CC'}$.

13. Yes. Suppose the size transformation with center O has a scale factor r. The image of any point P on the circle with radius d is P' such that $\dfrac{OP'}{OP} = r$. Thus OP' = r(OP) or OP' = rd. This means that the image of every point on the circle is at the same distance rd from O and hence on a circle with radius rd.

Open-ended

14. Answers vary; for example, a 50% reduction in size when making a photocopy

Cooperative Learning

15. (**a**) If p is the perimeter of the figure and p' the perimeter of the image, then p' = 3p. (**b**) If A is the area of the figure and A' the area of the image, then A' = 9A. (**c**) O' = rp (**d**) A' = r^2A

16. Answers vary.

Review Problems

17. (**a**) The translation given by slide arrow from N to M (**b**) A counterclockwise rotation of 75° about O (**c**) A clockwise rotation of 45° about A (**d**) A reflection in m and translation from B to A (**e**) A second reflection in n

18. (**a**) (4, 3) reflects about m to (4, 1); (4, 1) reflects about n to (2, 1). (**b**) (0, 1) → (0, 3) → (6, 3) (**c**) ($^-$1, 0) → ($^-$1, 4) → (7, 4) (**d**) (0, 0) → (0, 4) → (6, 4)

ONGOING ASSESSMENT 13-4

1. (**a**) (i) Yes. A line may be drawn through the center of the circle, either horizontally or vertically. A line may also be drawn through any of the sets of arrows. (ii) Yes. The figure will match the original figure after rotations of 90°, 180°, or 270° about the center of the circle. (iii) Yes. Any figure having 180° rotational symmetry has point symmetry about the turn center. (**b**) (i) Yes. A vertical line through the middle of the bulb is a line of symmetry. (ii) No. The figure will not match the original under rotation of less than 360°. (iii) No. The figure does not have 180° rotational symmetry. (**c**) (i) Yes. A vertical line through the stem is a line of symmetry. (ii) No (iii) No (**d**) (i) Yes. A horizontal line through the middle of the plane is a line of symmetry. (ii) No (iii) No

2. Answers may vary, but some possibilities are the following: (**a**) The Yellow Pages symbol (**b**) A regular pentagon (Chrysler symbol) (**c**) The letter N

3. Reflect the given portions about ℓ.

(a)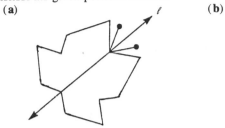

(b)

4. (a) (i) Four lines of symmetry; the diagonals and horizontal or vertical lines through the center
  (ii) No lines of symmetry
  (iii) Two lines of symmetry; horizontally and vertically through the center
  (iv) One line of symmetry; vertically through the center

(b) (i)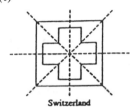

Switzerland

(ii)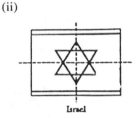

Israel

(iii)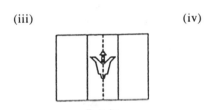

Barbados

(iv)

5. (a) 6 (b) Yes. The figure has 60° rotational symmetry.

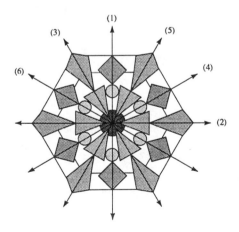

6. (a) One; vertically through the center (b) One; vertically through the center (c) None (d) Five; one through each vertex and its opposite face

7. (a)

(b)

8. (a) Seven; three through the "peaks," three through the "valleys," and one perpendicular to the others through the width of the figure (b) Two; one through the middle "peak" and one through the width (c) Seven; three through the vertices, three through the faces, and one perpendicular to the others through the width of the figure (d) 33; 16 through the peaks, 16 through the valleys, and one through the width

9. TO TURN.SYM :S :N :A
    REPEAT :N [SQUARE :S :RIGHT :A]
  END

  TO SQUARE :S
    REPEAT 4 [FORWARD :S RIGHT 90]
  END

(a) Execute TURN.SYM 50 6 60 (b) Execute TURN.SYM 50 3 120 (c) Execute TURN.SYM 50 2 180 (d) Execute TURN.SYM 50 3 240 (e) Execute TURN.SYM 50 6 300

10. TO TURN.SY :S :N :A
    REPEAT :N [EQTRI :S RIGHT :A]
  END

  TO EQUITRI :S
    REPEAT 3 [FORWARD :S RIGHT 120]
  END

(a) Execute TURN.SY 50 6 60 (b) Execute TURN.SY 50 3 120 (c) Execute TURN.SY 50 3 240 (d) Execute TURN.SY 50 6 300

Communication

11. (a) Yes. The definition of point symmetry is that it is rotational symmetry of 180°. (b) No. It may have rotational symmetry of other than 180°; an equilateral triangle is an example. (c) Yes. A circle is an example, as is the figure in Problem 1(a). (d) No. Consider the letter Z. (Nor is the converse true.) (e) Yes. Point symmetry implies 180° rotational symmetry.

Open-ended

12. (a) A scalene triangle (b) An isosceles triangle which is not equilateral (c) Not possible (d) An equilateral triangle

13. Answers may vary, but examples include the letter S and the Chevrolet logo.

14. (a) All figures will have two line symmetries. Some will have other symmetries. (b) All figures will have only two line symmetries.

15. Answers vary.

Cooperative Learning

16. Answers vary.

17. Answers vary; for example, consider a rectangle. You would report that your figure has two lines of symmetry and a rotational symmetry of 180°.

Review Problems

18. One method is to trace over the figure. Then fold at ℓ and trace along the figure as seen through the paper.

19. Find the images of the vertices.

ONGOING ASSESSMENT 13-5

1. (a)

(b)

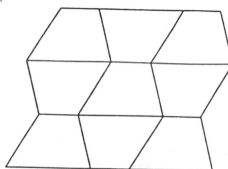

2. (a) Perform half-turns about the midpoints of all sides.
(b) Yes. If a polygon tessellates the plane, the sum of the angles around every vertex must be 360°. Successive 180° turns of a quadrilateral about the midpoints of its sides will produce four congruent quadrilaterals around a common vertex, with each of the quadrilateral's angles being represented at each vertex. These angles must add up to 360°, as angles of any quadrilateral do.
3. Experimentation by cutting shapes out and moving them about is one way to learn about these types of problems.
(a)

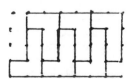

(b) Cannot be tessellated.
(c)

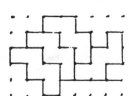

(d) Tessellate as in (a).

4. Hint: Consider figures like a pentagon formed by combining a square and an equilateral triangle, or the figure in Problem 7 of this Ongoing Assessment.
5. (a) The dual is another tessellation of squares (congruent to those given). **(b)** A tessellation of equilateral triangles
(c) The tessellation of equilateral triangles illustrated in the statement of the problem
6. (a) TO TESSELSQUARE
 PENUP BACK 70 PENDOWN
 REPEAT 9 [SQUARE 20 FORWARD 20]
 PENUP BACK 180 RIGHT 90
 FORWARD 20 LEFT 90 PENDOWN
 REPEAT 9 [SQUARE 20 FORWARD 20]
 END
 TO SQUARE :SIDE
 REPEAT 4 [FORWARD :SIDE RIGHT 90]
 END
(b) TO TESSELTRI
 PENUP BACK 70 PENDOWN
 REPEAT 9 [TRIANGLE 20 FORWARD 20]
 PENUP BACK 180 RIGHT 60
 FORWARD 20 LEFT 60 PENDOWN
 REPEAT 9 [TRIANGLE 20 FORWARD 20]
 END

 TO TRIANGLE :SIDE
 REPEAT 3 [FORWARD :SIDE RIGHT 120]
 END
(c) TO TESSELHEX
 PENUP BACK 70 LEFT 90 PENDOWN
 REPEAT 4 [HEXAGON 20 RIGHT 120
 FORWARD 20 LEFT 60 HEXAGON 20
 FORWARD 20 LEFT 60]
 END

 TO HEXAGON :SIDE
 REPEAT 6 [FORWARD :SIDE RIGHT 60]
 END
7. TO TILESTRIP :S
 REPEAT 4 [TILE :S PENUP RIGHT 180 FORWARD
 3*:S PENDOWN]
 END

 TO TILE :S
 RIGHT 180
 REPEAT 3 [REPEAT 4 [FORWARD :S LEFT 60]
 RIGHT 120]
 END
8. (a) The image ABCD under a half-turn in M (the midpoint of CD) is the following trapezoid FEDC. Because the trapezoids are congruent, ABFE is a parallelogram. The area of the parallelogram is AE · h or (a + b) · h. The parallelogram is the union of two nonoverlapping congruent trapezoids. The area of each trapezoid is (a + b) · h/2.

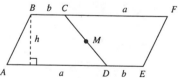

(b) To tesselate the plane with △ABC we find △A'BC the image of △ABC under a half turn about M the midpoint of $\overline{BC}$. If N is the midpoint of $\overline{AB}$ then the image of N is N'. It can be shown, that N, M and N' are collinear and hence that ANN'C, is a parallelogram. Because the image of $\overline{NM}$ is $\overline{MN'}$ it follows that NM = MN'. Hence NM $= \frac{1}{2}$ NN' $= \frac{1}{2}$ AC. Thus

NM $= \frac{1}{2}$ AC. Also $\overline{NM} \parallel \overline{AC}$.

9. See the explanation in Section 13-5.

Open-ended
10. Answers vary. In the given design, the tessellation can be obtained by half-turns followed by reflections.
11. Answers vary.
12. Answers vary. For example, a right rectangular prism, as well as a tetrahedron, will tile the space, but a cylinder or a square pyramid will not.

Cooperative Learning
13. Answer vary.
14. (a) Two such figures can be put together to form a parallelogram. Because parallelograms tessellate the plane, the original figure tessellates the plane. (b) There are 17 such figures. Two figures are different if they are not congruent and not similar.
(c) Answers vary. For example the following figure is a reptile.

Chapter Review
1. (a)   (b)

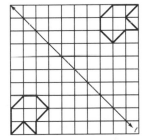   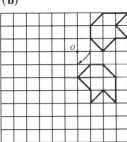

(c)

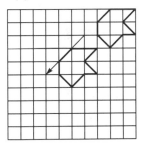

2. In each part find the images of the vertices.
3. (a) 4 (b) 1 (c) 1 (d) None (e) 2 (f) 2
4. (a) Line and rotational (b) Line, rotational, and point
(c) Line
5. (a) Infinitely many (b) Infinitely many (c) 3 (d) 9
6. This answer depends totally upon how the letters are made, but generally we have the following: c has line symmetry; i has line symmetry; o has line, rotational, and point symmetry; s has rotational and point symmetry; t has line symmetry; v has line symmetry; w has line symmetry; x has

line, rotational, and point symmetry; z has rotational and point symmetry.
7. (a) Let B' be the image of B under reflection in line r. The pumping station should be built at the point of intersection of the line connecting A and B' with line r. (b) 60/7 mi or approximately 8.57 mi
8. A = A', B is the midpoint of $\overline{A'B'}$, and C is the midpoint of $\overline{A'C'}$.
9. In each case, half-turn about X.
10. (a) Rotation by 120° about the center of the hexagon
(b) A reflection in the perpendicular bisector of $\overline{BY}$
11. Reflection in $\overset{\leftrightarrow}{SO}$
12. Let $\triangle H'O'R'$ be the image of $\triangle HOR$ under a half-turn about R. Then $\triangle SER$ is the image of $\triangle H'O'R'$ under a size

transformation with center R and scale factor $\frac{2}{3}$. Thus $\triangle SER$ is

the image of $\triangle HOR$ under the half-turn about R followed by the size transformation described above.
13. A($^-$3, 4.91), B($^-$8, 0.07), C(1.83, 5)
14. Rotate $\triangle PIG$ 180° (half-turn) about the midpoint of $\overline{PT}$, then perform a size transformation with scale factor 2 and center P'(= T).
15. The measure of each exterior angle of a regular octagon is

$\frac{360°}{8}$ or 45°. Hence the measure of each interior angle is

180° − 45° or 135°. Because 135 ∤ 3 a regular octagon does not tessellate the plane.
16.   TO RHOMSTRIP :S
              IF YCOR + :S > 100 STOP
              RHOM :S
              FD :S
              RHOMSTRIP :S
         END

APPENDIX I

ONGOING ASSESSMENT A-I-1
1. (a)   (b)

(c)   (d)

(e)   (f)   (g)

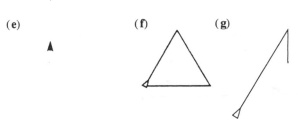

2. The answer may vary depending upon the type of computer being used.

3. (a)

(b)

(c)

4. Answers may vary.
(a) TO RECT
    REPEAT 2 [FORWARD 30 RIGHT 90
        FORWARD 60 RIGHT 90]
END
(b) TO FLAG
    FORWARD 40
    REPEAT 2 [FORWARD 20 RIGHT 90
        FORWARD 40 RIGHT 90]
END
(c) TO HAT
    REPEAT 2 [FORWARD 60 RIGHT 90 FORWARD 30
        RIGHT 90]
    PENUP LEFT 90 FORWARD 30 PENDOWN
    REPEAT 2[LEFT 90 FORWARD 6 LEFT 90
        FORWARD 90]
END
(d) TO T
    FORWARD 60 LEFT 90
    FORWARD 30 BACK 60
END
(e) TO RHOMBUS
    RIGHT 20
    REPEAT 2[FD 40 RT 70 FD 40 RT 110]
END
(f) TO CENTER.SQUARE
    REPEAT 4[FORWARD 70 RIGHT 90]
    RIGHT 45 PENUP
    FORWARD 35 LEFT 45
    PENDOWN
    REPEAT 4[FORWARD 20 RIGHT 90]
END
5. Answers may vary.
TO LOGO
    PENUP LEFT 90 FORWARD 90 RIGHT 90
    PENDOWN L
    SPACE O
    SPACE G
    SPACE O
END
TO L
    FORWARD 40 BACK 40
    RIGHT 90 FORWARD 20
    BACK 20 LEFT 90
END

TO O
    REPEAT 2[FORWARD 40 RIGHT 90 FORWARD 25
        RIGHT 90]
END
TO G
    FORWARD 40 RIGHT 90 FORWARD 25
    PENUP RIGHT 90 FORWARD 20
    PENDOWN
    RIGHT 90 FORWARD 10 BACK 10
    LEFT 90 FORWARD 20 RIGHT 90
    FORWARD 25 RIGHT 90
END
TO SPACE
    PENUP RIGHT 90
    FORWARD 35 LEFT 90
    PENDOWN
END
6. Answers may vary.
TO SQUARE1
    REPEAT 4[FORWARD 50 RIGHT 90]
END
TO TRIANGLE1
    REPEAT 3[FORWARD 50 RIGHT 120]
END
(a) TO SQUARE.PILE
    REPEAT 4[SQUARE1 RIGHT 90]
END
(b) TO DIAMOND
    RIGHT 30 TRIANGLE1
    RIGHT 60 FORWARD 50 RIGHT 120
    TRIANGLE1
END
(c) TO RECT1
    REPEAT 2[FORWARD 60 RIGHT 90 FORWARD 30
        RIGHT 90]
END
TO RECT.SWIRL
    RIGHT 30
    REPEAT 4[RECT1 LEFT 90]
END
(d) TO TRI.SWIRL
    REPEAT 3[TRIANGLE1 RIGHT 120]
END
(e) TO STAR
    RIGHT 30
    REPEAT 4[TRIANGLE1 RIGHT 60 FORWARD 50
        RIGHT 30]
END
(f) TO FLAG1
    FORWARD 10
    REPEAT 2[FORWARD 5 RIGHT 90 FORWARD 8
        RIGHT 90]
END
TO FLAG.TOP
    SQUARE1
    FORWARD 50 RIGHT 30
    TRIANGLE1
    FORWARD 50 LEFT 30
    FLAG1
END
7. Answers may vary.
(a) TO SQUARE.FACE
    SQUARE 60
    FORWARD 5 PENUP RIGHT 90
    FORWARD 25
    LEFT 90 PENDOWN
    SQUARE 10 PENUP FORWARD 18
    PENDOWN RIGHT 30

```
      TRIANGLE 10
      PENUP LEFT 30 FORWARD 15 LEFT 90
      FORWARD 10
      RIGHT 90 PENDOWN
      SQUARE 10 PENUP RIGHT 90
      FORWARD 20 LEFT 90 PENDOWN
      SQUARE 10
   END
   TO SQUARE :S
      REPEAT 4[FORWARD :S RIGHT 90]
   END
   TO TRIANGLE :S
      REPEAT 3[FORWARD :S RIGHT 120]
   END
(b) TO BUILD.SQR :S
      SQUARE :S
      SQUARE :S + 10
      SQUARE :S + 20
      SQUARE :S + 30
      SQUARE :S + 40
   END
(c) TO TAIL :S
      SQUARE :S
      FORWARD :S RIGHT 90 FORWARD :S LEFT 90
      SQUARE :S/2
      FORWARD :S/2 RIGHT 90 FORWARD :S/2 LEFT 90
      SQUARE :S/4
   END
(d) TO TOWER :S
      SQUARE :S
      FORWARD :S RIGHT 90 FORWARD :S/4 LEFT 90
      SQUARE :S/2
      FORWARD :S/2 RIGHT 90 FORWARD :S/8 LEFT 90
      SQUARE :S/4
   END
8. TO DOG
      FULLSCREEN
      PENUP BACK 50 LEFT 90 FORWARD 50 RIGHT 90
      PENDOWN
      BODY BACK 50
      LEG PENUP RIGHT 90 FORWARD 90 LEFT 90
      PENDOWN
      LEG RIGHT 90 FORWARD 10 LEFT 90
      FORWARD 100
      TAIL LEFT 90 FORWARD 100 RIGHT 90 BACK 20
      HEAD FORWARD 20 EAR
      PENUP LEFT 90 FORWARD 25 RIGHT 90
      FORWARD 15 PENDOWN
      EYE PENUP BACK 30 LEFT 90 FORWARD 15
      RIGHT 90 PENDOWN
      NOSE
   END
   TO BODY
      REPEAT 2[FORWARD 50 RIGHT 90 FORWARD 100
         RIGHT 90]
   END
   TO LEG
      REPEAT 2[FORWARD 50 RIGHT 90 FORWARD 10
         RIGHT 90]
   END
   TO TAIL
      REPEAT 2[FORWARD 30 RIGHT 90 FORWARD 10
         RIGHT 90]
   END
   TO HEAD
      REPEAT 2[FORWARD 50 LEFT 90 FORWARD 40
         LEFT 90]
   END
   TO EAR
      REPEAT 2[FORWARD 30 LEFT 90 FORWARD 15
         LEFT 90]
   END
   TO EYE
      REPEAT 4[FORWARD 5 RIGHT 90]
   END
   TO NOSE
      REPEAT 2[FORWARD 15 LEFT 90 FORWARD 5
         LEFT 90]
   END
9. TO KITE
      LEFT 45
      REPEAT 4[FORWARD 40 RIGHT 90]
      RIGHT 45
      REPEAT 3[BACK 20 K.TAIL RIGHT 60]
      BACK 20
   END
   TO K.TAIL
      RIGHT 60
      REPEAT 3[FORWARD 10 RIGHT 120] LEFT 120
      REPEAT 3[FORWARD 10 LEFT 120]
   END
10. (a) TO RECT :L :W
         REPEAT 2[FORWARD :L RIGHT 90
            FORWARD :W RIGHT 90]
      END
(b) Use the RECT procedure from part (a).
      TO FLAG :S
      FORWARD :S
      RECT :S/3 :S/2
   END
(c) TO HAT :S
      RECT :S :S/2
      PENUP LEFT 90 FORWARD :S/2
      PENDOWN
      REPEAT 2[LEFT 90 FORWARD :S/10 LEFT 90
      FORWARD :S + :S/2]
   END
(d) TO T :S
      FORWARD :S LEFT 90
      FORWARD :S/2 BACK :S
   END
(e) TO RHOMBUS :S :A
      REPEAT 2[FORWARD :S RIGHT (180 – :A)
      FORWARD :S RIGHT :A]
   END
(f) TO CENTER.SQUARE :S
      SQUARE :S
      RIGHT 90
      PENUP FORWARD :S/3 LEFT 90 FORWARD :S/3
      PENDOWN
      SQUARE: S/3
   END
   TO SQUARE :S
      REPEAT 4[FORWARD :S RIGHT 90]
   END
11. TO BLADE :S
      REPEAT 12[FORWARD :S PARALLELOGRAM
         :S*3/2 :S 30 RIGHT 30]
   END
```

TO PARALLELOGRAM :S1 :S2 :A
  REPEAT 2[FORWARD :S1 RIGHT :A FORWARD
  :S2 RIGHT (180 − :A)]
END
12. TO RECTANGLES :S
  LEFT 90
  REPEAT 4[RECTANGLE :S/3 :S RIGHT 90
    FORWARD :S/3]
END
TO RECTANGLE :S1 :S2
  REPEAT 2[FORWARD :S1 RIGHT 90 FORWARD :S2
    RIGHT 90]
END
13. Type the procedures on the computer.
14. Type the procedures on the computer.
15. Answers may vary.
(a) TO STRETCH :S
  IF :S<5 STOP
  SQUARE :S
  FORWARD :S RIGHT 90
  FORWARD :S LEFT 90
  STRETCH :S−10
END
(In LCSI, replace IF :S<5 STOP with IF :S<5 [STOP.])
(b) TO TOWER :S
  IF :S<5 STOP
  SQUARE :S
  FORWARD :S RIGHT 90 FORWARD :S/4
  LEFT 90 TOWER :S/2
END
(In LCSI, replace IF :S<5 STOP with IF :S<5 [STOP.])
(c) TO PISA :S :A
  IF :S<5 STOP
  SQUARE :S
  FORWARD :S LEFT :A
  PISA :S*0.75 :A
END
(In LCSI, replace IF :S<5 STOP with IF :S<5 [STOP.])
(d) TO CONSQRS :S
  IF :S<5 STOP
  SQUARE :S
  PENUP FORWARD :S/3 RIGHT 90
  FORWARD :S/3
  LEFT 90 PENDOWN
  CONSQRS :S/3
END
(In LCSI, replace IF :S<5 STOP with IF :S<5 [STOP.])
(e) TO ROW.HOUSE :S
  IF :S<5 STOP
  HOUSE :S
  SETUP :S
  ROW.HOUSE :S/2
END
(In LCSI, replace IF :S<5 STOP with IF :S<5 [STOP.])
TO HOUSE :S
  SQUARE :S
  FORWARD :S
  RIGHT 30 TRIANGLE :S
  LEFT 30
END
TO SETUP :S
  BACK :S RIGHT 90
  FORWARD :S LEFT 90
END
(f) TO TRI.TOWER :S
  IF :S<5 STOP
  RIGHT 30 TRIANGLE :S

SETUP :S
TRI.TOWER :S/2
END
(In LCSI, replace IF :S<5 STOP with IF :S<5 [STOP.])
TO TRIANGLE :S
  REPEAT 3[FORWARD :S RIGHT 120]
END
TO SETUP :S
  FORWARD :S LEFT 120
  FORWARD :S/4 RIGHT 90
END
16. TO NEST.TRI :S
  IF :S<10 STOP
  RIGHT 30 TRIANGLE :S
  FD :S/2 RIGHT 30
  NEST.TRI :S/2
END
(In LCSI, replace IF :S<10 STOP with IF :S<10 [STOP.])
TO TRIANGLE :S
  REPEAT 3[FORWARD :S RIGHT 120]
END
17. Answers may vary.
TO SPIN.SQ :S
  IF:S<5 STOP
  SQUARE :S
  RIGHT 20
  SPIN.SQ :S−5
END
(In LCSI, replace IF :S<5 STOP with IF :S<5 [STOP.])
TO SQUARE :S
  REPEAT 4[FORWARD :S RIGHT 90]
END
18. Answers may vary, for example, STAR 0 30
TO STAR :N :S
  IF :N=6 STOP
  PENUP
  FORWARD :S*(SQRT 2)/3 LEFT 45
  PENDOWN
  SQUARE :S PENUP RIGHT 45 BACK :S*(SQRT 2)/3
  RIGHT 60 PENDOWN
  STAR :N+1 :S
END
(In LCSI, replace IF :N=6 STOP with IF :N=6 [STOP].)
TO SQUARE :S
  REPEAT 4[FORWARD :S RIGHT 90]
END

APPENDIX II

ONGOING ASSESSMENT A-II

1. Approximately 11.896 or 11.9 years.
2. 96
3. (−10, 257) and (10, 357)
4. (a) The graphs all pass through the point (0, 3) and all are linear. (b) They differ in steepness. (c) As the slope becomes greater, the graph becomes steeper. The lines have slopes of 1, 2, 3, and 4, respectively.
5. (a) The graphs are all linear and are parallel to each other. They all have the same slope. (b) They cross the y-axis at different points. (c) The point where each graph crosses the y-axis is the y-intercept and it is the point at the end of each of these equations. In general, in the equation $y = mx + b$, the point b tells where the graph crosses the y-axis.
6. Approximately (1.22, −0.55)
7. (a) She needs to find the intersection points of Y_1, Y_2, and Y_3 with Y_4. (b) two hours

8. (**a**) Sign changes occur at x = 1 and x = 4. (**b**) Graph on calculator. (**c**) The graph crossed at x = 1 and x = 4.
9. 18 dimes and 15 quarters

APPENDIX III

1. The areas of a rectangle and a parallelogram with the same base and height are the same.
2. The area of a triangle is one-half the area of a parallelogram with the same base and height.
3. The ratio of the areas of two similar figures is the square of the ratio of two corresponding sides of the similar figures.
4. (**a**)–(**g**) Drawings may vary. An example answer using a regular pentagon follows. The entire pentagon is labeled as polygon 3. The triangle with the white oval is labeled as polygon 2. The height of the triangle is 1.15 in. The area of each triangle is approximately 0.96 in^2. The area of the pentagon is approximately 4.79 in^2. The perimeter of the pentagon is approximately 8.34 in. The ratio of the area to the perimeter is 8.34/4.79, or approximately 0.57. The ratio 0.57 is approximately one-half of 1.15. This approximation tends to support the formula for the area of a regular polygon as (1/2)ap, where a is the apothem and p is the perimeter.

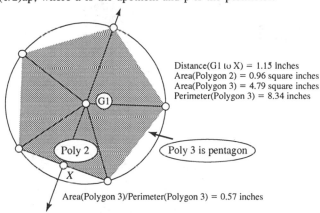

Distance(G1 to X) = 1.15 inches
Area(Polygon 2) = 0.96 square inches
Area(Polygon 3) = 4.79 square inches
Perimeter(Polygon 3) = 8.34 inches

Area(Polygon 3)/Perimeter(Polygon 3) = 0.57 inches

5. (**a**)–(**c**) A pentagon is given as a demonstration. The ratio of the perimeter to the length of the longest diagonal is approximately 3.10 in.

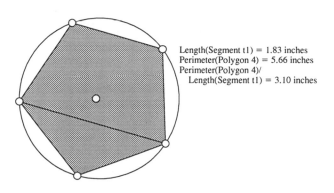

Length(Segment t1) = 1.83 inches
Perimeter(Polygon 4) = 5.66 inches
Perimeter(Polygon 4)/
  Length(Segment t1) = 3.10 inches

(**d**)–(**e**) Continuing the process should approximate π because the regular polygons inside the circle approach the circle. The longest diagonal approaches a diameter and the perimeter approaches the circumference of the circle.
6. (**a**) The percent of area in the square not covered by the circle is approximately 21%. (**b**) The percent of area in the circle not covered by the square is approximately 36%.

(**c**) The answers in parts (a) and (b) suggest that the circular peg will fit better in the square hole than vice versa.
7. (**a**) Approximately 21% (**b**) Approximately 21% (**c**) The answer doesn't change.
8. This exercise can be used to practice fair division. The geometry utility allows the moving of the line and the finding of areas with relative ease.
9. This exercise can be used to practice estimation of areas and the estimation of percentages.

APPENDIX IV

1. Answers will vary. An example follows:
(**a**) 5, 9, 13, 17, 21, ... (**b**) Column A should contain the numbers 1, 2, 3, 4, 5, 6, ... (**c**) The formula =A1+1 should be used to find A2 and then to fill down the rest of the column. (**d**) Column B for this example will start with 5, and each successive term is 4 more than the previous one. (**e**) The formula =B1+4 could be used here. (**f**) The Σ key should be used when the cell where the sum is wanted is highlighted. (**g**) In an arithmetic sequence, no matter which one was used the data should lie along a line.
2. Answers will vary. An example follows:
(**a**) 3, 6, 12, 24, 48, ... (**b**) Column A should contain the numbers 1, 2, 3, 4, 5, 6, ... (**c**) Column B for this example will start with 3, and each successive term is 2 times the previous one. (**d**) The formula =B1*2 could be used here. (**e**) The Σ key should be used when the cell where the sum is wanted is highlighted. (**f**) In a geometric sequence, no matter which one was used the data should lie along an exponential curve. For example, it should cross the y-axis at the point with coordinates (0, 1) and curve up sharply if the common ratio is greater than 1. It will approach the x-axis if the common ratio is less than 1 but greater than 0.
3. If all the data is listed in the first 14 cells of column A, the Σ key can be used to find the sum of all the data, and the sum can be placed in cell A15. The formula =A15/14 can be used to place the mean in cell A16.
4. Column B can be used to find the individual data items minus the mean using the formula =A1–A16 with the Fill Down feature. Column C can be filled with the square of the items in column B using the formula =B1^2 and filling down appropriately. Cell C15 might be used to find the sum of the first 14 cells of column C. The standard deviation might then be found using the formula =sqrt(C15/14), or approximately 25.60, and placed in cell C16. The spreadsheet then might appear as follows:

	A	B	C
1	23	⁻39.285714	1543.36735
2	45	⁻17.285714	298.795918
3	67	4.71428571	22.2244898
4	78	15.7142857	246.938776
5	98	35.7142857	1275.5102
6	54	⁻8.2857143	68.6530612
7	36	⁻26.285714	690.938776
8	76	13.7142857	188.081633
9	75	12.7142857	161.653061
10	24	⁻38.285714	1465.79592
11	43	⁻19.285714	371.938776
12	54	⁻8.2857143	68.6530612
13	100	37.7142857	1422.36735
14	99	36.7142857	1347.93878
15	872		9172.85714
16	62.2857143		25.59695

5. A sample spreadsheet follows. All decimals have been truncated to two places. In reality, the lending agency would probably not truncate. The value in C1 was created as $1000 + 0.015*1000 - 40$. For all cells in Column C after C1, the formula $=0.015*C1 - 40$ was used.

	A	B	C
1	1	40	$ 975.00
2	2	40	$ 949.63
3	3	40	$ 923.87
4	4	40	$ 897.73
5	5	40	$ 871.19
6	6	40	$ 844.26
7	7	40	$ 816.93
8	8	40	$ 789.18
9	9	40	$ 761.02
10	10	40	$ 732.43
11	11	40	$ 703.42
12	12	40	$ 673.97
13	13	40	$ 644.08
14	14	40	$ 613.74
15	15	40	$ 582.95
16	16	40	$ 551.69
17	17	40	$ 519.97
18	18	40	$ 487.77
19	19	40	$ 455.08
20	20	40	$ 421.91
21	21	40	$ 388.24
22	22	40	$ 354.06
23	23	40	$ 319.37
24	24	40	$ 284.16
25	25	40	$ 248.42
26	26	40	$ 212.15
27	27	40	$ 175.33
28	28	40	$ 137.96
29	29	40	$ 100.03
30	30	40	$ 61.53
31	31	40	$ 22.79

Note that the last payment was for only $22.79 and not $40. The payments took 31 months.

6. The first step is to create a column A that is the number of the term by placing 1 in cell A1 and using the formula $=A1+1$ to fill down for a total of 100 cells in column A. Next we could use the formula $=13*A:A$ and fill down for a total of 100 cells in column B.

7. Answers may vary depending upon the method used for computing grade points at your college. In general, you may use 4 quality points for each hour of A, 3 quality points for each hour of B, 2 for each hour of C, 1 for each hour of D, and 0 for each hour of F. After multiplying each hour by the respective number of quality points, find the total of all quality points, then divide by the total number of hours.

8. (a) A sample spreadsheet follows where the A column is created by entering 1 in cell A1 and using the formula $=A1+1$ and Fill Down to create a total of 25 cells. The B column is found by entering 1 in cell B1 and 1 in cell B2. The remainder of the cells are created using the formula $=B1+B2$. Column C is created using the formula $=B1^2$. Column D is created by filling cell D1 with $=C1$, and using the formula $=D1+C2$ to create the remainder of the cells.

	A	B	C	D
1	1	1	1	1
2	2	1	1	2
3	3	2	4	6
4	4	3	9	15
5	5	5	25	40
6	6	8	64	104
7	7	13	169	273
8	8	21	441	714
9	9	34	1156	1870
10	10	55	3025	4895
11	11	89	7921	12816
12	12	144	20736	33552
13	13	233	54289	87841
14	14	377	142129	229970
15	15	610	372100	602070
16	16	987	974169	1576239
17	17	1597	2550409	4126648
18	18	2584	6677056	10803704
19	19	4181	17480761	28284465
20	20	6765	45765225	74049690
21	21	10946	119814916	193864606
22	22	17711	313679521	507544127
23	23	28657	821223649	1328767776
24	24	46368	2149991424	3478759200
25	25	75025	5628750625	9107509825

(b) The sum of the squares of the first n terms of the Fibonacci sequence is $a_n a_n + 1$. (c) The same conjecture is not true.

9. The A column can be created by entering 1 in cell A1 and using the formula $=A1+1$ and Fill Down to fill as many cells as wanted. The B column can be created by entering $=A1$ in cell B1 and $=B1*A2$ with the Fill Down feature to complete the wanted cells.